BELIEVE

UK DESIGN FOR PERFORMANCE
2011–2015

MAKE / BELIEVE

UK DESIGN FOR PERFORMANCE
2011–2015

14 – 31 JANUARY 2015:
NOTTINGHAM TRENT UNIVERSITY
NEWTON BUILDING, GOLDSMITH STREET,
NOTTINGHAM NG1 4BU

Nottingham Trent University is delighted to host the launch exhibition of Make/Believe, the latest quadrennial celebration of excellence in UK design for performance by the Society of British Theatre Designers, in collaboration with the V&A museum.

BA (Hons) Theatre Design at NTU is a firmly established, industry respected course with over 40 years of teaching expertise. Our students benefit from an extensive network of links with a wide range of performance, heritage, educational and professional theatre companies; live projects, competitions and work placements ensure that we continuously connect right across the industry.

Our Theatre Design course is a member of the International Organisation of Sceneographers, Theatre Architects and Technicians, the Association of Courses in Theatre Design, and the Society of British Theatre Designers. This is also the only course in the UK to be accredited by the Chartered Society of Designers.

All course information: www.ntu.ac.uk/art
Exhibition information: www.boningtongallery.co.uk

Published in Great Britain
by The Society of British Theatre Designers
Theatre Design Department,
Royal Welsh College of Music and Drama,
Castle Grounds,
Cathays Park,
CARDIFF CF10 3ER

Registered Charity No. 800638

Text copyright © 2014

ISBN 13: 978 – 0 – 9529309 – 8 – 3

British Library Cataloguing in Publication Data:
a catalogue record of this book is available from
the British Library.

Design and Typography:
Marc Jennings - www.theundercard.co.uk

Editor and Curator: Kate Burnett

Printed by: PCP - www.pcp.biz

Photographs and illustrations are by the
contributing designers unless otherwise stated.

Information in this catalogue has been provided by
contributing designers and is published in good faith.

The Make/Believe National Exhibition is
dedicated to the memory of designer
Johan Engels, (1952 – 2014) who sadly died
during the preparation of the exhibition.

The Society of British Theatre Designers is
deeply grateful to all the sponsors, from private
individuals to large organisations who have made
this exhibition, its catalogue and programme of
educational events possible.

CONTENTS

Cover Image: *Barber of Seville*
Gary McCann
Nationale Reisopera, Netherlands, 2013
Karin Strobos as Rosina
Photo: Marco Borggreve

Inside covers image: *RIOT Offspring*
Abigail Hammond
RIOT Company, Sadler's Wells 2012,
Photo: Bettina Strenske

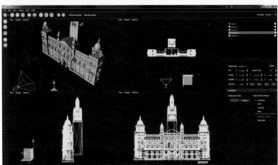

SPONSORS FOREWORD

Backstage Academy is delighted to be sponsoring Make/Believe: UK Design for Performance 2011-15.

The United Kingdom has a justly deserved global reputation for the quality and innovation of both its designers and technicians, all of whom play an integral part in creating and realising the vast range of live events we bring to the world's stages and stadiums each year. From live events and product launches through to film and TV, the integration of digital and new technologies helps us immerse and challenge our audiences, whilst driving the convergence of design disciplines, creating new roles and skillsets.

Although digital technologies and the 'virtual' world occupy one frontier for exploring space and performance, it is vital we do not forget or lose the traditional craft and practical skills that form the foundations for both design and realisation – without these skills the link between the virtual and the real world becomes ever distant - in a world based upon science and technology let us not forget it's the creative and artistic that dictates our use of technology. The transition between concept and reality is hugely important, otherwise we might as well just switch off the lights and gather round the latest games console.

Backstage Academy is committed to evolving the skills, aspirations and work ethos of all those who might design and deliver the stages and live experiences of tomorrow. Thanks to our unique industry partnerships we see first hand the evolving career opportunities, roles and skillsets required, and we understand the importance of keeping alive the traditions and practical skills that have driven the high standard of design and production work. We look forward to meeting you on the road during the travels of Make/Believe 2015-2016.

SBTD FOREWORD

Since its foundation in 1975 the Society of British Theatre Designers has evolved into an increasingly relevant and important institution, and the quadrennial National Exhibition with the accompanying catalogue are now an essential showcase for new and established designers from all over the UK.

For this reason it is important that it is not entirely London based, and we are extremely grateful to Nottingham Trent University and its staff and students, for hosting the current exhibition, and for supporting the National Curator Kate Burnett. Exhibiting in a venue outside London has several advantages - cost, space, the backup of a Higher Education facility and, hopefully, a new and diverse public.

Embarking on a venture of this scale inevitability involves an army of sponsors, technical teams and volunteers. We would like to thank the Backstage Academy for their major sponsorship of the project and the catalogue, as well as the contribution of their staff and students to exhibition events.

Thanks also to the Victoria and Albert Museum for their partnership in the exhibition, its journey to the Prague Quadrennial, and the subsequent six month residency in the Theatre and Performance Galleries at the V&A.

Another institution that has once again been invaluably helpful is the Royal Welsh College of Music and Drama, led by Sean Crowley and his dedicated team.

I work abroad a great deal, and meet people from all disciplines in the theatre. It is gratifying how often practitioners of all ages and backgrounds tell me how inspiring the SBTD exhibition catalogues are. The collaboration, vision, skills and hard work evidenced in the catalogue and exhibition are something of which we can ALL be proud.

Richard Hudson
President
Society of British Theatre Designers

WELCOME

The SBTD's Make/Believe national exhibition project commenced in the newly redesigned Newton atrium exhibition spaces at Nottingham Trent University from 14 - 31 January 2015. Selected work represents the UK at PQ2015 in Prague from 17 - 28 June 2015, at the Victoria and Albert Museum in London from 9 July 2015 - 3 January 2016.

Make/Believe is the sixth UK national exhibition in an unbroken line of quadrennial exhibitions since 1994, but only the ninth national exhibition since the SBTD started in 1975. Contextualised and to some extent motivated by the corresponding Prague Quadrennials, these exhibitions, and more enduringly their accompanying catalogues, chart the careers of many of the UK's designers with changes in aesthetics, construction and recording materials and technologies, performance and audience contexts shaping the journey.

Over the years designers have bowed in and out of the exhibitions, taken family/career 'breaks', developed their practice in specific directions, collaborated and built enduring partnerships with directors, lighting designers, costumiers, and diversified into other areas of design including events, the music industry, film and TV, heritage and display, education and alternative training and careers in, most fequently, art therapy and midwifery! We are delighted to include established designers such as Robin Don and Russell Craig whose memorable designs for *A Midsummer Marriage* and *Oberon*, respectively, featured in the '83-'87 SBTD exhibition as well as emerging designers and the latest in a remarkable line of Linbury Prize winners, Ana Inés Jabares Pita and Alexander Ruth (2013). We are sorry to record here the recent sudden death of Johan Engels, whose wonderful set designs have been included in the past 4 exhibitions, and are here represented, accompanying Marie-Jeanne Lecca's costume designs for *The Magic Flute* on the Bregenz Festspiel lake stage.

The exhibition title, Make/Believe, indicates the skills, vision and commitment found in the diversity of performance design today. It encompasses the wide range of work that defines both the heart and wider contexts of this artform-in-industry - in music festivals, large scale events such as the Olympics, Paralympics, community opera, found space and promenade performance, in digital, landscape, heritage and media contexts, as well as the intimate and highly valued work that designers are currently doing in education, health and various community settings.

We celebrate the high quality of designs for a variety of theatre spaces, the traditions of pantomime design, the ravishing visuals that transform many children's books into stage spectaculars as well as the dance and opera designs by UK designers that are notable around the world.

Make/Believe also acknowledges and promotes the development of new performance spaces, the re-envisioning of old and existing buildings and the increasing commitment to sustainable design and practices in both production and performance environments.

Performance design lives on in memorable images for those who have seen or been a part of productions and events. Exhibitions of this artform enable many more children, students, industry professionals and interested public to enjoy and engage with the imagination and skills of designers – and importantly the huge number

MAKE / BELIEVE

of technical and crafts practitioners who develop and realise the designs. This catalogue is intended as both accompaniment to the Make/Believe exhibition in its various iterations, but also as a stand-alone publication that creates a time frame and gives insights into designers' conceptual and production processes and collaborations. The SBTD catalogues are unique in the world in this continuous record and showcase of design for performance.

The title Make/Believe with its various connotations and resonances is, as ever, an umbrella, applicable to all the work within, so there are no separate sections and designers are listed alphabetically (mostly). While the designers' commentaries provide context and process insights, short essays have been commissioned, have arisen from interviews, or developed from responses to our Research Project questions. Most of the essays are by individual designers, but the Birmingham Opera, Wildworks and DragonBreath companies featured are exemplars of collaborative art-form led practice that we are proud to include.

We have been talking about – and finally achieved the inclusion of Sound Designers into an SBTD catalogue (they have been included in the past 3 exhibitions) with an attached and integral CD presentation coordinated by tireless Sound Designer Karen Lauke. Our huge thanks to Marc Jennings, catalogue designer who has so carefully and inspirationally brought all this work together.

Thanks also to 3 institutions that have demonstrated the vital interdependence of Higher Education and Industry in this sector. The Backstage Academy, our major sponsor, is offering education and training originating from and based in the industry context that employs designers such as Es Devlin and Misty Buckley. Nottingham Trent University are hosting the SBTD national exhibition for the second time, a testament to their continuous support and recognition of excellence in the development of design for performance. The BA Hons Theatre Design course at NTU originated in the Nottingham Playhouse in 1975 and again the industry – HE relationship is strongly and practically supported here. The Royal Welsh College Of Music And Drama, now the registered and administrative home of the SBTD, hosted the previous national exhibition, Transformation & Revelation as well as the 2013 World Stage Design exhibition. The commitment and skills delevoped there under Sean Crowley, Head of Drama and Chair of the SBTD are evident in the brilliant exhibition team of Make/Believe, led by Patricia Grasham. Perhaps the most significant partner in Make/Believe is the Victoria & Albert Museum, through whose agency, this work can be made available to far more visitors and participants in the UK and abroad. The Make/Believe project is made possible with the support of all these institutions, of national organisations, our many industry sponsors and supporters as well as that of members and exhibitors in the SBTD, ASD, ACTD, ABTT and ALD.

I hope that Make/Believe will provide a rich source of pleasure, fantasy, contemplation as well as stimulation, or provocation to develop new ideas, projects, technologies and contexts.

Kate Burnett,
Curator
Make/Believe: UK Design for Performance 2011-2015

DICK BIRD

NOTES ON A CONVERSATION ABOUT THE DESIGN PROCESS FOR BEFORE THE DAWN

HOW DID YOU COME TO WORK ON BEFORE THE DAWN AND HOW DID THE DESIGN DEVELOP?

Before the Dawn was Kate Bush's first stage show for 35 years. She never appeared weighed down by the expectations that this would produce, and approached the whole process empirically with a great appetite for experiment.

The show divided into three parts—the first was to be and look like a conventional rock concert, and Kate was very keen that the audience wouldn't suspect that after 30 minutes it would break apart, and out of it would emerge two para-theatrical experiences, The Ninth Wave and A Sky of Honey.

Both were based on song cycles, one from 1985, the other from 2005. By the time we first spoke, Kate had already conceived them as a series of images, a visual narrative, and the design job seemed to be to find a way to contain those images without asphyxiating them.

Kate assembled her design team gradually, based on work she had seen, starting with the lighting designer Mark Henderson. Robert Allsopp the costume props maker, with whom she'd already worked on a variety of different projects, then a set designer, myself. Adrian Noble was brought in as co-director, Kate's eyes when she had to step inside the piece as a performer. Other members of the design team were put in place as the need for them became apparent. In my case she had seen and liked an opera based on Philip Pullman's Firework Maker's Daughter.

It was the most experimental and evolutionary of processes, partly because of Kate's desire to experience and understand every aspect of the creation of the material. In the early days this meant a lot of sitting around exchanging ideas and images, and a lot of standing around in aircraft hangars, invariably freezing, watching different densities of LED video wall behave with different grades of acrylics, BPs, silks, smokes, lazers. Some of the things we explored and hung on to for a very long time turned out to be simply impossible to achieve, but always they led to some other means of expressing the initial idea, and it was often this circuitousness of approach that led to the unusual freshness of the final product.

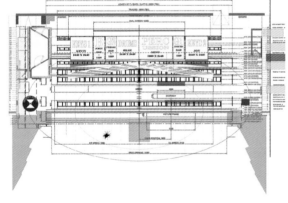

IT WAS THE MOST EXPERIMENTAL AND EVOLUTIONARY OF PROCESSES, PARTLY BECAUSE OF KATE'S DESIRE TO EXPERIENCE AND UNDERSTAND EVERY ASPECT OF THE CREATION OF THE MATERIAL.

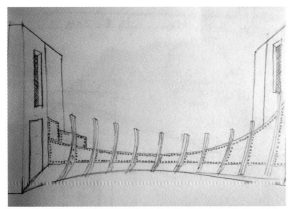

DID YOUR WORKING PROCESS INCLUDE MODEL MAKING, DRAWING, OTHER 3D METHODS AND DIGITAL PROCESSES?

Models were a more than usually useful tool in trying to tease out what was in Kate's imagination—also, very practically, to discuss what was possible on stage. In fact the show was originally planned to take place at the Alexandra Palace, and I made a model of the venue to take along to our first meeting. Even at 1:100, this was a massive object, and when Kate saw her tiny self represented, 36 millimetres high, she quickly looked for other venues.

The Apollo Hammersmith seats 3,500 while retaining a sense of connection between the stage and the farther reaches of the auditorium. A converted cinema from the 1930's, it presents its own challenges, having an extremely wide proscenium, practically no wings and relatively little depth. With three distinct settings to achieve, a lot of effort and ingenuity went into hiding those parts that weren't in use, and while the discrete elements of the design continued to evolve and morph like clouds, I spent a lot of time, and foamboard, designing masking. Although useful for concealment, however skimpy we tried to make it, this always had the function of reducing what we really liked about the stage, its volume—particularly for the big skies in the third section. When we stripped it all away, we finally had the basic design, an empty space. The one really large object we had to hide and couldn't fly was a hydraulically rocking box set living room, which was put up against a side wall, covered in vacform brick, fire extinguishers and ladders and painted to look like part of the theatre. What the audience could and couldn't see of the succession of objects and performers that then entered the stage was controlled by Mark Henderson, backlight and haze creating the murk out of which these elements appeared.

The stage also had to accommodate the band - two percussionists, three guitar players, two keyboard players and their equipment – a really gorgeous thing to look at. Their placement in the three parts of the show, and moving them between those positions had a big impact on the visual language of the show. We developed a set of interlocking platforms that allowed them to be pulled eight metres upstage as a unit to clear the stage for the Ninth Wave, and then scattered more informally stage right for The Sky of Honey.

The scenario of the Ninth Wave played with the tension between dream and reality, the reality represented in film, upstage on an oval screen, the dream world played out in a series of often surreal settings on stage. The visual style of those settings developed very gradually in a series of models; a wave became a skeleton fish which became a rusted wreck and then ended up having elements of all three. The rocking room, a comfortable sitting room adrift on an angry sea, went through twelve versions before finding a geometry improbable enough to exist in the dream world.

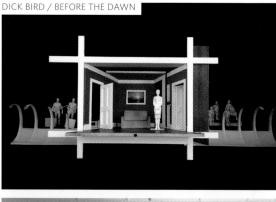

THERE WERE A LOT OF DIFFERENT VISUAL INGREDIENTS TO THIS SHOW. HOW DID THEY DEVELOP? HOW MUCH WERE YOU ABLE TO COLLABORATE?

As the year went on the team of designers grew, with Robert Allsopp creating masks and costume props; Brigitte Reiffenstuel on costume, puppetry and waves by Basil Twist; illusion by Paul Kieve. The projection designer Jon Driscoll came on board relatively late, and was hugely important to the look of the piece, particularly A Sky of Honey which used state-of-the-art video walls and projectors with old nineteenth century theatrical techniques of painted gauzes and silks, to create a wonderful sense of depth and dimension. I always think a production manager is a hugely important part of the creative team, and Simon Marlow was endlessly supportive and inventive in making the impossible actual. The very exploratory and interdisiciplinary atmosphere in which we worked was instrumental in creating the complex and layered feeling of the visual world.

Through a month of technicals at the Apollo, Kate showed little interest in getting on stage and rehearsing, and spent most of the time between the lighting desk and the video console shaping her show. This made her performance in the end all the more extraordinary.

For me a strong image of the piece is watching a screen made from 50 metres of moving silk tumble from the 10 metre grid, a projected bird swooping to the ground in the unnaturally extended moment of the screens existence.

THROUGH A MONTH OF TECHNICALS AT THE APOLLO, KATE SHOWED LITTLE INTEREST IN GETTING ON STAGE AND REHEARSING, AND SPENT MOST OF THE TIME BETWEEN THE LIGHTING DESK AND THE VIDEO CONSOLE SHAPING HER SHOW. THIS MADE HER PERFORMANCE IN THE END ALL THE MORE EXTRAORDINARY.

BEFORE THE DAWN
Kate Bush

Hammersmith Lyric, London
September 2014

Directors: Kate Bush and Adrian Noble
Lighting Designer: Mark Henderson
Set Designer: Dick Bird
Sound Designer: Greg Walsh
Costume Designer: Brigitte Reiffenstuel
Choreographer: Sian Williams
Masks, Costume Propmaker,
Creative Consultant: Robert Allsopp
Puppetry Director: Basil Twist
Projection Designer: Jon Driscoll
Illusion Designer: Paul Kieve
Photographer: Dick Bird

1/
BECS ANDREWS
DIRECTION, COSTUME AND VIDEO DESIGN

TRANSMISSION
Becs Andrews (2013-14)

Becs Andrews Company
TFTV, York
June 2014

BA: TRANSMISSION is a design-led interactive installation and contemporary dance piece that explores infectious networks (disease, memes) and how changes at a molecular / personal level can have global consequences.

The large floor projection tracks the dancers' or audience members' movements, and generates networks through which they see an infection spread.

Sound and video are triggered by specific movements (eg: proximity) and display immune system information (ie: spine lights) through our sensor-imbedded costumes, which I designed to hide and cushion the metal sensors, and allow for maximum movement.

Each of the seven sections in the performance explores an aspect of transmission through this kinetic-visual-aural interactive system - from the hubs such as airports and playground where mass infections occur to the microscopic 'lock and key' cellular mechanisms that allow infection to happen.

Before and after each performance the audience are invited to experience the environment from within - triggering the sound and video and setting up infection networks with each other.

Director: Becs Andrews
Choreographer: Simon Birch
Costume Designer: Becs Andrews
Electronic Engineer (costume sensors): Seb Madgwick
Lighting Designer: Louise Gregory
Sound Designer: Composer: Jon Hughes
Sound Programmer: Tom Mitchell
Video Design: Becs Andrews and Phill Tew
Visual Programmer: Phill Tew
Lead Scientist: Mike Brockhurst
Photographer: Chris Nash (Images 1 and 2), Becs Andrews (image 3)

2/
BECS ANDREWS
SET AND COSTUME DESIGN

THE CRACKLE / THROUGH HIS TEETH (2014)
Author/Composer: Matthew Herbert / Luke Bedford

Royal Opera Company
Linbury Studio Theatre, Royal Opera House
April 2014

BA: One set, two very different operas, both loosely based on Faust.

The Crackle set is a surreal cardboard world of fruit shoots and charity phone-ins, with strange music machines operated by Mephistopheles. My open-walled design, reminiscent of barcodes and matches, enabled the 2-D settings to slide on and off stage, and the ROH children's opera company to instantly appear.

Through His Teeth is a psychological thriller about sex and obsession and additionally used sliding screens with spy holes. Video projections of CCTV and live video feed through these, invoking the paranoia and shifting reality for the central character, 'A' (Faust), tricked by her conman lover.

Director: Matthew Herbert / Bijan Sheibani
Set and Costume Designer: Becs Andrews
Lighting Designer: Paul Knott
Production/Media Designer: Sam Meech
Photographer: Becs Andrews (images 1 and 2),
Stephen Cummiskey (image 3)

3/
BECS ANDREWS
SET AND COSTUME DESIGN

TERRARIUM
Simon Birch (2012)

Simon Birch Dance Company
North York Moors / SALT Festival Cornwall
August 2012 / August 2013

BA: Terrarium was a duet danced in an inflatable bubble in rural outdoor locations on the North York Moors and the Cornish coast. My costume designs were a response to the textures of the landscape and its seasonal changes - stags shedding velvet in autumn, naked hatchlings in spring, the wildness of winter and the abundance of summer. Profound transformations of the costumes took place without the dancers leaving the bubble; a ruched skirt became a parachute and floral suits appeared seemingly from nowhere.

The work was shortened and the costume designs adapted for urban outdoor festivals in Hull, Sheffield, London and Leeds.

Director and Choreographer: Simon Birch
Set Designers: Simon Birch and Becs Andrews
Costume Designer: Becs Andrews
Sound Designer: Composer: Jon Hughes
Photographer: Simon Birch (image 2);
Becs Andews (image 3)

THE WIND TUNNEL PROJECT

ARTLINER AND BKKR
2014

*Q121 and R52, Heritage Buildings,
Farnborough
June 2014*

THE WIND TUNNEL PROJECT: Shrouded in secrecy since their inception, Q121 and R52 were two of the earliest aerodynamic testing facilities in the world, which reveal themselves to the public for the first time via The Wind Tunnel Project. McIntyre-Burnie's work within this multi-faceted project, 'Flying into the Dawn' transformed both buildings into an immersive journey, delving into the dichotomy of flight: the wonder and the terror.

Drawing on a team of sound, light, food and exhibition designers, the piece developed in situ, responding both to the unique qualities of this momentous site and to its role as the harbinger of flight. Flying into the Dawn explores how flight offered an almost spiritual escape from the horrific reality of World War 1, a period when, instead of reconciling the past, people made believe in the future. An historic recording from 1942 parries a new choral piece performed and recorded in situ; illuminated zones vie with darkness; slippers encourage a silence, whilst popping candy jars with anechoic alcoves. An insect filmed at 10,000 frames a second provides a surreal insight into the invisible realm, whilst paper planes amidst a starling murmeration offer us a place to play. The work reawakened the space as a place to transport us into an imagined past and a preternatural now, mechanised threat and childhood wonder.

Director: Artliner and BKKR

Lighting Designer: Isometrix

Artist and Sound Designer:
Thor McIntyre-Burnie

Curator: Salma Tuqan

Images
THE WIND TUNNEL
PROJECT

1/
MEGAN BAKER
COSTUME DESIGN

UNION
Tim Barrow (2013-14)

Royal Lyceum Theatre, Edinburgh, Scotland
March 2014

MB: This play is about the original 1707 Union of Scotland and England. It took real history and historical characters and events but approached them with a freedom that was playful, anachronistic and had an epic sweep through time and place, taking on politicians, royalty and bankers. I wanted the costumes to reflect the need for an audience to trust the historical truth and arguments of the piece, but to get away from a literal accuracy. I used colour and texture to give each world its own sensual definition from bawdy taverns and the Scottish Parliament, to the Court of Queen Anne. We wanted to feel that we could taste and smell the worlds of the characters to understand how they lived and therefore who they were. I was playful in using contemporary references such as 'pin stripe' to hint at modern city bankers, alongside period cuts to create a visual dialogue between the period of the play and the audience who were watching it.

Lyceum Theatre Company
Director: Mark Thomson
Set Designer/Video Artist: Andrzej Goulding
Costume Designer: Megan Baker
Lighting Designer: Chris Davey
Sound Designer: Philip Pinsky
Photographer: Tim Morozzi

2/
MEGAN BAKER
COSTUME DESIGN

THE GUID SISTERS
Michel Tremblay (1968)
Translated by Martin Bowman and Bill Findlay

Co-production between the Royal Lyceum Theatre
and the National Theatre of Scotland
The Royal Lyceum Theatre, Edinburgh
The King's Theatre, Glasgow
September 2012

MB: There is a long history of cultural connection between Scotland and French Quebec and Michel Tremblay's play about a group of working class women filling books of green shields stamps connected the two cultures in perfect understanding. A key decision was to celebrate the play in its own period in the early 1960's. Both set and costumes sought to reflect Serge's vision of the play as a truthful and theatrical world of wonderful grotesquery. To achieve this I rooted the costume in the cut and prints of the period using fabric and colour to heighten and exaggerate, to achieve a sense that we were watching something real but with the contrast and colour turned up too high. So we were always watching something real without settling into absolute naturalism.

Director: Serge Denoncourt
Set Designer: Francis O'Connor
Costume Designer: Megan Baker
Lighting Designer: Charles Balfour
Sound Designer: Philip Pinsky
Photographer: Richard Campbell

Images 1 & 2   Images 3 & 4
Union   The Guid Sisters

CATHERINE BAINES
COSTUME DESIGN

THERE IS A WAR
Tom Basden (2011)

Mountview Theatre School
Jacksons Lane Theatre,
February 2013

CB: There is a War is set in a non-specific
war zone, where the blue and the grey
armies are waging war against each other.
The play focuses on the bureaucracy of the
military, through an amusing and sometimes
deliberately confusing portrayal of a war zone
where no one quite knows what is happening.
The colours of the armies' blue grey uniforms
are indistinguishable. Despite this, the
characters continue fighting until the bitter end.
The play is darkly comedic and contains many
unsettling, bewildering yet amusing characters.

Director: Dan Bird
Set Designer: Matt Hope
Costume Designer:
Catherine Baines
Lighting designer:
Matthew 'Lux' Swithinbank
Sound designer: Hannah Pardon

Image
There Is A War

LARA BOOTH
SET AND COSTUME DESIGN

IL RITORNO D'ULISSE IN PATRIA
Claudio Monteverdi (1640)

Royal Northern College of Music
Opera theatre, RNCM
December 2012

LB: The design grew from an early discussion about Homer's
Odyssey; the notion of a story being retold over centuries,
passed on from one generation to the next. The set takes the
form of a book, the cover of which, woven, weather-worn and
richly textured, becomes Penelope's Palace wall. The structure
revolves to reveal the book's inner pages, carved out to form
the rocky shores of Ithaca. The singers move through caves
and transcend cliff tops. A strip of sky is lit with a godlike
eye in the form of the sun or moon. The costumes belong to
our Ithaca alone, influenced by both traditional clothing and
contemporary fashion design from the Asian continent.

A number of illusions were incorporated to achieve
the magic elements in the plot such as Ulysses' onstage
transformation to a beggar, and a bow and arrow that
could be seen to shoot the three suitors dead on stage.

Director: Stefan Janski
Set and Costume Designer: Lara Booth
Lighting Designer: John Bishop
Illusionist: Darren Lang
Photographer: Paul Cliff

Images
Il Ritorno d'Ulisse in Patria

REBECCA BRADBURY
SET AND COSTUME DESIGN

ALICE'S ADVENTURES IN WONDERLAND

Trent Repertory Company
May Hall, Trent College
June 2014

RB: With so many adaptations everyone has their own idea of what Wonderland should be. I wanted to create a world that was unexpected but instantly recognisable. The design emerged from a request by director Donnaleigh Bailey, to make the audience feel the same surprise and wonder Alice does when falling down the rabbit hole, and discovering Wonderland. Upon entering, the audience were met with a simple black and white set including a large screen surrounded by John Tenniel's original illustrations. A tree that rooted Alice to the real world and a compass painted across the floor show that ultimately, it is the journey of a girl through a nonsensical and disparate world. By having a stark colourless set we were able to produce, through lighting, colourful scene transformations that created a strong visual narrative.

Director: Donnaleigh Bailey
Set and Costume Designer: Rebecca Bradbury
Lighting Designer: Tom Olding
Photographer: Helen Boyd

MARIE BRENNEIS
INSTALLATION/SCULPTURE/PERFORMANCE

DELIBERATE DIGRESSION
Marie Brenneis

The Performance Pad Depot
The Performance Pad, Mainz, Germany
May 2012

MB: Deliberate digression is an installation/ performance/dance piece which explores hysteria and irrationality.

Director, Choreographer,
Set and Costume designer: Marie Brenneis
Photographer: Marie Brenneis

SIMON BANHAM:

If I pick up my current sketchbook, open it, the first clear drawing I come across is this:

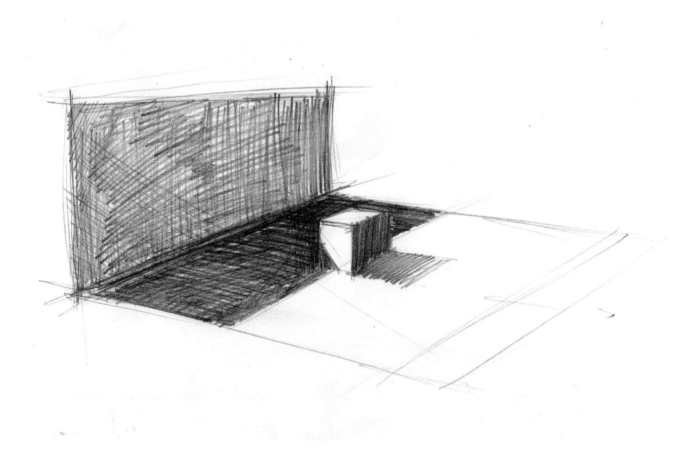

    This drawing and the following drawing don't strike me as too dissimilar; they're both shaping, framing and suggesting a simple space with form and light. At the moment they are nothing, they are waiting to become, I know what they might be, but at this stage I don't know what they are.

    The drawings start at opposite ends of a sketchbook and develop in different directions, peopled as they are by different ideas and communities.

A YEAR IN TWO DRAWINGS

If I pick up the same sketchbook, turn it over, open it, the first clear drawing I come across is this:

However, despite these conflicting demands, as they move physically closer through the pages of the book, perhaps the initial intention to frame a situation (rarely a place) in space with light and form and then through time (so the scenography is always becoming something new) becomes even clearer and hasn't shifted so far from those first drawings. The same clay.

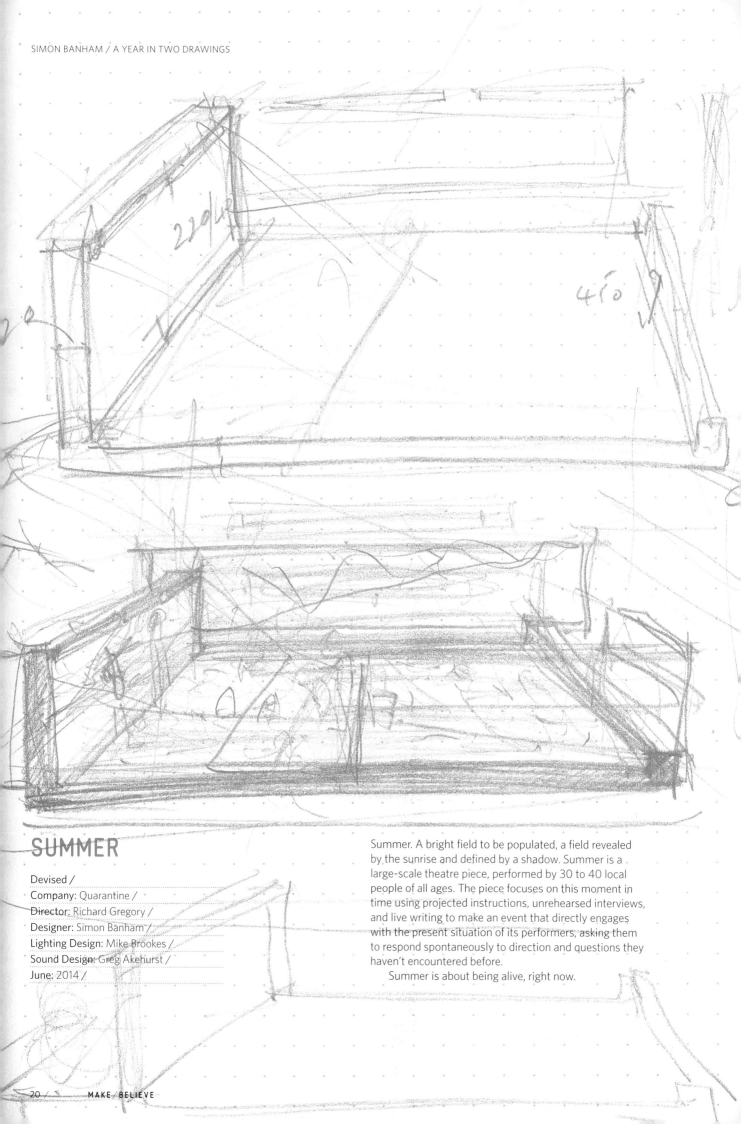

SUMMER

Devised /
Company: Quarantine /
Director: Richard Gregory /
Designer: Simon Banham /
Lighting Design: Mike Brookes /
Sound Design: Greg Akehurst /
June: 2014 /

Summer. A bright field to be populated, a field revealed by the sunrise and defined by a shadow. Summer is a large-scale theatre piece, performed by 30 to 40 local people of all ages. The piece focuses on this moment in time using projected instructions, unrehearsed interviews, and live writing to make an event that directly engages with the present situation of its performers, asking them to respond spontaneously to direction and questions they haven't encountered before.

Summer is about being alive, right now.

The drawing at the the front of my sketchbook becomes 'Summer'
created by Quarantine, performed in a warehouse in Salford.
    It looked like this:

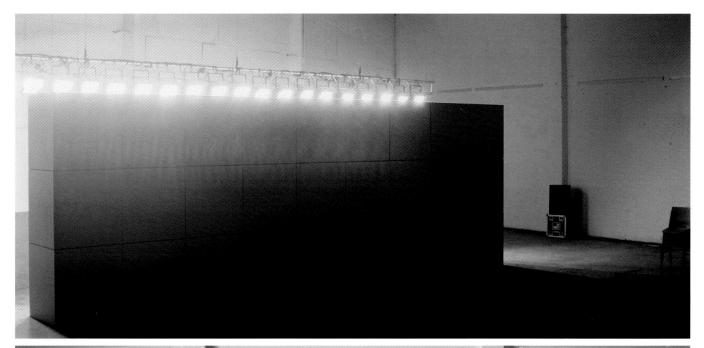

THE TRIAL

Composer: Philip Glass /
Libretto: Christopher Hampton /
Company: Music Theatre Wales /
Director: Michael McCarthy /
Conductor: Michael Rafferty /
Set & Costume Design: Simon Banham /
Lighting Design: Ace McCarron /
October: 2014 /

THE TRIAL: Josef K is confined to one space that becomes many places. Whilst appearing to be solid the space is fluid and permeable, doors and windows open within the walls, hands and arms appear through the joins, a small cupboard becomes a larger cupboard and becomes a dark void, until the whole back wall disappears, but there is still no escape. Surrounded by an ever changing array of characters, sharing moustaches and beards, he is constantly observed and his actions and environment manipulated until he accepts the inevitability of his own death.

WASHING LINGS
FAUSE BEARDS

TINY CONSTRICTED SPACE

The drawing at the back of my sketchbook becomes 'The Trial', a new Philip Glass opera staged by Music Theatre Wales at the Royal Opera House, London.
It looked like this:

Images
Crocodiles

SARAH BEATON
SET AND COSTUME DESIGN

CROCODILES
Lee Mattinson (2014)

Royal Exchange Theatre Company
The Studio, Royal Exchange Theatre, Manchester
October 2014

SB: Crocodiles transforms the Royal Exchange
Studio into an isolated and decaying seaside
guest house. The subsiding, fractured house
is thrust into the space, with the structure
of the theatre dissecting its distinctive blue
beams. The set becomes more saturated and
obscure as the play develops: transforming the
once-real buffet into a knitted party tea with an
invited knitted boyfriend and crocodile.

Director: Ng Choon Ping
Set and Costume Designer: Sarah Beaton
Lighting Designer: Matthew Haskins
Sound Designer: Dominic Kennedy
Video Designer: Gillian Tan

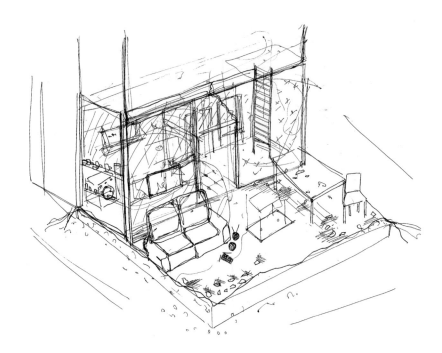

Crocodiles - Scene 10

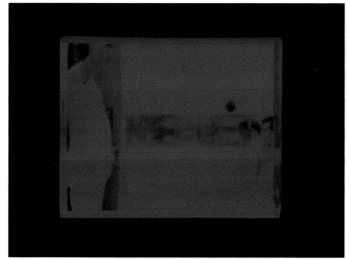

Images 1 & 2   Images 3 - 5
Peep / 69   Quiproquo

1/
SIGNE BECKMANN
SET AND COSTUME DESIGN

PEEP / 69
Leo Butler (69) (2012)

Natural Shocks
Peep venue / Pleasance Courtyard, Edinburgh Theatre
July 2012

SB: Peep is a unique pop up peepshow theatre with a series of performances taking place at the Pleasance Courtyard, Assembly Gardens and Latitude Festival 2012-13.

Each audience member is treated to an individual peep booth, where they put on headphones and sit back and enjoy the show through a one-way mirror. They can see the performers but the performers can't see the audience, creating a very private and anonymous experience for the viewer.

Director: Donnacadh O'Briain
Venue designer: Signe Beckmann
Set and Costume Designer: Signe Beckmann
Lighting Designer: Ben Ormerod
Sound Designer: Nick Powell
Photographer: Signe Beckmann

2/
SIGNE BECKMANN
SET AND COSTUME DESIGN

QUIPROQUO
Samuel Gustavsson and Niclas Stureberg (2012)

Rapid Eye
Dansehallerne, Copenhagen
March 2012

SB: Can people be manipulated to perform actions they would not have chosen to do themselves? Does free will exist? Quiproquo sets out on a quest to find the answers to these questions and more. The performers are exploring the relationship between cause and effect, using their bodies and a string of objects. It is a fusion of the theatrical stage image and the virtuosity of juggling.

Director: Mads Rosenbeck
Choreographer: Mads Rosenbeck and Samuel Gustavsson
Composer/ Music: Sture Ericson
Set and Costume Designer: Signe Beckmann
Lighting and Sound Designer: Tobias Staal
Photographer: Tobias Staal

1/
TANJA BEER
DIRECTION, SET AND COSTUME DESIGN

STRUNG (THIS IS NOT RUBBISH)
Tanja Beer (concept) 2012/2013

The Arts Centre (Melbourne), World Stage Design (Cardiff), Royal Central School of Speech and Drama (London)
February 2013

TB: Strung is a performance installation that dissolves boundaries between performer and designer, installation and costume, site and material. The work is part of This is Not Rubbish, a larger research project that explores the journey of a material rescued from landfill, and its capacity to create immersive performance spaces and wearable artefacts. After the final performance of Strung, the set material (reclaimed salami netting) was knitted into unique fashion accessories and auctioned off for charity. A major focus of eco scenographic practice is the elimination of landfill waste in the production of sets and costumes. This is Not Rubbish embraces the potential of ecological practice, emphasising what is possible in a world of limited resources, rather than what is not.

Director: Tanja Beer
Set and Costume Designer: Tanja Beer
Active Scenographers (London): Ella Marie Fowler, Jacquie Holland and Natalie Jackson
Photographer: Alex Murphy

2/
TANJA BEER
CONCEPT AND SET DESIGN

THE LIVING STAGE
Tanja Beer (concept) 2012/2013

The Living Stage/Plantable Research Collective Castlemaine State Festival (Australia), World Stage Design (Wales)
March 2013

TB: The Living Stage combines stage design, permaculture and community engagement to create a recyclable, biodegradable and edible performance space. Part theatre and part garden, the project collaborates with local permaculturists to build 'living' stages that are specific to site and community. The Living Stage considers ecological principles and environmental impact as opportunities rather than constraints: ethics that can illuminate, and be integral to aesthetics. Celebrating the multisensory aspects of scenography, the project seeks to engage with its audiences on a haptic, olfactory and gustatory level. The Living Stage was created as part of the Castlemaine State Festival (image above) and for World Stage Design as the Trans-Plantable Living Room. Moving beyond recycling and efficiency, the project posed a more radical question: 'Can we create designs that not only enrich our audience, but our community and environment as well?'

Director: Various devised works by CreateAbility, Born in a Taxi and Plantable
Set Designer: Tanja Beer
Costume Designer: Adrienne Chisholm (Castlemaine)
Permaculture Designers: Hamish MacCallum and Sas Allardice (Castlemaine) and Sam Holt and the Riverside Community Allotments (Cardiff)
Photographer: Gisela Beer (Castlemaine)

3/
TANJA BEER
SET DESIGN

SEA CHANGE
Richard Osborne (2014)

The Place, London
2014

TB: My initial design concept for Sea Change – a dance piece about climate change – was to create a hanging sculpture of 'ice' that could 'melt' on stage. However, the idea was soon reconsidered when I was advised that all set fabric would need to be fire-retarded using a toxic substance that I was keen to avoid. Back in the rehearsal room, the choreographer and I decided to simplify. Rejecting the separate sculpture idea, we asked the dancers to explore their costumes scenographically, using their bodies to connect with the fabric more abstractly, physically and spatially. The result was a piece of visual dramaturgy that was far more integrated and successful than my original idea: the costumes were first hung as a sculpture, and then became wearable items, before being used as scenic elements to help support the narrative and emotion of the piece.

Choreographer: Richard Osborne
Set Designer: Tanja Beer
Costume Designer: Rosie Gibson
Lighting Designer: Anna Sbokou and Sarah Crocker
Photographer: Tracey Fahy

1/
GIUSEPPE BELLI
SET DESIGN

A SOLDIER AND A MAKER
Iain Burnside (2012)

The Pit, Barbican, London
April 2012

GB: Ivor Gurney's studies at the Royal College of Music were interrupted by World War 1. He suffered shell shock in the trenches in France and became increasingly ill. Ivor Gurney spent the last 15 years of his life in the City of London Mental Hospital in Dartford where he continued to work and rework his music and poetry until his death from tuberculosis in 1937.

The design for the set is moulded by his life and correspondences including poetry, music and letters from the trenches.

I experimented with lighting gels on a blue composite installation of images taken in the countryside of Gloucestershire which was frequented, loved and written about by Gurney and his contemporaries, together with text from his poetry written in the trenches. Matching many gels to colours in the set, I was able to affect the graphic quality, and manipulate the image and depth of field, making things appear and dissipate with scenes remaining grounded in the desolation of burnt tree spikes at the battlefield of Ypres.

Images 1 & 2:
A Soldier and a Maker

Images 3 & 4:
Journeying Boys

Director: Iain Burnside

Set Designer: Giuseppe Belli

Costume Designer: Emma Belli

Movement: Victoria Newlyn

Lighting Designer: Rob Dyer

Photographer: Rob Dyer

2/
GIUSEPPE BELLI
SET DESIGN

JOURNEYING BOYS
Iain Burnside (2013)

Britten Theatre Royal College of Music
February 2013

GB: An RCM commission and part of the Britten Centenary celebrations, it explores Les Illuminations, Britten's settings of Arthur Rimbaud's extraordinary prose poems.

Faced with multiple quick scenes, split staging, multiple period settings and a complex narrative with cross period dialogues I drew inspiration from the teachings of my first Theatre Design tutor – Christopher Morley, RSC designer and Minimalist. I began to consider the design in a more painterly way, rendering and transforming through colour and accent on form.

Consideration of the lighting dimensionally on the painterly 2D forms allowed me to experiment with shapes and colours. This themed the scenes, accentuating morphing and transfiguring them with architecture and unobtrusive life.

Director: Iain Burnside

Set Designer: Giuseppe Belli

Costume Designer: Jools Osborne

Movement: Stephen Pelton

Lighting Designer: Paul Tucker

Photographer: Giuseppe Belli

NABUCCO

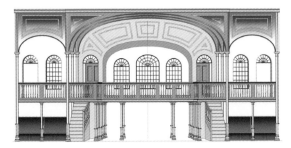

OPERA NATIONAL DE LORRAINE NOVEMBER 2014

Verdi's Nabucco tells the story of the destruction of the Temple of Solomon in Jerusalem by Nebuchadnezzar, and the forcing of the captured Hebrews towards enslavement, exile and death in Babylon. It is unusual in the almost constant presence and participation of the chorus. It seemed possible that this was the sort of story that might be enacted by a community almost as a ritual, like a Nativity play in a Christian church, and that this would be a Hebrew community. I am always depressed travelling in Europe to see, increasingly, synagogues under special protection measures, with sentries outside. In Nancy, where the performance is taking place at the Opera National de Lorraine, there is a synagogue from the late 18th century in a compound behind a bullet deflecting fence which makes it all but invisible, despite being

in the very centre of a bourgeois French town. This synagogue was stripped in the 1940s with its contents destroyed and burnt and most of its congregation transported and killed. It has now been restored, and the Jewish community has come back to something like its pre-war level. There are plenty of others that remain empty shells, and it was one of these spaces that we began to think of as the gathering place for this ritual, performed by a congregation of what might be ghosts or memories.

The beautiful Opera House at Nancy shares some geometry with synagogues put up around Europe at the end of the 17th century, in making the design, I wanted to make the stage space a reflection, or extension, of the auditorium. The proscenium is echoed in the shape of the arch at the back of the set, and the balconies run at the same height as the boxes at the side of the dress circle. The set runs to a vanishing point suggested by the horseshoe of the auditorium.

The set needs to accommodate a chorus of 60, on stage most of the time. The balcony level aims to accommodate them, with at times a small banda (12 musicians), while

leaving the downstage centre clear for the rather conventional 19th century love story in which love conquers history. The set goes very high into the grid and far into the wings so that there is little sense of it ending, and the space appears cavernous.

Most of my physical process takes place in the model box. I use a fairly basic desk top publishing programme both for drawing up and printing out parts of the models, and for producing the final drawings. This keeps the process between models and drawings quite fluid, and in the early stages allows the sketching out and throwing away of quite detailed pieces which are quick and easy to resize and reconfigure. It stops the process from becoming too precious. It's the part I find most instructive, when you see the shapes that have existed in the back of your mind or a bad drawing begin to resolve themselves, or otherwise, in three dimensions. Later, as the work becomes more detailed, there's a degree to which the many laborious repetitive tasks involved in making a model, all requiring complete attention and focus, keep the left brain occupied well enough to free up the

HOWEVER EVOCATIVE A MODEL IS, THERE IS STILL A HUGE AMOUNT IN TERMS OF FINISH THAT CAN ONLY BE ACHIEVED AT FULL SIZE...

right side for more inspirational and creative thought. Often interesting ideas and solutions crop up while cutting out.

I've included some pictures showing early models being cut about in discussion with the director, leading towards more finished versions at white card stage, and the final model—also a final drawing in which you can still see elements of the first model.

I would normally have a pretty strong idea of what the finish and textures on the final set are while working on the white card model, based on an accumulation of visual references, and where not, the process of making the final model tends to ask and answer those questions. In a set like this one, patina is the most eloquent voice in telling the visual story, and colour choices have been led by the desire to show a passage of time and neglect. The few flecks of paint are there to set off the rust.

Between an accurate model and good paint and texture references there is probably enough to go on, but I think the more of your intentions you can put into a final model, the easier it is to inform and enthuse a distant workshop. It can also be a very useful tool to

motivate managements.

However evocative a model is, there is still a huge amount in terms of finish that can only be achieved at full size. At a scale of 1:25, after all, a millimetre in the model is an inch (2.5cm) in real life, and there is some detail that can only be hinted at and supported with references. The set for this Nabucco has had the luxury of four weeks on stage for rehearsal, with three full day paint calls spread out over the month, giving plenty of time to watch the space evolve under light, and move on. The atelier in Nancy has done a terrific job, but as everywhere, different workshops have very different ideas of representation, and much of the first paint calls were spent adding volume and texture to rust and paint. The most effective and unifying element has turned out to be pigeon shit, liberally and crustily splattered throughout, on the floor, the balustrades and the red stair carpets - specially installed to set it off.

Dick Bird 21/11/2014

NABUCCO
Giuseppe Verdi (1841)
Opera National de Lorraine
November 2014

Conductor: Rani Calderon
Director: John Fulljames
Set Designer: Dick Bird
Costume Designer: Christina Cunningham
Masks: Cecile Kretschmar
Lighting Design: Lee Curran
Photographer: Dick Bird

1/
JOHN BISHOP
LIGHTING DESIGN

MIGNON
Ambroise Thomas (1866)

Buxton Festival
Buxton Opera House
July 2011

JB: Mignon tells the story of the kidnapping of a little girl The harsh reality of a troupe of unemployed travelling performers, their inspired performance of A Midsummer Night's Dream in a Baron's theatre, the attempted arson of the theatre and the rescue of Mignon from the fire are all intertwined with the homeless tramp Lothario's endless search for his long lost daughter. The feeling of old fashioned theatre mixed with simple poverty and the triumph of love over adversity figured prominently in my design decisions while I was creating the lighting design for Mignon. Disguising my use of 21st Century moving lights and a large rig of conventional lighting equipment was paramount to my portrayal of a visual likeness to traditional 19th Century footlights and greasepaint.

Director: Annilese Miskimmon
Choreographer: Diane Smith
Set and Costume Designer: Nicky Shaw
Lighting Designer: John Bishop
Photographer: John Bishop

2/
JOHN BISHOP
LIGHTING DESIGN

KASHCHEI THE IMMORTAL
Nikolai Rimsky-Korsakov (1901-1902)

Buxton Festival
Buxton Opera House
July 2012

JB: Stephen Lawless, the director of this Buxton Festival production wove an intricate and sometimes fantastical thread through a double bill of two unconnected fairy tale operas, Maiden in the Tower and Kashchei the Immortal. Russell Craig's vivid set design for the birthday party of a bailiff's son in a make believe nursery in the first opera, became the seedy apartment of an abuser in the second opera. Similarly, the young girl bullied and locked in the doll's house of the first opera became the abused princess imprisoned in a cage of the second. Developing a captivating visual fantasy for the world of the nursery to contrast and conflict with the harshness of the abuser's apartment became my main concern. The result was a coherent series of visually striking semi-realistic and imaginary settings illustrating the convoluted and make believe passions of the operas as their stories unfolded.

Director: Stephen Lawless
Choreographer: Lynne Hockney
Set and Costume Designer: Russell Craig
Lighting Designer: John Bishop
Video Designer: Stanley Orwin-Fraser
Photographer: John Bishop

Images 1 & 2
Mignon

Images 3 & 4
Kashchei the Immortal

Images 5-7
Tannhäuser

3/
JOHN BISHOP
LIGHTING DESIGN

TANNHÄUSER
Richard Wagner (1842-1845)

Opéra National du Rhin
Opéra National du Rhin, Strasbourg
March 2013

JB: My overall challenge in creating
the lighting design for Keith Warner's
extraordinary production of Tannhäuser
was to overcome the practical difficulties
presented by Boris Kudlička's architecturally
complex and inventive set design, whilst
providing a rich and varied tapestry of light.
Unable to utilise conventional spotbars due
to the vast ceiling towering over the set, I
chose to light the many scenes through the
central, articulating cone which descended
through the ceiling. The scenes ranged from
the bordello excesses of Venusberg, to the
mysterious hunting forests outside the castle
of Wartburg through which the pilgrims
pass, to the interior of the grand hall of the
Wartburg in which Tannhäuser competes in
a song contest for the love of Elizabeth. They
continue through the journey of the exhausted
pilgrims returning from Rome, to the death
of Elizabeth and finally the re-birth of hope
through the green shoots on the papal staff
suggesting God's forgiveness of Tannhäuser.

Director: Keith Warner
Choreographer: Karl Alfred Schreiner
Set Designer: Boris Kudlička
Costume Designer: Kaspar Glarner
Lighting Designer: John Bishop
Video Designer: Mikolaj Molenda
Photographer: John Bishop

Images 1 - 3
The Tempest

Images 4 & 5
Il Ritorno d'Ulisse in Patria

1/
HAZEL BLUE
SET AND COSTUME DESIGN

THE TEMPEST
William Shakespeare (1611)

Tron Theatre Company
The Tron, Glasgow
May 2011

HB: This Tempest was set in a rusted industrial jungle gym. The Tron's Mayfesto '14 was a response to the Glasgow Commonwealth Games, and the theme of all the productions and play readings was colonisation and the defiance, poetry and power that is found in colonial literature. Cesaire's 'A Tempest' was quoted both at the beginning and at the end of the play. The set used as much of the height and space of the venue as possible to create many different levels,which were accessible to the actors, while the moving, rotating spiral staircase related to a swirling hurricane. The characters were generally quite absurdly costumed, while Caliban's robes were reminiscent of a dignified indigenous person, representing his connection with the earthy, bountiful territory he has lost to Prospero. It is essential to believe in what we make to ensure that what we make is believed.

Director: Andy Arnold
Set and Costume Designer: Hazel Blue
Lighting Designer: Sergey Jakovsky
Sound Designer: Barry McColl
Production Media Designer: JamHot
Scenic Artist: Ashleigh Blair
Photographer: John Johnston

2/
HAZEL BLUE
SET AND COSTUME DESIGN

IL RITORNO D'ULISSE IN PATRIA
Claudio Monteverdi (1639/40)

Royal Conservatoire of Scotland
Alexander Gibson Opera Studio RCS
October 2013

HB: This production was set 30 years after World War 1 with Ulisse returning from the Front. The mortals are dressed appropriately for the period, while the gods' costumes are more a reflection of their roles in the manipulation of the mortals. The fabrics for their costumes were screen printed by myself, with images relating to their characters. The black and white theme unifies the group and is continued into their otherworldly make up. Although these gods walk among the mortals who are oblivious to their presence, the audience is led to believe in their supernatural powers by the transformative power of costume, make up, lighting and music

Director: Mark Hathaway
Set and Costume Designer: Hazel Blue
Lighting Designer: Chris Hayes
Photographer: Ken Dundas

1/
MARIE BLUNCK
PRODUCTION DESIGN

MASQUERADE
Slung Low and Clay Interactive Ltd

Slung Low and Clay Interactive Ltd
Victoria & Albert Museum, London
2014

MB: In this permanent interactive installation for the V&A's new Europe 1600-1800 galleries, the life-sized door opens to reveal a young English debutante (Phoebe Sparrow) at the Venetian Carnival in the early 1760s.

Harlequin, played by Dan Watson, jumps in to the scene to encourage the audience to mimic his gestures. Upon striking the right pose, the story proceeds with the audience accompanying the debutante through a masked ball, a gambling hall (Il Ridotto) and a Commedia Del'Arte performance on a public piazza.

Working with the V&A curatorial team to maintain strong historical accuracy, the design captures the atmosphere of Venetian life found in the sketches and paintings of Carlevarijs, Guardi and Tiepolo. Surrounded by the artefacts of the period, the installation avoids a documentary style in favour of immersing the audience into sketchy vignettes.

The live cast consisted of community volunteers from diverse groups, who went through an intensive series of workshops run by theatre company Slung Low to learn about the choreography, mannerisms and deportment of 1760s Venice.

Live footage was shot on green screen, whilst the background spaces are drawn visualisations of 1760s Venice, bringing the scenes to life with a painterly quality and giving the right feel for the era.

Director: Alan Lane
Choreographer: Lucy Hind
Sound Designers: Heather Fenoughty and Georgi Marinov
Production/Media Designer: Marie Blunck
Director of Photography: Jonny Franklin

2/
MARIE BLUNCK
PRODUCTION DESIGN

59 MINUTES TO SAVE CHRISTMAS
Oliver Senton and Alan Lane (2012)

Slung Low
Barbican Centre, London and CAST, Doncaster Theatre Company:
December 2012 and December 2013

MB: This site-specific performance is an exciting, fantastical adventure for young people during the festival period. Christmas has been taken hostage by the evil Professor Meanwood, and the audience of children follow Jack and Sergeant Hiccup on an interactive adventure through the venue in an attempt to rescue it. The interactive journey takes the audience to an elf workshop, a Christmas fairy on a tree, a lonely snowman and culminates in the professor's secret lair. Moving objects such as a remote controlled Christmas tree on wheels and a speeding smoke maker leads the audience between locations.

Recalling a world of Ruritania and inspired by cuckoo clocks and Lady Gaga, the design transports the audience into small worlds, whilst giving them activities to complete. Upon completing each task, the children are one step closer to saving Christmas. For example, the lonely snowman stuck in his over sized snowglobe is encouraged to break free once the audience has sung a Christmas carol.

Each audience member wears a set of radio headphones, and the performance is a mixture of live dialogue and prerecorded soundtrack composed by Heather Fenoughty.

Director: Alan Lane
Choreographer: Lucy Hind
Set and Costume Designer: Marie Blunck
Lighting Designer: Rick Mountjoy, Kelli Zezulka
Sound Designer: Heather Fenoughty
Photographer: Kelli Zezulka

Images 1 & 2
Masquerade

Image 3
59 Minutes To Save Christmas

1/
MISTY BUCKLEY
PRODUCTION DESIGN

COLDPLAY - GHOST STORIES
International tour
April 2014

Images from Royal Albert Hall, London
July 2014

MB: The concept of the show was based on the Dark Night of the Soul poem by Saint John of the Cross in 1578, which reflected a process of immense change. Winter trees with delicate paper origami stars blossoming from them reflected the somewhat sombre but delicate tone of the album. In Japanese tradition origami is synonymous with transformation, taking the seemingly ordinary and transforming it in to something sculptural and beautiful.

The materials held great importance: paper for its delicacy and magical qualities, wood for its strength and resilience and light for its warmth. Paper is also symbolic in so many cultures as a representation of love, luck, birth and death. Five hundred paper stars were duly created and individually folded by the art department; each one with hand written lyrics from A Sky Full of Stars. All this sat within the inky backdrop of Mila's Furstova's haunting backdrops.

Director: Phil Harvey
Set Designer: Misty Buckley
Lighting Designer: Paul Normandale

2/
MISTY BUCKLEY
PRODUCTION DESIGN

GLASTONBURY FESTIVAL
Pilton, Somerset

The Park and other areas

MB: It was a real honour. Glastonbury is a working farm and a very family run festival. Everyone who works there has a special affinity with the festival or the site, or the spiritual time of year. Despite 187,000 people it is still the most intimate, friendly, warm, creative atmosphere.

There were lots of challenges, from weather conditions to having to build everything from scratch. We lived on site together for three weeks, everyone bringing their creativity and ideas along. The art department was from all over - prison workers, lawyers, tree surgeons, all with a burning creativity. The role of the designer was also the facilitator of everyone's creativity and it was amazing to be part of that with scenic painters, welders, carpenters, costume designers.

The best part was when the gates opened and tens of thousands of people run down the fields... That's what completes the scene

Directors: Emily Eavis & Michael Eavis
Designer: Misty Buckley

Images 1 & 2   Image 3
Coldplay - Ghost Stories   Glastonbury Festival

3/
MISTY BUCKLEY
PRODUCTION DESIGN

PARALYMPICS CLOSING CEREMONY

*Olympic Stadium, Greenwich, London
August 2012*

MB: This was the embodiment of our dreams, ideas, passions and goals; symbol of the desire and drive to achieve the seemingly impossible for the underbelly of society who achieve in spite of misfortune - the artists, poets, dreamers, musicians, thinkers, all of those who create and strive for a better place. This is a representation of the journey of the athletes, who achieved greatness against the odds.

The ceremony began in an almost empty stadium, with just a simple sundial in the centre. A war veteran, Rory, climbs the 10m high staircase with prosthetic limbs; an arduous climb and delivers a speech from the top inviting everyone to join him in celebrations in the stadium.
A huge truck invasion happens of different vehicles and machines...

And the festival begins...
Festivals are a great leveller where anything goes and all are welcome. We didn't want to emulate festival so we created our own. I drew on follow festival creators to help realize my ideas and designs, bringing their wonderful creativity with them. I brought in Joe Rush, founder of Mutoid Waste Company, to help realize my vision it was an incredibly creative and inclusive environment; Kinetika Community Arts, Joe's amazing team, Help for Heroes as the cast, Candoco, Charles Hazlewood's Paralympic Orchestra - and our wonderful friends, Coldplay.

Director: Kim Gavin
Set Designer: Misty Buckley
Costume Designer: Michael Sharp
Lighting Designer: Patrick Woodroffe

Image 1
Paralympics Closing
Ceremony 2012

Image 2
Paralympics Closing
Ceremony concept board -
Spring (No2 of 8)

1/
SAMAL BLAK
SET AND COSTUME DESIGN
....
GHOST PATROL

Composer / Libretto: Stuart MacRae / Louise Welsh (2012)

Scottish Opera and Music Theatre Wales
Edinburgh International Festival
Traverse Theatre, Edinburgh, Theatre Royal Glasgow,
ROH2 London & UK Tour
August 2012
....

SB: The opera is set in a bar. It tells the story of two ex-soldiers who meet again some years after fighting in the army together. They share a secret: the killing of civilians, which was covered up. Both are still haunted by the event.

The aim of the design was to merge two worlds - the present time of the bar and the past of the war - allowing the set to morph into the landscape of their suppressed memories.

In designing the bar, I chose iconic references, in which colours and material evoked the battlefield - the hard metal bar top, the desert sand-coloured tiles, tv screens showing news of the ongoing war. At the climax bottles fell like bombs, 'ghost' images of the victims appeared on the screens, and the bar was transformed into the road where the horrifying killing took place.

Conductor: Michael Rafferty

Director: Matthew Richardson

Set and Costume Designer: Samal Blak

Lighting: Ace McCarron

Video: Tim Reid

Photographer: Robbie Jack

2/
SAMAL BLAK
SET AND COSTUME DESIGN
....
MACBETH

William Shakespeare (1611)

Guerilla Theatre
Miryang Theatre Village, Seoul, South Korea
February 2011
....

SB: The play starts with war. Like an infectious disease, the violence spreads, moving into the home for the most gruesome of all acts.

The design takes the war into the living room of a military wife and, by placing several scenes in this location, makes the act of murder all the more daring and reckless: the chance of getting caught is always present. The design allows several locations at the same time on stage, with the possibility of merging locations and situations fluently together. The aim was to depict both the home as well as the atmosphere of a corporate world in which the characters live and work. A world where... "there's no art To find the mind's construction in the face.."

In the play, humans are constantly at the mercy of weather and nature, an unknown force that can overwhelm. In contemporary society, we live most of our lives indoors, where we, in a disconnected manner, can experience the natural, outdoor world on television. This creates an unnatural atmosphere, an interesting equivalent to that imagined by Shakespeare.

Director: Alexander Zeldin

Set and Costume Designer: Samal Blak

Lighting: Kim Ing Gon

Photographer: Samal Blak

Image 1   Images 2 & 3
Ghost Patrol   Macbeth

NOT WHAT YOU EXPECT FROM OPERA

From interviews by Kate Burnett with Richard Willacy: Executive Director
of Birmingham Opera Company (BOC) and discussions with designers
Paul Brown and Samal Blak about their work with BOC on productions
Mitttwoch Aus Licht (2012) and Khovanskygate: an Enquiry (2014)

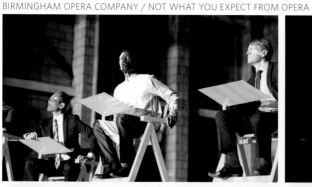

Images
Mittwoch Aus Licht
World Parliament (1)
Orchestra Finalists (2)
Helicopter String Quartet
(3 & 4)

RICHARD WILLACY:

The title of the company is **Birmingham Opera Company- Not what you expect from opera.** Graham Vick, founder and Artistic Director has led the company in Birmingham for almost 30 years. In 2000 the company opened the doors and volunteers were placed at the centre of its mission to make the highest quality work in partnership with the peoples of Birmingham. What BOC does is to bring people into the art, and, as a natural consequence of that, they bring other people with them who come because they have first hand contact with people in the show.

The company is multi-scale so chooses the right repertoire for different situations and spaces. We change our activity depending on who we're talking to and what we're trying to achieve. So for example, we will go and do a session in a community centre; we can't bring an orchestra, but a singer and instrument brings the experience up close. As our first port of call, we will bring somebody who is actually a leading person within the show, and in terms of the creative team, one of the directors, or the choreographer.

There is a link between every activity that happens through the year, whether it's 'just' a session in a community hall or whether it's the large-scale show, everything feeds back and forth. When we go to a community centre we check whether the libretto, which is in English, is understandable to an audience that's never heard it before. If it's not, we change it, or we sing it better. We uncover through practice what a composer intended and it all seeds together to create more resonant performances.

MITTWOCH AUS LICHT

Karlheinz Stockhausen's *Licht* (Light) is a modern masterpiece; a cycle of 7 operas, one for each day of the week. *Wednesday from Light* is the day of co-operation between the cycle's three driving forces; Lucifer, Eve and Michael. Regarded by many as 'unstageable' since its completion in 1998, and the only piece in the cycle to remain unperformed, *Wednesday from Light* was finally produced by BOC in a disused chemical factory, The Argyle Works, Birmingham, as part of the London 2012 Festival.

Each *Day* has a colour. Wednesday's colour is Yellow. The 'story' isn't easily distilled... this is from the score... from Stockhausen himself.

Intuition is the divine principle,
Vision is the spiritual realisation,
Mercury is the planet,
Sight is the sense,
Yellow is the colour,
Understanding is the human trait,
Peace is the dream,
Kindness is the virtue,
Harmony – Beauty – Art is the fruit of conflict,
Singing is the language,
Air is the element,
Raphael is the guardian angel.

PAUL BROWN DISCUSSING MITTWOCH AUS LICHT:

A lot of Mittwoch is very prescribed, for instance requiring 4 helicopters, so its perceived as unstageable. The directions can be a bit of a strangle-hold, especially in the Michaelion, which is completely choreographed and defined. It is all notated and has the least freedom, like an end-on piece of theatre needs wings, whereas the Orchestra Finalists section is so mad we just had to find a way to do it.

We had to meet the Stockhausen Foundation to discuss how it might be done in a found space. They expressed their acoustic demands, - it is slightly subjective how you hear it, and they came to see the space. It was an organic process, and is a different experience for the audience for each section. Its about glass skyscrapers and things better imagined than visualised. Its playful, it needs naivety, not hydraulics.

The music is sophisticated and electronic, he (Stockhausen) needs it to be listened to and understood in the brain. It comes across as playful – because of its name. But it is sophisticated and childlike. Allowing oneself as a listener to reach a space that isn't artful,- its joyful. At Birmingham Opera Company you are working with people with a story to tell and letting art and music release something that general life doesn't.

Working with the volunteers on costume, - you have to understand who they are to work out what they are going to wear. The principal is that people don't bring their own costumes, we costume them. Its under-designing (you don't want to drown them in a design idea), so that when there is an audience, the performers still feel a part of them too. Its important that the audience are surprised and seduced, - brought on the journey.

Hearing the helicopters for the first time was wonderful, - life and art!

MITTWOCH AUS LICHT
Karlheinz Stockhausen

Birmingham Opera Company
London 2012 Festival
Argyle Works, Digbeth, Birmingham
August 2012

Director: Graham Vick
Music Director: Kathinka Pasveer
Designer: Paul Brown
Lighting: Giuseppe Di Iorio
Choreography: Ron Howell

Images
Khovanskygate: A National Enquiry

DURING 2013 BIRMINGHAM OPERA COMPANY WORKED ON A PROGRAMME OF WORKSHOPS. EVENTS AND FILMS THAT LED TO THEIR PRODUCTION OF KHOVANSKYGATE: A NATIONAL ENQUIRY IN APRIL 2014. THIS WAS A NEW ENGLISH VERSION (LIBRETTO) BY MAX HOEHN OF MODEST MUSSORSKY'S OPERA KHOVANSCHINA.

A new dawn for Russia. Tsar Peter is unleashing a full-scale cultural revolution that will transform his country into a modern, European state. But first he must take back control of his capital from Ivan Khovansky and his corrupt police force. Khovansky has eliminated Peter's ministers in a bloody coup and is ready to proclaim his son, Andrei, as Tsar. The people of Russia, disillusioned and disenfranchised, await the outcome of this momentous day in their history.

RICHARD WILLACY:

Khovanschina raises strikingly modern parallels; Musorgsky paints a devastating portrait of a nation on the brink of collapse; torn apart by state corruption, religious fanaticism, social inequality and ethnic cleansing. Our version, Khovanskygate: A National Enquiry is both politically and personally challenging, its about now, especially around religion and ways of living. What do you want from *this* world? Would you rather live in the next? It was also a challenge for our mainly volunteer chorus, it would put them at the heart of the work. One of the things we do is to create an appetite for (taking part in) challenging work - we couldn't have imagined doing it (Khovanschina) 5 years ago.

SAMAL BLAK. DESIGNER:

Normally one would start off with an audience or a space, but not this time as none was confirmed, so I just designed speculatively for a space 40m x30m. I did rough sketch-ups, went to see spaces in Birmingham, started rehearsals. It was interesting working speculatively, looking at spaces for the worlds they could be... but we did know all the characters.

A tent is about temporary-ness, it comes and goes, its more about the people and events that would happen in such a space, small private moments crowded in behind the main stage or big open moments like the political campaign. We got the tent four weeks before opening, the aesthetics of it were to do with the real earth floor of the space it was in (outside the MAC in Birmingham). The aesthetic is about 'real', the aesthetic of real people, a lot of bad taste, ... a space meant for the camera - like a tv studio, or a sponsors' backdrop to a press conference.

We needed to be clear about the identity of different groups in that big space - there is no audience overview [because they are in amongst the performers], we had to use reality. The 'True Believers' were in black and white - mostly white. Placards were important, they fitted in with a world of messaging and selling. They could be lifted high or go on the ground; like the leaflets - flyers which ended up on the ground, stepped on.

The sound wins! You can't be too precious. So in the tent we added plywood cladding to structures and created other hard surfaces; we hung felt to absorb and balance the sound - we never start with sound, it comes organically, but it is the biggest thing.

With Birmingham Opera you can go up close and touch. You can feel liberated by moving around.

It's about 'how can you tell this?' interestingly, simply and clearly, about working in the moment. Working with Graham (Vick) is very inspiring. There is no such thing as beautiful or ugly, its about who or what is on stage.

KHOVANSKYGATE: A NATIONAL ENQUIRY
Opera by Modest Musorgsky (1880)
A new English version by Max Hoehn (2014)

Director: Graham Vick
Designer: Samal Blak
Movement Director: Ron Howell
Lighting Designer: Giuseppe Di Iorio
Conductor: Stuart Stratford
Chorus Master: Jonathan Laird
Birmingham Opera Company Chorus
Birmingham Opera Company Actors and Dancers
CBSO Children's Chorus
City of Birmingham Symphony Orchestra
BANDA formed by students of Birmingham Conservatoire

Photographer: Paul Brown
Lighting Designer: Wolfgang Goebbel
Set and Costume Designer: Paul Brown
Director: Graham Vick
Photographer: Paul Brown

Images
Nabucco

1/
PAUL BROWN
SET AND COSTUME DESIGN

NABUCCO
Giuseppi Verdi (1841)

New National Theatre Tokyo
May 2013

PB: The Temple of Consumerism is under attack by the forces of Anarchy. The audience watch the windows being broken and paint smeared over the 'desirable' merchandise. Eventually the anarchists end up worshipping what they sought to destroy and it is only through Nature that a resolution is reached, as rain pours down on the escalators and the marble floor slabs reveals earth beneath them.

Director: Graham Vick
Set and Costume Designer: Paul Brown
Lighting Designer: Wolfgang Goebbel
Photographer: Paul Brown

Images
Hippolyte et Aricie

2/
PAUL BROWN
SET AND COSTUME DESIGN

HIPPOLYTE ET ARICIE
Jean-Philippe Rameau (1733)

Glyndebourne Opera
June 2013

PB: This is an eclectic voyage illustrating an argument between Cupid and Diana. The opera opens in the glacial kingdom of Diana. Cupid creates a thaw by building a vegetable Arcadia out of the ingredients of the fridge. Our journey takes us to Hell-the soiled and grimy area behind the appliance inhabited by baroque flies, then via the domestic living room and bedroom of a couple locked in a loveless relationship. The final act set in a refrigerated mortuary which houses the bodies of the victims of Diana and Cupid's experiment.

Director: Jonathan Kent
Choreographer: Ashley Page
Set and Costume Designer: Paul Brown
Lighting Designer: Mark Henderson
Photographer: Mike Hoban

Images 1-3
Faust

1/
ISABELLA BYWATER
DIRECTION, SET AND COSTUME DESIGN

FAUST
Charles Gounod (1859)

Mariinsky Theatre, Saint Petersburg
2013

IB: Faust is a story of a man struggling with his demon. I gave him a simple lodging room as an academic bachelor in search of knowledge, which can transform as in a dream, to contain his obsession with a young girl. This simultaneously shows the everyday surroundings and his subconscious, or later, Marguerite's subconscious thoughts.

Director: Isabella Bywater
Choreographer: Dan O Neill
Set Designer: Isabella Bywater
Costume Designer: Isabella Bywater and Nicky Shaw
Lighting Designer: Jen Schriever
Production Media Designer: Nina Dunn
Photographer: Natascha Razina

2/
ISABELLA BYWATER
DIRECTION, SET AND COSTUME DESIGN

LUCIA DI LAMMERMOOR
Gaetano Donizetti (1835)

Danish Opera tour
March 2014

IB: Lucia di Lammermoor is a psychological thriller in which the young Lucia is mistreated. The space I decided on is a desolate decaying building (based on an asylum) where we could imagine Lucia and her only brother played cruel games, as children and where in adulthood her brother's games are life-threatening and Lucia is pushed to the edge of insanity.

Director: Isabella Bywater
Choreographer: Dan O Neill
Set and Costume Designer: Isabella Bywater
Lighting Designer: Hans Ake Sundqvist
Photographer: Anders Bach

Images 4-6
Lucia di Lammermoor

Images
The Burning Fiery Furnace

1/
KITTY CALLISTER
SET AND COSTUME DESIGN

THE BURNING FIERY FURNACE
Benjamin Britten (1966)

Mahogany Opera
Orford Church, Aldeburgh Festival
June 2013

KC: As part of the Britten100 Celebrations in 2013 Mahogany Opera decided to
stage Benjamin Britten's Church Parables and return them to Orford Church in
Suffolk, the location for which they were originally written and were first performed.

Because two of the parables were performed on the same evening and with
limited changeover time, the design had to be kept simple. Monks process down
the central aisle by candlelight, key characters then remove their habits to don the
colourful and opulent clothes of King Nebuchadnezzar's court. We were keen for the
costumes to capture the feel of an ancient Babylonian court. To do this, many of the
pieces and fabrics used for the costumes were sourced from antique shops, charity
shops and markets.

In the Burning Fiery Furnace a stained glass window forms the centrepiece of
the set. It is erected as part of the performance to become the shrine to the image
of the false God Merodak, and later the furnace in which the three Israelites are
condemned to burn.

The use of light was important, even to the timing and duration of the performance.
The fading daylight outside the church helped mirror and add to the atmosphere and
drama of the performance inside, casting colourful shadows on the church walls.

The Church Parables were also performed in Southwark Cathedral, London /
Buxton Festival /The Hermitage and St Ekaterina's in St Petersburg.

Director: Frederic Wake-Walker
Set and Costume Designer: Kitty Callister
Lighting Designer: Ben Payne
Musical Director: Roger Vignoles.
Photographer: Robert Workman

Images
The Yellow Sofa

2/
KITTY CALLISTER
SET AND COSTUME DESIGN

THE YELLOW SOFA
Julian Philips (2010)

*Glyndebourne Jerwood Studio,
Glyndebourne & Touring
October 2012*

KC: As part of Glyndebourne's aim to promote new opera in a more intimate studio environment, The Yellow Sofa was commissioned for and performed during the Glyndebourne Touring Opera schedule in 2012.

Set on and around a yellow sofa, the opera was designed to be an inclusive experience, with interaction starting from the moment the audience enter the room.

The set was designed as a deconstructed late 19th century town house, the cast having space to freely move and interact between set and orchestra who, like the singers, remained fully visible on stage throughout. The yellow sofa was not only a key piece of set, but also appears in the form of a seductive cabaret-type singer, stepping in and out of the action. Like the bright yellow of the sofa her costume reflects the sensual nature of her character, and stands in direct contrast to the other characters of the piece. The main elements of the design were created in muted tones, helping to accentuate the difference between the character of the sofa and everything else in the story.

Conductor: Gareth Hancock

Director: Frederic Wake-Walker

Set and Costume Designer: Kitty Callister

Lighting Designer: Andy May

Photographer: Robert Workman

1/
PAUL BURGESS
SET AND COSTUME DESIGN

HARD PLACES
Farhad Sorabjee (2004)

Mercury Theatre Company (UK), Tinderbox (UK)
and Rage Productions (India)
Mercury Theatre, Colchester, Prithvi (Mumbai, India),
Choice (Cochin, India), Epicentre (Gurgaon, India)
September 2012

PB: This production had two main scenographic challenges: how initially to create a border in a desert (a fictional location inspired by the Golan Heights) and then how to transform this from naturalism to something suggesting a post-death experience. It also had a major practical challenge: how to make it tour to some very different venues in India, from a small horseshoe space to large proscenium arch. The solution was a flexible strip, which could be extended across any size of stage and could also be carried with the team on domestic flights in India. The strip was strewn with rubbish, which in the play's last minutes, as the line between life and death become blurred, floats upwards, free from gravity. The UK team created the first version of the show, then collaborated with a parallel Indian team to adapt it for Indian audiences and logistics.

Director: Chris White
Set Designer: Paul Burgess (with Dhanendra Kawade for India)
Costume Designer: Paul Burgess
Lighting Designer: Cis O'Boyle (with Hidayat Sami for India)
Composer: Ansuman Biswas
Sound Designer: Marcus Christensen (with Gautam Dhanu for India)
Photographer: Paul Burgess

2/
PAUL BURGESS
SET AND COSTUME DESIGN

A MIDSUMMER NIGHT'S DREAM
William Shakespeare (1605)

Deafinitely Theatre
Shakespeare's Globe, London
June 2014

PB: This British Sign Language production aimed to find a modern resonance for the play without losing any of the joyfulness and magic in the script. Our court became a world of banking: materialistic, wasteful, hierarchical and in opposition to the natural world of our forest, which was anarchic, transformative and sustainable. Our fairies were magical recyclers, attempting to mend the mess made by humans. Their world, including their clothes, was made from repurposed office rubbish woven with blossoming plant life. As a BSL production, albeit one with a musical score, all our ideas had to be expressed visually. This made it a tremendously exciting project to design.

Director: Paula Garfield
Composer: Philippa Herrick
Set and Costume Designer: Paul Burgess
Photographer: Simon Kane

Images 1 & 2
Hard Places

Images 3 & 4
A Midsummers
Night's Dream

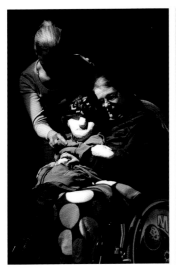   

1/
NERISSA CARGILL THOMPSON
SET AND COSTUME DESIGN

BEYOND THE 4TH WALL
Proud and Loud Arts/Cathy Crabb (2011)

Proud and Loud Arts
The Lowry Studio + Touring Theatre Company:
January 2012

NCT: In 2011 Proud and Loud Arts, a disability-led theatre company based in Salford, created a new play called 'Beyond the 4th Wall' with writer Cathy Crabb. This questioned whether a perfect world where every want and need is catered for without prejudice or unnecessary medical intervention would really be so perfect. As usual with their work there is a lot of comedy, but also some bold truths. With the current government cuts to disability allowances, and the reduction in social care hours, 'Beyond the 4th Wall' seems even more relevant than when first devised. How should people in need of care be treated? Are we really offering care or a form of well-intentioned incarceration?

I drew on references to Sixties sci fi in creating a 'Commune', a white world with flowing drapes and curved furniture. In contrast, and to keep the Commune theme, the costumes were in a rainbow of bright colours using a uniform of Eastern yoga trousers and loose long sleeved tops. I peppered the set with accents of these colours to give a feel of unity. The show premiered at The Lowry Studio in 2012, then toured the northwest in Feb/March 2013. As it was the first time the company had toured, there were many additional considerations for them. On tour, we used a white dance floor and adapted the exact formation of the drapes to the rigging/track available at each venue.

I suggested that we use a puppet for the part of young Taylor, rather than an actual child or video as we have done in the past. I made him the correct size for a five year old and used real clothes, but chose not to attempt a naturalistic finish in case it made him seem doll like. After initial apprehension from the group saying he was scary, this worked very well and everyone fell in love with him. This was thanks to Aisling Leyne from Puppet Pool who brought him to life so beautifully. Integrated signing was provided by Siobhan Rocks.

Director: Tom Hogan
Set and Costume Designer: Nerissa Cargill Thompson
Lighting Designer: Tom Dexter Scott
Photographer: Nicola Jaye

2/
NERISSA CARGILL THOMPSON
SET AND COSTUME DESIGN

AMOROUS CONGRESS
Aqueous Humour (2013)

Aqueous Humour/Action Factory Community Arts
Blackburn Festival, Witton Country Park Theatre Company:
June 2013

NCT: Aqueous Humour were commissioned in 2013 by Action Factory Community Arts to create a new comedy strolling piece for Blackburn Festival. We worked closely with one of their women's groups to explore attitudes to female mental health as a starting point for the show. In particular, we looked at obsession, delusion, name-calling and slang. The three characters are searching for a husband, for acceptance, for a contract of care. They may be utterly bonkers and desperate but they try hard to maintain a sense of poise and decorum expected in a convivial society.

As the event was being held at Witton Country Park, the grounds of a now demolished old mansion, we chose a historic theme/look. The elaborate wigs of Marie Antoinette gave a great opportunity for visual messages. I took the wigs as high as I could by using a withy base to reduce weight. These were ornamented with literal interpretations of the slang phrases. I followed through, from the wigs into the costumes, with a feel of the same era. Making these from scratch would have been extremely costly and time consuming, so I adapted full-skirted wedding dresses, in particular, by adding pannier style underskirts to give the correct silhouette. The creams and golds of the dresses were chosen to stand out against the green of the parks at this and other festivals and historic houses/gardens, but also to add a hint of ghostliness to characters from a bygone time.

Director: Tom Hogan
Costume Designer: Nerissa Cargill Thompson
Photographer: Carl Gibson

Images 1 & 2
Beyond the 4th wall

Image 3 & 4
Amorous Congress

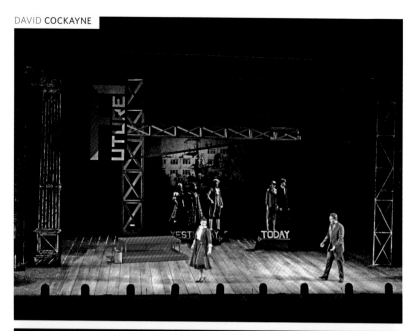

DAVID COCKAYNE
SET AND COSTUME DESIGN

PARADISE MOSCOW
Dmitri Shostakovich (1958)

Royal Northen College of Music
RNCM Opera Theatre
March 2013

DC: Paradise Moscow was composed when many public housing schemes were underway throughout Russia. They were much improved dwellings but their provision, in Paradise Moscow, involves all of the problems that would be expected in the Russia of the time, bribery not being the least. The seven 'good' characters are unsurprisingly confronted by enemies who have conflicting interests. In the end honesty, love and a bright future triumph.

The production needed to reflect the reality of Russia at the time, but also elements of fantasy combined in a design strongly based in the traditions of the musical. The original work is an operetta, a form that persisted in Russia long after it had died out in the West. We used sources such as constructivist theatre, architecture and graphics. Some of the design employed architect's drawings to suggest an imagined future. Projections, sometimes onto black/grey gauze, gave flexibility, a link to graphics and text and a clock that could go backwards. The latter was in the final scene, 'The Magic Garden'. This felt like some invention to resolve plot lines until we found a photograph with a caption explaining that about twenty gardens were created by the new residents across Moscow.

Conductor: Clark Rundell
Director: Stefan Janski
Choreographer: Bethan Rhys Wiliam
Set and Costume Designer: David Cockayne
Lighting and Projection Designer: Arnim Friess
Photographer: David Cockayne

Image 1
The Museum of the Future - Moscow
Image 2
The Courtyard of the Flats
Image 3
A Street in Moscow

1/
FIONA CHIVERS
SET AND COSTUME DESIGN

BEHIND THE MIRROR
Anee Holke Ekenes and Pia Holden (2013)

Panta Rei Danse Teatre
Black Box Oslo and touring
2013

FC: Staged in the round, with the audience seated 'in a rabbit hole', Behind The Mirror revisits Lewis Carroll's phantasmagoric Wonderland through a high paced language of dance.The dance sequences bring to life the surreal narrative foregrounding the more absurd moments, characters enter a world of giant chess pieces, tiny tea sets and hundreds of jam tarts. A dusty old looking-glass provides a portal to a topsy turvy world of endless possibilities. This is a journey which involves unexpected puzzles, questions, and random meetings for both audience and performer. Behind the mirror is suitable for children and young at heart adults.

Directors and Choreographers:.
Anee Holke Ekenes and Pia Holden

Set Designer: Fiona Chivers

Costume Designers: Fiona Chivers, Caroline Ekornes

Sound Designer: Nathaniel Reed

Photographer: Pia Holden

2/
FIONA CHIVERS
SET AND COSTUME DESIGN

THE EDGE
Based on 'I Only Came To Use The Phone' by Gabriel Garcia Marquez (1992)

Ourspace, The Drum,
Theatre Royal Plymouth
July 2013

FC: Our starting point was a short story by Gabriel Garcia Marquez, I Only Came To Use The Phone. It's about a woman who breaks down on the motorway and gets a lift on a bus that goes to an asylum. She only goes in to use the phone, but never gets out. She is admitted as a patient. This piece of devised physical theatre was atmospheric working with feelings more than naturalistic dialogue. Three layers of screens are used with haunting effect, a hospital screen becomes the host for some dynamic shadow work, a projection screen and a full stage gauze reveal the echoes of past lives.

Director: Lee Hart

Set and Costume Designer: Fiona Chivers

Lighting Designer: John Perkins

Sound Designer: Greta Henessy

Production/Media Designer: Matt Holmes

Photographer: John Allen

Image 1
Behind The Mirror

Images 2 & 3
The Edge

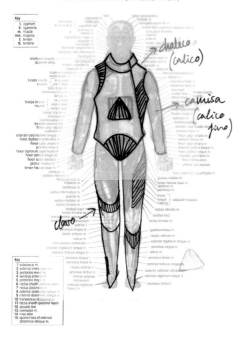

1/
LUCÍA CONEJERO RODILLA
SET, COSTUME AND LIGHTING DESIGN

BALLAST
Jesús Capel Luna (2010)

Collective La Strada Fashion Circus
Proud2 at the O2 Arena Venue, London
April 2011

LCR: The performer's costume in 'Ballast' symbolizes mind pains which are externalized through physical lesions, allowing alternating sensations of heaviness and its opposite, weightlessness. This is the losing of an overload: a pain-free body, like a hot air balloon which gains height when the ballast is thrown. This costume is a dynamic interactive element in the scenography, enriching the performer's communicative capacity. The metal pieces of ballast are located inside the costume and the performer removes them during his escape from emotional troubles.

Director and Choreographer: Jesús Capel Luna
Set, Costume and Lighting Designer:
Lucía Conejero Rodilla
Sound Designer: Oceane Peillet Sunniva
Photographers: Lucía Conejero Rodilla (Image 1 and 2) and Conrad Hafenrichter (Image 3)

Images
Ballast

Images
The Moonflower

2/
LUCÍA CONEJERO RODILLA
SET, COSTUME AND LIGHTING DESIGN

THE MOONFLOWER (OPERA)
Mario Ferraro (2011)

Boii Theatre
Riverside Studios (Tête à tête Festival))
August 2011

LCR: 'The Moonflower' is inspired by the lives of Margaret Mee, a British botanist and artist explorer, and Chico Mendes, a Brazilian rubber tapper, environmentalist and human rights activist. This opera transmits the compromise of mankind with the defence of the Amazon forest. The ephemeral exploitation and devastation of these forests is symbolized by the Moonflower that opens once in a lifetime and dies when appears the first morning star. The costumes and props were conceived to confer movement and interplay between the performers. For instance, Yara, the Amazonian siren plays with her net-tail while captures Margaret or the cocoon where the moonflower is hidden.

Director: Maja Milatovic-Ovadia
Set and Costume Designer:
Lucía Conejero Rodilla
Lighting Designer: Ricardo Gomes
Video Artist: Mafalda Cruz
Assistant Costume Designer:
Mariona Sala de Buen
Photographer: Lucía Conejero Rodilla (Image 1) and Jana Chiellino (Image 2)

Images 1 & 2
Veriditas – Costume,
Beauty & The Beast -
A Space Adventure

Image 3
Splosh! Sixth Sense

1/
SUE CONDIE
SET AND COSTUME DESIGN

BEAUTY & THE BEAST – A SPACE ADVENTURE
Andy Pollard (2013)

The Round, Stephen Joseph Theatre, Scarborough
November 2013

SC: This new and unusual version of Beauty and the Beast is set in Scarborough (Yorkshire) but in the year 2525. The water levels have risen and people now live in cradles raised above the earth's surface.

The design developed around themes of nature vs technology and we enjoyed the challenge of reinventing the theatre space to accommodate the action. Visuals included wireless glowing orbs, floating rings, and snap-on teleporter bracelets. The biggest test of all was filling the stage from above with vine-like fronds which was particularly tricky in the round. The floor design grew partly out of inspiration from Kandinsky paintings and from the chaotic forms of space junk and fractals.

Director: Adam Sunderland
Set and Costume Designer: Sue Condie
Lighting Designer: Jason Taylor
Sound Designer: Joel Sinclair
Photographer: Sue Condie
Costume Supervisor: Julia Perry-Mook
Costume Maker: Jenny Reeves

2/
SUE CONDIE
SET AND COSTUME DESIGN

SPLOSH!
Benedict Eccles (2012)

Sixth Sense/Salisbury Playhouse
National tour- Arts centres and community venues
February 2014

SC: Splosh! developed as a play for early years with an aim to encourage children's language skills through play, and empower families to develop communication at home.

The design was based around a bath tub and we enjoyed an R&D week exploring bathtime play culminating in a story using dance, puppetry and music. The final set had to be flexible enough to fit into a wide variety of spaces with access and height restrictions, but ultimately be able to accommodate many elements of surprise to enchant our very young audience. A theatrical 'shower' curtain was used effectively to conceal and reveal and portholes cut into the side of the bath were used in many inventive ways. The design provided a colourful playground where the two performers went on a journey from under the sea, into the air, a car chase, a boat trip and finally to a birthday party.

Much of the material chosen for the props and puppets derived from regular bathroom stuff including toothbrushes, loofas, towels, facecloths, sink plugs and sponges. At the end of the play the children were invited to come and play with a lot of bath time paraphernalia and the bubble machine was switched on..... so the experience continued!

Director: Mark Powell
Set and Costume Designer: Sue Condie
Sound Designer: Jack Merivale
Photographer: Charlotte Fryer

PATRICK CONNELLAN
SET AND COSTUME DESIGN

THE TAMING OF THE SHREW
William Shakespeare (1593)

Derby Live
Derby Theatre
February 2012

PC: Our interpretation of The Taming of the
Shrew is unashamedly Marxist. We have set
the play at the height of 19th Century industrial
capitalism to show how marriage, sex and even
love are simply commodities to be won, lost or
tamed. The set is an industrial prison built on
coal and steam. A weedy apple tree hangs on to
life and freedom but is ultimately snuffed out by
the barbarities of capital.

Director: Pete Meakin
Set and Costume Designer: Patrick Connellan
Lighting Designer: Chris Ellis
Sound Designer: Adam McCready
Video Designer: Will Duke
Photographer: Robert Day

Images
The Taming of the Shrew

FRANK CONWAY
SET DESIGN

A PARTICLE OF DREAD
(OEDIPUS VARIATIONS)
Sam Shepard (2013)

Field Day Theatre Co.
The Playhouse Theatre, Derry/Londonderry
December 2013
Signature Theatre Company, New York
November 2014

...in 1991 Seamus Deane made perhaps the most coherent and succinct attempt to describe the Field Day plays when he wrote: "All the Field Day dramatists have had in common a preoccupation with freedom, won by coming through, not skirting around, historical experience."
Thomas Kilroy, Derry 2013

FC: The production of 'A Particle of Dread (Oedipus Variations)' evolved during a series of Field Day workshops in Derry throughout 2013 with Sam Shepard, Stephen Rea, Nancy Meckler, a number of actors, musicians and myself. Sam, a generous collaborator, was involved in every aspect of the production. He spoke of his interest in the Oedipus story, as being a crime investigation; the murder by Oedipus of his father. We wanted to create a space where examination was its purpose, where there was no place to hide, no shadows and no escape. I looked at forensic laboratories, morgues and abattoirs.

The venue in Derry was a hall three floors up in a former Catholic convent. We initially planned to adapt the existing space to our purposes, but the scheduling restrictions were insurmountable. Instead we created a large, all-enveloping set, horrendously challenging physically.

I redesigned the Field Day production for the Signature Theatre in New York, a traditional proscenium theatre creating a different set of challenges.

Director: Nancy Meckler
Set Designer: Frank Conway
Costume Designer: Lorna Marie Mugan
Lighting Designer: John Comiskey
Composer and Cellist: Neil Martin
Sound Designer: Sam Jackson
Photographer: Ros Kavanagh/Frank Conway

Images
Particle of Dread (Oedipus Variations)

RUSSELL CRAIG
SET AND COSTUME DESIGN

THE MAIDEN IN THE TOWER / KASHCHEI THE IMMORTAL
Sibelius / Rimsky Korsakov (1896 / 1901)

Buxton Opera Festival
Buxton Opera House
July 2012

RC: The fairytale operas The Maiden In The Tower and Kashchei The Immortal both deal with the theme of captivity and rescue. A bullied girl locked in a nursery doll's house in the first opera becomes an abused woman in a rotting cage in the second.

Director: Stephen Lawless
Set and Costume Designer: Russell Craig
Lighting Designer: John Bishop
Media Designer: Stanley Orwin-Fraser
Photographer: Robert Workman

Image 1
The Maiden In The Tower

Images 2 & 3
Kashchei The Immortal

1/
CHARLIE CRIDLAN
SET AND COSTUME DESIGN

EDDIE AND THE GOLD TOPS
Kate Bramley (2011)

Bad Apple Theatre
Touring Regionally and Nationally Halls
and Studio Spaces
April 2011

CC: Bad Apple Theatre Productions tour in a large transit van. It is a challenge to create epic, multi-faceted worlds which tour nationally to packed village halls on stages the size of a postage stamp as part of the much acclaimed 'Theatre On Your Doorstep' programme.

'Eddie and the Gold Tops' is a musical play for which I conceived a revolving milk float that opened up to create a number of diverse locations around a Yorkshire village. This included the back of the village pub, a swinging 60's London recording studio and the milk float itself.

The ensemble cast had perfect comic timing. Using costumes and puppets which added on, turned inside out and upside down, the ensemble cast of three played a host of characters. 'Eddie' and his arch enemy 'Peter Purdick ' were cleverly conjured by a single actor with the simple addition of a moustache. The curtain call felt very sparse as one looked around to see where the rest of the cast were.

Director: Kate Bramley
Composer: Jez Lowe
Set and Costume Designer: Charlie Cridlan
Lighting Designer: John Bramley
Photographer: Karl Andre

CHARLIE CRIDLAN
SET AND COSTUME DESIGN

LIGHTS OUT LAND GIRLS
Kate Bramley (2012)

Touring Regionally and Nationally Halls
and Studio Spaces
Theatre Company: Bad Apple Theatre
April 2012

CC: This was the second show I designed for Bad Apple Theatre in their 2012 season. In contrast to 'Eddie', 'Land Girls' was a travelling piece, a road movie. It was a comic play with songs set in 1946, the story of two Land Girls, and their adventures on the way to Blackpool to sing in a talent contest. The third character has a guardian angel quality and appears in a number of different guises to help them on their way. Bad Apple Theatre are based in North Yorkshire where the play is set; these lush green landscapes inspired the tonal aesthetic to the set and costumes.

With strains of 'The Wizard of Oz' the play also has a poignant edge, set against a background of the end of World War 2 and Hiroshima. To emphasise the road movie feel of the piece, I quickly set upon a perspective floor and fences which, moved easily by the cast, served as both interior and exterior.

In front of a cyc that allowed for glorious sunsets, posts and rails continued into a fretwork backdrop reminiscent of the Japanese flag, indicating a whirlwind of chaos, which transformed the finale.

Director: Kate Bramley
Composer: Jez Lowe
Set and Costume Designer: Charlie Cridlan
Lighting Designer: John Bramley
Photographer: Karl Andre

CHARLIE CRIDLAN
SET AND COSTUME DESIGN

CONNECT 2014
Wavelength Connect Ltd (2014)

Sheepdrove Organic Farm and Conference Centre
2014

CC: For Wavelength Connect Ltd, I respond to the buildings in which they hold the four events of their year long programmes. Wavelength bring the leaders of the corporate and social business sectors out of their usual environments to learn from each other. I use theatrical techniques, methods of staging and seating to change and enhance the environments, inspiring and enhancing conversation.

The fifth time I worked for Wavelength Connect at Sheepdrove I needed to keep the floor space free to seat 120 people, a stage and speakers. Five different seating configurations across the two day event changed the space and anglesfor each session.

To use the vast vaulted ceiling space to best effect I created a 'helix' of circular screens flowing from one end of the room to the other in response to the stunning green oak and lime walled structure of the RIBA award winning building. This formed a visual 'spine' incorporating circular projection screens at either end, the backbone of Wavelength, a metaphor of its 'Connectivity' and allowing me space below to move the seating around, whilst securing good sightlines in every configuration.

The third event, Re-Connect2, also at Sheepdrove, was about 'landing the learning'. I installed three circular screens back in the Oak Room fragments of the 'helix' of March. We needed an 'end on' arrangement for the whole event; it was as if the helix had grounded and we could walk on it, a tabula rasa. In this way each Wavelength event has a visual story which links through the year programme, an underground language of its own. Its members pick up on this and are inspired, so that in some way I am contributing to the experiential learning at the very heart of what Wavelength do.

Director: Jessica Stack
Set and Costume Designer: Charlie Cridlan
Lighting Designer: Steve Cohu, Cue Media
Media Designer: Neil Denbow, Cue Media
'Helix' installed by Creative Draping
Photographer: John Owen

Image 1
Eddie and the Gold Tops
Image 2
Lights out Land Girls
Image 3
Wavelength Connect

1/
SET AND COSTUME DESIGN

THE HOUSE OF BERNADA ALBA

Federico Garcia Lorca - translated by David Johnston (1936)

The Department of Drama and Theatre Arts, University of Birmingham
George Cadbury Hall Theatre
March 2013

DC: The director wanted to explore the subtext of the translation through the use of traditional Spanish music and dance such as flamenco; the stamp of a foot or the swish of a skirt became the grammar to the text. When developing the costume designs I looked at stances that represented certain movements in flamenco as well as poses that emphasise character traits. The daughters' costumes were made up of many pieces but always fluid for movement, whereas Bernada Alba was stiff and restricted. I also used elements of the set as part of the presentation of the costume drawings, such as the huge archways and the bright yellow seen through them, thus communicating how the shapes could be made or silhouetted on the set.

Director: Mollie Guilfoyle

Set and Costume Designer: David Crisp

Lighting and Sound Designer: Daniel Warboys

Production Media Designer: Daniel Warboys and David Crisp

Costume Supervisor: Lucy Nye

Photographer: David Crisp

2/
SET AND COSTUME DESIGN

TRUST NOT YOUR DAUGHTERS' MINDS

Sam Fox of Kindle Theatre Company and Cast, Devised January - February 2014

Department of Drama and Theatre Arts, University of Birmingham
George Cadbury Hall
February 2014

DC: The piece ... Othello, as it ... them. Workin ... we explored ... seen and the se ... ear defenders, the audie... room containing a bed and a ... and around them. They then moved to a second stage on to experience a piece with live spoken words, soundscapes, Foley and sensory elements. One of the challenges was creating a space where twenty audience members could inhabit a room alongside five performers. The set design aided the lighting by having two large window spaces that could be backlit, as well as using a white palette to enable the lighting to bounce.

Director: Sam Fox, Kindle Theatre Company

Set and Costume Designer: David Crisp

Lighting and Sound Designer: Daniel Warboys

Photographer: David Crisp

Image 1
The Winters Tale

Image 2
Skylight

Image 3
The Glass Menagerie

1/
BOB CROWLEY
SET AND COSTUME DESIGN

THE WINTER'S TALE
William Shakespeare/Joby Talbot
(1611/2013-14)

Royal Ballet

Royal Opera House, Covent Garden
April 2014

BC: The 'Wishing Tree' is a place of pilgrimage in Bohemia. The young lovers Perdita and Florizel meet there. Its natural sculptural shapes and verdant colours are the opposite of the grey spartan Sicilian Court.

Director and Choreographer:
Christopher Wheeldon

Set and Costume Designer: Bob Crowley

Lighting Designer: Natasha Katz

Media Designer: Daniel Brodie

Photographer: Jaimie Todd

2/
BOB CROWLEY
SET AND COSTUME DESIGN

SKYLIGHT
David Hare/Paul Englishby (1995)

Robert Fox Ltd

Wyndhams Theatre, London
June 2014

BC: A flat/apartment looking estate in North London in 1995

Director: Stephen Daldry

Set and Costume Designer: Bob Crowley

Lighting Designer: Natasha Katz

Sound Designer: Paul Arditti

Photographer: Ros Coombes

3/
BOB CROWLEY
SET AND COSTUME DESIGN

THE GLASS MENAGERIE
Tennessee Williams (1944)

American Repertory Theatre
Booth Theatre
September 2013

BC: The Glass Menagerie is a 'memory play' as described by the central character Tom. The living, dining room and fire escape of the tiny St Louis apartment in which he (Tennessee Williams) grew up. The set floats in the middle of a pool of total blackness with no entrances or exits to the wings of the theatre. A world 'suspended' in time.

Director: John Tiffany

Set and Costume Designer: Bob Crowley

Lighting Designer: Natasha Katz

Sound Designer: Clive Goodwin

Photographer: Bob Crowley

Image 1
Annabelle Schmidt,
The 39 Steps

Image 2
Mr Memory,
The 39 Steps

Image 3
The Creature,
Frankenstein

1/
ANNE CURRY
COSTUME DESIGN

THE 39 STEPS
John Buchan (1915) Alfred Hitchcock (film 1935)
Patrick Barlow Stage adaptation (2005)

Blue Orange Arts
The Blue Orange Theatre Theatre, Birmingham
28 August 2014

AC: I prefer designing for intimate spaces, and was delighted to discover this new theatre venue which is helping build a sense of community and bringing urban regeneration to part of Birmingham's Jewellery Quarter.

This production tested the power of 'Make:-Believe', as there were only four actors while the script included 150 characters and the director added a further eleven!

I am committed to sustainable design and strive to produce quality 'live' performance design work on limited budgets, using recycled fabrics and materials. This methodology encourages creativity - it makes you think, consider and justify how to solve problems. Designing these costumes I learned more about synthetic and natural materials, developing my craft skills in fabric dying and hand sewing, which is versatile and enables manipulation of both vintage and contemporary textiles.

The set design concept was minimalist, but the vast costume narrative and need to create a sense of period became very important, especially for the main characters. As rehearsals progressed I developed a style of costume which focused on the head and shoulders of characters who made only brief appearances. The audience had only time to look at heads and faces, the comic dramatic action was so furiously fast.

With just one female and three male actors I designed hair and make up, for total characterisation. For the three different female characters we utilised different wigs and found time for different make up effects to develop their characters.

Director: Simon Ravenhill
Collaborative Design & Production Team: Ian Craddock; Anne Curry; Nusra Nazir; Holly Phillips; Gemma Rose; Mark Webster.
Costume Designer: Anne Curry
Lighting Designer: Jon Bates

2/
ANNE CURRY
COSTUME DESIGN

FRANKENSTEIN OR THE MODERN PROMETHEUS
Mary Shelley (1818)

Blue Orange Arts
The Blue Orange Theatre
October 2014

AC: These comments are based on reading the script and having the first design discussion with the director. The show previews on 24 October 2014. I am designing the costumes and working with the creative team on the set design.

I continue my commitment to sustainable design and production practices, working with mainly recycled synthetic and natural materials, including adapting items of stock and sourced costume and clothing.

I will be deconstructing and reconstructing garments, to create 19th century style costumes for a cast of approximately 20 actors. The director wants a 'period' feel. I agree and am excited to design and create for this classic text, at minimal or no cost, using what can be found, adapted and changed into something 'new' for our world on stage.

Director: Oliver Hume
Set Designer: Simon Ravenhill
Costume Designer: Anne Curry
Lighting Designer: Jon Bates

Images
Mother Courage

JUDITH CROFT
SET AND COSTUME DESIGN

MOTHER COURAGE
Bertold Brecht (1939)

Library Theatre Company
Quays Theatre, Lowry, Manchester
February 2013

JC: Mother Courage is the story of a woman who believes she can profit from war and still remain untouched. She is a strong woman; courageous indeed, but her wit, her cunning, her self belief still cannot save her from war's merciless cost. Her 'Make Believe' is that she is unassailable, but in the end, war exacts its price. The design tries to provide a setting which could be any 20th century war and yet is always consciously within a theatrical space.

Director: Chris Honer

Musical Director: Greg Palmer

Set and Costume Designer: Judith Croft

Lighting Designer: Nick Richings

Sound Designer: Paul Gregory

Photographer: Judith Croft

ANGELA DAVIES
SET AND COSTUME DESIGN

THE MOUSE AND HIS CHILD
Russell Hoban (1967)

Royal Shakespeare Company
RST Stratford-upon-Avon
November 2012

AD: The Mouse and his Child is the story
of two clockwork mice, a father and child
searching for the notion of 'home'. This is
an epic story of self discovery and darkness
as the characters travel through toyshops,
fields, a pond and the rubbish dump. They
encounter and overcome many challenges.
The design developed from workshops
with the company. The challenge of the
multi locational design, was to respond to
an inventive and creative company and to
allow the freedom, anarchy and sense of
'play' to develop from rehearsal room to
stage. The design played with scale and
the set became a flexible 'clockwork box of
tricks'. Design elements were inspired by the
original art work in the 1967 Russell Hoban
book, a dog food can, clockwork mechanics,
including the original toy and images of the
Universe. Many costumes were designed in
collaboration with the company.

Director: Paul Hunter
Movement: Sian Williams
Set and Costume Designer: Angela Davies
Lighting Designer: Paul Anderson
Music: Iain Johnstone
Sound Designer: Andrew Franks
Projection and Animation: Maxwell White
Photographer: Hugo Glendinning

Images
The Mouse and His Child

1/
SIMON DAW
SET AND COSTUME DESIGN

THE METAMORPHOSIS
Franz Kafka (1915) dance adaptation
by Arthur Pita (2011)

*The Royal Ballet
Linbury Studio, ROH, London
September 2011*

SD: Arthur Pita's adaptation of Franz Kafka's
1915 novella, staged in claustrophobic traverse,
tells the horrifying story of Gregor Samsa's
(Royal Ballet Principal Edward Watson)
extraordinary transformation. This is evoked by
startling physical distortions and a black liquid
that seeps from his body, infecting the clinical
white apartment he inhabits.

Director and Choreographer: Arthur Pita
Set and Costume Designer: Simon Daw
Lighting Designer: Guy Hoare
Music: Frank Moon
Photographer: Simon Daw

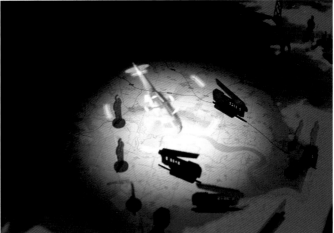

Images 1-3   Images 4-6
The Metamorphosis   3rd Ring Out

2/
SIMON DAW
SET AND COSTUME DESIGN

3RD RING OUT
Zoe Svendsen/ Simon Daw (2010/2011)

Metis
Shipping containers, Edinburgh and Watford
2011

SD: 3rd Ring Out is performed inside a
converted shipping container placed in the
public realm, and puts the audience in control
of an emergency planning centre on the UK
coast in 2033. Charged with making a series of
difficult choices relating to this climate changed
future, the audience vote using a bespoke
digital system, the results of which define
the journey through a multi-routed narrative.
A second shipping container provided an
open space for the public to contribute to a
web of possible narratives and to discuss the
challenges of rehearsing the future.

Directors and Set Designers:
Zoe Svendsen and Simon Daw
Sound Designer: Carolyn Downing
Photographer: Simon Daw / Jamie Archer

BECKY DAVIES
SET AND COSTUME DESIGN

AS YOU LIKE IT
William Shakespeare, script adapted
by Elise Davison (2014)

Taking Flight Theatre Company
Outdoor, promenade, site-specific production,
national tour including Wales Heritage Sites
May-August, 2014

BD: Taking Flight Theatre Company tours and responds directly to striking outdoor spaces across Wales with its annual Shakespeare production. Unlike many theatre companies, Taking Flight places inclusion and accessibility at the heart of the theatre-making process. Visual and hearing impairment, incorporating wheelchairs (in terms of costume and access across the performance site), BSL (British Sign Language) Interpreters, live audio description and actors who do not conform to the usual Shakespearian stereotypes, form the basis from which ideas for design can geminate. As You Like It explores the eclectic aesthetic of a gypsy-come-fairground-come-circus land within which Duke Frederick and his court bejewel themselves in a manner inspired by pearly kings and queens. In contrast, the forest folk are adorned by animal features such as ram horns and rabbit tails. The use of colour and tactile qualities provide a multi-sensory and immersive experience, suitable for Touch Tours.

Director: Elise Davison
Set and Costume Designer: Becky Davies
Photographer: Jorge Lizalde

Image 1
Adam (Fortune Teller)

Image 2
Rosalind

Images 1 & 2:
iTMOI

Image 3
Shadows of Memory

Image 4
Emerald Tour Celtic Woman
at Comcast Arena

1/
MATT DEELY
SET DESIGN

ITMOI
Akram Khan (2013)

Akram Khan Company
MC2 Grenoble, Sadlers Wells and world tour
May 2013

MD: A contemporary dance piece, inspired by
The Rite of Spring. Akram was interested in the
dynamics of how Stravinsky transformed the
classical world of music by evoking emotions
through patterns. I wanted to support this
concept with the design of a simple floating
frame, which came to life on the stage with
smoke, lighting, movement and shadows.

Choreographer: Akram Khan
Composers: Nitin Sawhney, Jocelyn Pook
and Ben Frost
Set Designer: Matt Deely
Costume Designer: Kimie Nakano
Lighting Designer: Fabiana Piccioli
Photographer: Jean-Louis Fernandez

2/
MATT DEELY
SET DESIGN

SHADOWS OF MEMORY
Solange Umuhire, Didier Ntwali
and Moise Mutangana (2014)

Kwibuka20
Amahoro Stadium Kigali Rwanda with
international broadcast
April 2014

MD: A live stadium event which was a 20th
commemoration ceremony of the genocide
against the Tutsi. The performance depicted
a brief account of Rwandan history from
the time of the colonialists, through to the
genocide of 1994 and to the present day. The
set comprised of three curved ramps leading
to a central focus, a flame shaped bamboo
tower, a symbolic structure of hope and the
spirit of Rwanda.

Director: Hope Azeda and Matt Deely
Mass Choreographer: Penny Jones, Detail
Choreography: Jonas Byaruhanga
Dramaturge & Drama Consultant:
Dorcy Rugamba
Set Designer: Matt Deely
Costume Designer: Kimie Nakano
Lighting and Sound Designer:
East African Promoters

3/
MATT DEELY
SET DESIGN

EMERALD TOUR
David Downes (2014)

Celtic Woman
Nashville and world tour
March 2014

MD: A set for a world touring show.
   Celtic Woman are an all female Irish musical
ensemble, with band and traditional dancers. I
was asked to design a set with a Celtic theme
that would be easy to set up for a world tour. I
created artwork combining iconic Celtic symbols
with rock texture. It was all mass printed onto
touring canvases and gauzes.

Director: David Downes
Choreographer: Daryn Crosbie
Set Designer: Matt Deely
Costume Designer: Synan O'Mahony
Lighting Designer: Jim Mustapha
Photographer: David Conger

1/
ES DEVLIN
SET DESIGN

MILEY CYRUS 'BANGERZ' WORLD TOUR (2014)
Arenas Across The World
2014

ED: Sometimes the most immediate ideas are the ones that I long to see in huge scale on stage.

When I was introduced to Miley in late 2013 she was 21 and had just become notorious for sticking out her tongue and twerking her way out of the Hannah Montana Disney character she had embodied since she was 14 years old.

Her story intrigued me. She seemed driven by an anarchic need to overthrow a persona that had dominated her adolescence. I am always alert to the 'need' at the core of any creative endeavour and hers seemed entirely real to me. It was unsurprising that one of the first references that came up at our meeting was Miley's favourite film: The Truman Show.

Our show began with Miley sliding down her own notorious tongue and ended with her flying out astride a giant plastic hotdog through Truman Show exit doors in a painted sky.

Diane Martel spent a lot of time with Miley, entered the world of her friends, her language, her range of references, and gathered a collection of emblems, icons, like the stickers or emoticons that form a visual lexicon in text-speak. The emblems are planted like a treasure trail through the show - in props, costume, film.

Miley is a dog rescuer and dog fanatic and one of the key emblems was her beloved Alaskan Klee Kai dog Floyd. We took photographs of Floyd and printed them onto the 12 metre high inflatable sculpture.

Director: Miley Cyrus / Diane Martel
Choreographers: Rich and Tone
Designer: Es Devlin
Lighting: Rob Sinclair

2/
ES DEVLIN
SET DESIGN

LONDON 2012 OLYMPIC CLOSING CEREMONY
Olympic Stadium
August 2012

ED: My brief was to create a floor design based on the Union Jack flag. I was concerned that it was a problematic concept: potentially narrowly nationalist, rather than 'Olympic' and inclusive in spirit. But this was clearly and unavoidably the brief, so I therefore began to explore ways in which I could diffuse the singularity of meaning of the flag and reimagine it as an original statement appropriate to the event.

The closing ceremony was conceived essentially as a celebratory gesture of pop culture. The solution began to present itself when I ceased thinking of the flag design in terms of geometric forms, and instead translated it into fluid paint. In the form of a red, white and blue Damien Hirst 'spin painting', the flag became invested at once with the irreverence of a Sex Pistols poster and the explosive energy of an Olympic firework.

I began by researching the evolution of the Union Flag design; the design options that the graphic designers of James I submitted to him in 1601 when he was planning to unite England and Scotland; also the use of the Union Jack design in fine art and pop culture throughout history, particularly the past 50 years which is the period from which the music of the Closing Ceremony was drawn. I researched the work of 20th century graphic artists – especially those who focused on album cover art – including the work of Peter Blake and Storm Thorgerson.

This project was viewed by the Mayor, the Prime Minister and the Royal Family, not to mention a global television audience of just under one billion, including just about everyone I know. There are strict traditions, etiquette and taboos that have formed around the treatment of national flags: it's perilous territory.

Director/Choreographer: Kim Gavin
Designer: Es Devlin
Costume: Michael Sharp
Lighting: Patrick Woodroffe
Video: Treatment

Images
London 2012 Floor

A CONCEPT OF HELL...
DON GIOVANNI, ROYAL OPERA HOUSE, LONDON, JUNE 2014
ES DEVLIN

Don Giovanni has been called the graveyard of designers - it's notoriously difficult to create a design that works for every aspect of this tonally complex work. This is my second attempt - the first was with Keith Warner in Vienna in 2006 - and in both cases it took a series of iterations and multiple false starts before arriving at the design.

The temptation is to design the themes of the piece without taking into account the detail of the action.There's an instinct to express the profound contemplation of human identity and mortality, while the action of the piece is largely a farce which demands doors and hiding places.

The piece ends with the protagonist burning in hell. So no design process can really get off the ground until the designer and director have tackled: 'what does the concept of hell mean to us and to this production?'

Kasper and I continued the conversation for about a year before settling on the definition of Don Giovanni's hell.

I had been trying to understand David Deutsch's book 'The Fabric of Reality' since Nitin Sawhney gave it to me in 2008. I struggled to comprehend its theory that there are myriad parallel universes: every choice we do not take spawns a new parallel reality that we do not live. The Catalogue Aria in Don Giovanni made sense of it: each of the 1736 women that Giovanni has slept with can be viewed as a parallel possible identity for him; a life that exists as an option - currently chosen not to live - but hovering as available, potential.

Eros is the antidote to Thanatos, the impulse towards sex overwhelms fear of death. Giovanni's appetite for life, for immortality is expressed as a desire to live more than one life: how many lives can he live at once? Each woman that Giovanni sleeps with affords a new dimension to his identity, a new version of himself: the one that went to Italy to live with a dancer, the one that lived in Germany with a singer, the one that married a Spanish lawyer.

His hell would be the antithesis of this: social isolation, infinite loneliness, his identity definable only in relation to himself.

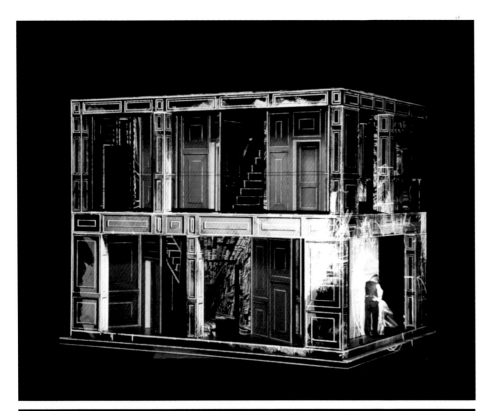

Image (top)
Don Giovanni (2014)

Image (below)
Chimerica (2012)

I had learned during Keith Warner's Vienna Don Giovanni to be attentive to the need for doors in the action. And doors became central to the machine for Kasper Holten's ROH production: It began as a wall. During the overture the Catalogue was written, name by name in response to the music, and the names formed architectural details - with every added name, a new door, new architectural potential was invested in the wall. Giovanni's encounter with Anna opened a new door, Elvira entered through the door that had been established for her, and by the time we reached the Catalogue aria, it was clear to the audience what game the set was playing: the wall had split into a revolving configuration of moving planes, doors and stairs.

Many of the most moving pieces of writing in Don Giovanni are those not written for him: the music that really breaks your heart is that of the 'collateral damage', the characters caught in the web of his parallel universes, existing in a state of unrealizable potential - kept alive to sustain Giovanni's illusion of immortality. It's one of the challenges of designing this piece: if the environment becomes Giovanni's psychological space, how do you manage the substantial chunks of time that he is offstage?

The choreographer Signe Fabricius had an instinctive response to the piece from the start: 'let's set the piece inside the catalogue'. Luke Hall's projected handwritten catalogue became the place where we allowed the collateral damage to be expressed: the music guided blots of ink, scrawls and smears to form expressively over the architecturally organized list of names. Giovanni never really left the stage - he observed Anna, Ottavio and Elvira from within the endlessly turning architecture that became progressively more scrawled and stained by the projected ink leaking between the catalogue names that afforded its endless architectural possibilities

Giovanni's descent into hell

GIOVANNI'S DESCENT INTO HELL WAS HIS PROPULSION OUT OF THE SET AND ONTO THE FORESTAGE - THE SET SPAT HIM OUT. THE WALL CLOSED BACK UP - THE APERTURES CLOSED. THE ARCHITECTURE WAS ERASED.

was his propulsion out of the set and onto the forestage - the set spat him out, the wall closed back up - the apertures closed, the architecture was erased. The lights came up, the singer, Mariusz Kwiecien, was left stranded - outside society, outside his production - left to sing about hell fire in front of a blank white wall.

The design required precisely mapped projection on every surface of a constantly revolving and shape-shifting box. Luke Halls and I had first collaborated in 2008 - in fact, on the film for Nitin Sawhney based on 'The Fabric of Reality'. So we had sort of begun this conversation 6 years ago. Luke had been using the D3 projection playback system on concert tours (especially U2), and introduced it to the Royal Opera House for this production: it enabled us to map onto the moving set throughout rehearsals - essential for Kasper to integrate performance and projection.

I had been working through a series of revolving box ideas over the course of 10 years: the first in 2003 on Keith Warner's Macbeth, then 2006 Pet Shop Boys Fundamental Tour, the MTV EMA Awards 2010, Chimerica at the Almeida in 2013, Machinal at the Roundabout in 2014. In each case, the design was arrived at via its own circuitous route and it was only in retrospect that I was able to trace the through line of thinking from one design to the next. I think the appeal has been the exploration of complexity and simplicity: the unquestionable stability and platonic certainty of a cube, infected with the myriad complex interventions required by the singular needs of each production.

Es Devlin
December 2014

THE LIGHTS CAME UP.
THE SINGER, MARIUSZ KWIECIEN,
WAS LEFT STRANDED -
OUTSIDE SOCIETY, OUTSIDE HIS
PRODUCTION - LEFT TO SING
ABOUT HELL FIRE IN FRONT OF
A BLANK WHITE WALL.

DON GIOVANNI
Wolfgang Amadeus Mozart / Lorenzo Da Ponte (1787)
Royal Opera House, London, 2014

Director: Kasper Holten
Designer: Es Devlin
Video Designer: Luke Halls
Costume: Anja Van Kragh
Choreography: Signe Fabricius
Lighting: Bruno Poet

Images 1 & 2   Images 3 & 4   Images 5 & 6
Othello   The Rest Is Silence   Baby Doll

1/
ROBIN DON
SET DESIGN

OTHELLO
William Shakespeare (1604)

Singapore Repertory Theatre
Fort Canning Park
April 2013

RD: The constructed environment encapsulated a present day Combat Unit in a make believe Overseas situation. As well as providing dynamic acting areas for Othello's forces, the real life shipping containers 'borrowed' from the main port in Singapore were able to be camouflage painted and hacked about and used as dressing rooms as well as lighting, sound and stage management control areas. This economically and artistically solved the problem of mounting an epic production in the open air in a public park. Even the rear projected helicopter arrival succeeded through torrential downpours.

Despite being a rather muscular design requiring vast cranes and workforce to assemble it in a natural grassy exterior amphitheatre (seating capacity 2500), the evening breeze added to the intimate quality required for concentration in the tensely focused bedroom scenes.

Director: Bruce Guthrie
Set Designer: Robin Don
Costume Designer: Penn O'Gara
Lighting Designer: Rick Fisher
Sound Designer: Mike Walker
Production Media Designer: Andrzej Goulding
Photographer: Marcus Tozini

2/
ROBIN DON
SET DESIGN

THE REST IS SILENCE
A Meditation On Hamlet
William Shakespeare (1602 / 2013)
Adaptation Tristan Sharps

Dream Think Speak
Constructed Multi-Media Environment Warehouse Tour
May 2013

RD: The Rest is Silence is a cinematic and dreamlike
deconstruction of Hamlet adapted by Tristan Sharps. It
interweaves performance and film to create an essence
that cuts to the heart of Shakespeare's great play.
The special environment was constructed to allow a
constant state of transformation within the elements. The
auditorium area is enclosed on all four sides within floor
to ceiling two way mirrors, allowing the action to take
place all around. The audience is free to roam and spy
on the live action as it dissolves through, or is swallowed
up by the reflective surfaces carrying the action at once
from make believe into truthful reality. Forty projectors are
required for the installation.

Director And Concept: Tristan Sharps
Design Consultant: Robin Don
Costume Designer: Berthe Fortin
Sound Designer: Pendle Poucher
Production Media Designer: Tristan Sharps
Photographer: Jim Stephenson

3/
ROBIN DON
SET DESIGN

BABY DOLL
Tennessee Williams (Film 1956 / Play 1970)

Nuffield Theatre Company
Nuffield Theatre, Southampton
September 2012

RD: Baby Doll is a 1956 American film drama directed by Elia Kazan,
starring Carroll Baker, Karl Malden and Eli Wallach. Williams adapted his film
script in 1970 into the play entitled 'Tiger Tail' The plot focuses on a feud between
two rival cotton plantation owners in rural Mississippi and the action takes place
in and around the haunted crumbling mansion. The drama is heightened with a
terrifying chase from the ground floor porch right up into the third floor attic where
the heroine falls through rotting floorboards.

Steeply perspected interior architecture behind an exterior image on
sharkstooth gauze allowed us to make believe that the room interiors were large
in scale within the confines of a very shallow depth. The set being so compacted
allowed the action to be played entirely in front of the iron.

The film was controversial when it was released due to its implicit sexual
themes, provoking the Roman Catholic National Legion of Decency to wage a
largely successful effort to ban it. Nevertheless, the film received multiple major
awards with Kazan winning the Golden Globe Award for Best Director.

The film is credited with originating the name and popularity of the legendary
babydoll nightgown, which derives from the costume worn by Baker's character,
the part originally written by Williams for Marilyn Monroe.

Director: Patrick Sandford
Set Designer: Robin Don
Costume Designer: Penn O'Gara
Lighting Designer: David W Kidd
Sound Designer: Rob Jones
Photographer: Robin Don

1/
MAX DOREY
SET AND COSTUME DESIGN

BLACK JESUS
Anders Lustgarten (2013)

HMD Productions
Finborough Theatre
October 2013

MD: The environment was created with found materials from abandoned buildings, made to reflect a derelict Zimbabwean office, in which the tools of democratic discourse are scattered.

Director: David Mercatali

Set and Costume Designer: Max Dorey

Lighting Designer: Howard Hudson

Sound Designer: Max Pappenheim

Photographer: Adam Trigg

2/
MAX DOREY
SET AND COSTUME DESIGN

I CAN HEAR YOU
EV Crowe (2014)

Royal Shakespeare Company
The Other Place at the Courtyard, RSC, Royal Court Upstairs
July 2014

MD: In 2013 the RSC began plans for converting the former Courtyard Place into the new 'Other Place'. The Midsummer Mischief Festival was a chance to dry run a new studio space built within the footprint of the Courtyard stage, one space to stage four new plays. Each piece included a feature wall designed for the festival, made to feel as if the floor of the courtyard stood on its end, with the design sympathising with the natural ambiance of the space.

Director: Jo Mcinnes

Set and Costume Designer: Max Dorey

Lighting Designer: Robin Griggs

Photographer: Topher Mcgrillis

Images 1-3
Black Jesus

Images 4 & 5
I Can Hear You

SUZI DOREY
SET AND COSTUME DESIGN

HAPPINESS REPEATS ITSELF
Sean Tuan John and company, (devised 2011 – 2013)

Sean Tuan John
Aberystwyth Arts Centre / Wales Millennium Centre, Cardiff
October 2013

SD: Happiness Repeats Itself is an exploration in dance and spoken word, reliving the precious lost moments and obliterated memories of child patients, both real and imagined, of the lobotomy pioneer Dr Walter Freeman, in the America of the 1950's.

A forest of the mind, once a place for dreams, but now burnt out, ravaged and turned to nightmare, with jumbled echoes of the past. Stories told and retold, love and terror combined and abstracted in the layered confusion of damaged minds. Towering burnt trees making vulnerable children of these broken patients, as their medical records lie in drifts like fallen, decaying leaves.

Director and Choreographer: Sean Tuan John
Set and Costume Designer: Suzi Dorey
Lighting Designer: Andy Hamer
Sound Designer: Peter Farago
Photographer: Alex Lloyd Jenkins

Images
Happiness Repeats Itself

On wall:

APRIL ASHLEY
Portrait of a lady

Born in Liverpool in 1935, April Ashley MBE, a former Vogue model and actress, is one of the first people in the world to undergo pioneering gender reassignment surgery. As one of the most famous trans* individuals and a tireless campaigner for transgender equality, she is an icon and inspiration to many.

Here, for the first time, we explore April's very public story through her previously unseen private archive, and investigate the wider impact of changing social and legal conditions for all trans* and lesbian, gay and bisexual people from 1935 to today.

Alongside this, members of the trans* and gender diverse communities also share their own remarkable life stories.

*trans - an umbrella term for people whose gender identity and/or gender expression differs from the sex they were assigned at birth.

1/
OLIVIA DU MONCEAU
SET AND INSTALLATION DESIGN

APRIL ASHLEY PORTRAIT OF A LADY
Curator Gary Everette (2013)

Homotopia
Museum of Liverpool, September 2013

ODM: Homotopia, the international festival of queer arts and culture, commissioned me as Exhibition Designer for their Heritage Lottery Funded project on the life of transgender icon April Ashley. With a Theatre Design background I was asked to avoid the standard museum format and to embrace a more operatic and striking approach to the exhibit aesthetic, which treated April's story along with the history and experiences of transgender people in Britain over the past 70 years. I used the full height of the gallery walls to display the oversized black and white photos of April's glamorous life. In contrast I recreated a make believe Parisian club, 'Le Carousel' famous for its 1950's female impersonators, in opulent colour at the heart of the exhibition. This theatrical installation was very successful in engaging the public while exploring issues of hate crime, shifting social attitudes and representations of gender and sexuality.

Director: Gary Everette
Set Designer: Olivia du Monceau
Production Media Designer: Tim Brunsden
Photographer: Courtesy of National Museums Liverpool

Images 1 & 2
April Ashely

Image 3
Harmony in Blue and Gold

Images 4-6
Gale Force Council House
Movie Star

2/
OLIVIA DU MONCEAU
SET AND INSTALLATION DESIGN

HARMONY IN BLUE & GOLD
ElDahab & Rosie Cooper (2014)

Liverpool Art Biennial
Bluecoat Gallery, Liverpool
August 2014

ODM: The brief was to reconstruct a slice of the famous Peacock Room, originally decorated by Victorian artist James McNeil Whistler. The real Arts and Crafts dining room is displayed in the Smithsonian in Washington DC. My role was to recreate the 6m x 4m wall as a sculpture, composed from photographs of the original. I oversaw all aspects of the project, starting with 3D renders outlining my interpretation, to technical drawings for the construction team and working with various scenic and graphic artists for the final treatments. Commissioned by the Liverpool Art Biennial as part of their Whistler exhibition, this theatrical installation was described by Margaret Macdonald, the world leading expert on Whistler, as 'the best reconstruction [she has] ever seen'.

Director: Mai Abu ElDahab & Rosie Cooper
Installation Designer: Olivia du Monceau
Photographer: Roger Sinek, Courtesy of Liverpool Art Biennial

3/
OLIVIA DU MONCEAU
SET AND INSTALLATION DESIGN

GALE FORCE COUNCIL HOUSE MOVIE STAR
Mark Edward (2012)

Homotopia
Camp & Furnace, Liverpool
October 2012

ODM: This piece works as a trilogy with the other two productions. Each design deals with the themes of make/believe, specifically the recreation of past worlds with a theatrical artistic licence. My role was to reconstruct the theatre set as an artistic installation. Whereas the first two designs are based on real places in history (a Parisian Female Impersonators Club and a Decorative Arts and Crafts Dining room) Gale Force, in contrast, looks at a fictionalised 1970's northern council house. In collaboration with Performance Artist Mark Edward and his ageing drag queen persona. Originally production designed for a short film 'Council House Movie Star' the set was later re-erected so the audience could experience it first hand. Emerging from the bathroom shower block, the audience was invited to watch the original film sitting on toilets surrounded by the surreal decor of a 1970's disco.

Director and Choreographer: Mark Edward
Set Designer: Olivia du Monceau
Costume Designer: Cast & Company
Photographer: Luis Santos

1/
ALEX EALES
SET DESIGN

**ALLES WEITERE KENNEN SIE AUS DEM KINO
(THE REST WILL BE FAMILIAR TO YOU FROM CINEMA)**
Martin Crimp after Euripedes (2013)

*Deutsches Schauspielhaus Hamburg
November 2013*

AE: An adaptation of The Phoenician Women, this
radical new version by Martin Crimp ripped the
characters from ancient Greece and resurrected them
in the modern world to relive their past conflicts and
attrocities. Props were treated as museum artifacts in
glass cases, the main characters were hostages and
the chorus were empowered as both teachers and
tormentors of the protagonists brought back to life in
a world they no longer understand.

Director: Katie Mitchell
Set Designer: Alex Eales
Costume Designer: Laura Hopkins
Lighting Designer: James Farncombe
Sound Designer: Donato Wharton
Photographer: Stephen Cummiskey

2/
ALEX EALES
SET DESIGN

**REISE DURCH DIE NACHT
(JOURNEY THROUGH THE NIGHT)**
Devised by Katie Mitchell based on the book
by Fredericke Mayröcker (2012)

*Schauspiel Köln
Halle Kalk, Cologne
October 2012*

AE: Based on the book by Fredericke Mayröcker, this
was a devised piece of 'live cinema' about one woman's
tormented journey back home on the Paris-Vienna night
train to attend her father's funeral.

The train carriage set was accessible from all sides
by actors and camera operators, the camera feeds were
edited live into a film that ran in real time, projected onto a
screen above the stage. The audience could see the entire
construct of the filming process: panels along the side of the
carriage could slide up to reveal interiors from the characters'
memories, the central compartment could be rotated to
see inside, a soundproof booth in one compartment was
for live voiceover and real footage of the journey from Paris
to Vienna was projected behind the carriage to provide the
filmic landscape rolling past the windows.

Director: Katie Mitchell
Set Designer: Alex Eales
Costume Designer: Laura Hopkins
Lighting Designer: Jack Knowles
Sound Designer: Gareth Fry and Melanie Wilson
Production Media Designer: Leo Warner for 59 Productions
Photographer: Stephen Cummiskey

Image 1
Alles weitere kennen Sie
aus dem Kino

Image 2
Reise durch die Nach

Image 3 & 4
Clemency

3/
ALEX EALES
SET DESIGN

CLEMENCY
James Macmillan and Michael
Symmons Roberts (2011)

Linbury Studio,
Royal Opera House, London
May 2011

AE: Based on the ancient biblical story of Abraham and
Sarah's visitation by three angels, this new chamber opera
explored ideas of vengeance and mercy. The setting and
design was timeless, but the three spaces were set as a
triptych behind massive hinged gilt frames. The action
became a living painting at once both contemporary and
reminiscent of religious painting of the 15th century. The
third panel of the triptych is a mirror image of the second,
allowing us to witness dialogues from both sides of a table
split down the middle, most crucially Abraham's pleas to
the avenging travellers for forgiveness.

Director: Katie Mitchell
Movement Director: Joseph Alford
Set Designer: Alex Eales
Costume Designer: John Bright
Lighting Designer: Jon Clarke
Photographer: Stephen Cummiskey

1/
MATT EDWARDS
SET AND COSTUME DESIGN

UNDER A FOREIGN SKY
Paula B. Stanic (2011)

Theatre Centre
Touring
2011

ME: The design for a contemporary narrative, particularly one that is a piece of new writing, requires a particular form of close collaboration between the director, writer, cast and designer. The actors will develop their characters with the writer and director during the rehearsal process, and the designer needs to help make the characters believable for both cast and audience.

Three of the characters arrive in the UK as refugees and the audience witnesses their experiences as they attempt to make new lives. Another has experienced a traumatic event in her past but believes she can prevent this happening to others, who end up in a similar situation.

The brief to provide a 'believable' environment for this small scale touring production was challenging. The travelling storage space for the set was minimal and the venues varied in controllable lighting, seating configuration and floor surfaces. The solution for 'Under A Foreign Sky' was to provide a composite setting that suggested a number of interior and exterior spaces for the cast to inhabit and for the audience to make believe.

Directed: Natalie Wilson
Set and Costume Design: Matt Edwards
Lighting Design: Aideen Malone
Sound Design and Composer: Dan Steele
Photographer: Matt Edwards

2/
MATT EDWARDS
SET AND COSTUME DESIGN

THE OLD WOMAN, THE BUFFALO AND THE LION OF MANDING
Created and performed by: Jan Blake, Raymond Sereba and Kouame Sereba (2012)

Adverse Camber and The Akua Storytelling Project
Touring 2012, Second Tour 2014.
Supported by Arts Council England

ME: Storytelling is a flexible form of performance. It allows for impromptu adaptation and interventions, particularly effective here with Jan's expressive and vibrant style and the accompaniment of Raymond Sereba and Kouame Sereba, two improvisational musicians, adding layers of diversity and resonance using both traditional African and contemporary Western instruments.

'With storytelling, the relationship between performer and designer has to be a close one, because the storyteller has to be able to share the story with the designer'.
(Jan Blake 2012 UTube Promotional Video by Gavin Repton, for Adverse Camber and the Akua Storytelling Project).

The design for this production had to 'flow' as each performance evolved. The costumes are a mixture of styles with reference to Medieval African and European tailored shapes; 18th Century European and contemporary African fashion. The set also suggests elements and shapes from the narrative with printed stylised symbols. The hand cut projection patterns provide an evolving environment that subtly adds to the audiences' immersive experience.

Artistic Advisor: Harmage Singh Kalirai
Designer: Matt Edwards
Lighting Designer: Stuart Walton
Photographer: Matt Edwards

Images 1 & 2
Under A Foriegn Sky

Images 3 & 4
The Old Woman,
The Buffalo And The Lion
Of Manding

PAUL EDWARDS
SET AND COSTUME DESIGN

LA COEUR DE CELIMENE
Ambrosia Thomas (1855)

Wexford Festival Opera
Wexford Opera House, Ireland
November 2012

PE: This opera is an 18th century love story of a girl deciding which of her suitors to marry. I set it in the centre of a topiary maze to highlight love's many twists and turns. Against this, the costume designs used the full spectrum of this period's chocolate box colour pallete.

Director: Stephen Barlow
Choreographer: Paula O'Reilly
Set and Costume Designer: Paul Edwards
Lighting Designer: Declan Randell
Photographer: Paul Edwards

Images
La Cour De Celimene

RICHARD EVANS
SET AND COSTUME DESIGN

THE ADDAMS FAMILY - A NEW MUSICAL COMEDY
Andrew Lippa/Marshall Brickman/Rick Elice (2007)

Royal Conservatoire of Scotland
Assembly Hall, Edinburgh
August 2014

RE: Creating a brand new, fresh and engaging audience experience from a subject as familiar to Western culture as the Addams Family was the first challenge that faced us. Throw into the mix staging a full scale Broadway Musical at an Edinburgh Fringe venue with 70 costumes, 30 wigs a hefty set and a 15 minute turn around and you have quite a challenging production. The latter was overcome with astounding stage management efficiency and the former by returning to the roots of the Addams in their original single panel comic form. There are personality traits and aesthetic characterisations in the original Charles Addams comics that have been lost in translation through films and TV, that we tried to bring to life on stage. These included the famous Addams Mansion, a house on the move with a personality of its own. I attempted to capture this on stage with constantly moving set pieces and broken, slatted walls which played with light and shadows of the Addams' ancestors.

Director: Ken Alexander
Choreographer: Chris Stuart-Wilson
Set and Costume Designer: Richard Evans
Lighting Designer: Grant Anderson
Sound Designer: Gerrie Victor
Photographer: R. Evans / K. Dundas

Image
The Addams Family

1/
JONATHAN FENSOM
SET AND COSTUME DESIGN

THE ACCRINGTON PALS
Peter Whelan (1981)

The Royal Exchange theatre Manchester
January 2013

JF: This is the workaday world of knockers-up, rain soaked cobbled streets, neighbourliness and matriarchal rule.

The journey we follow is set within the living and working quarters of the sturdy and busy women of Accrington. We decided to create a glistening cobbled street,in the round, drowned in familiar Lancashire rain, that filled the theatre with a bleak sense of realism. In the second half of the production we are transported to the front line to witness the tragic unfolding of the Accrington Pals' fate. The set was transformed from Accrington Streets, millworks, and parlours, to the horrors of northern France by the use of a few pieces of furniture, that never left the stage.

Director: James Dacre

Choreographer: Anna Yee

Set and Costume Designer: Jonathan Fensom

Lighting Designer: Charles Balforth

Sound Designer: Emma Laxton

Photographer: Jonathan Keenan

2/
JONATHAN FENSOM
SET AND COSTUME DESIGN

A MIDSUMMER NIGHT'S DREAM
William Shakespeare (1590)

Shakespeares Globe Theatre
July 2013

JF: Feral fairies, mud spattered lovers and clumsy mechanicals come together in Shakespeare's most effervescent comedy.

The fairies here are not the dainty, winged variety you might imagine fluttering gracefully between flowers on a hot summer's day. Nor are they the kind that have costumes bearing floral motifs that might have been salvaged from the flower-power era. No, these fairies are more earthy and more animal, and thus more mysterious and a touch scary.

Director: Dominic Dromgoole

Composer Claire Van Kampen

Choreographer: Sian Williams

Set and Costume Designer: Jonathan Fensom

Photographer: John Heynes

Images 1 & 2
The Accrington Pals

Images 3 - 5
A Midsummer
Night's Dream

JONATHAN **FENSOM**

1/
RICHARD FOXTON
SET AND COSTUME DESIGN

CHICAGO
Kander & Ebb, Fosse (1975)

Coliseum Theatre, Oldham
Sept 2013

RF: Chicago is a vaudeville style musical based on a 1926 play of the same name by reporter Maurine Dallas Watkins. It satirises the criminal justice system and the media obsession with celebrity criminals.

I created the feel of a vaudeville performance by incorporating the three piece permanent band (supplemented by actor musicians) into a 1920's fantasy architectural frame, with stylised scenic elements to create locations in a fluid variety theatre oeuvre. Costumes were influenced heavily by original vaudeville and variety styles of the 1920's and 1930's.

Director: Kevin Shaw
Choreographer: Beverley Edmonds
Musical Director: John Morton
Set and Costume Designer: Foxton
Lighting Designer: Jason Taylor
Sound Designer: Lorna Munden
Photographer: Andrew Billington

2/
RICHARD FOXTON
SET AND COSTUME DESIGN

TAKEAWAY
Robert Lee/Leon Ko (2011)

Theatre Royal Stratford East
June 2011

RF: The central character of Eddie is a student who works in his father's takeaway, but dreams of emulating his musical idol Tom Jones. The design enabled Eddie's real world to melt away into a fantasy TV special world of Eddie (the new Chinese Tom Jones) in which he morphed into his hero.

Costumes reflected the real world of east London and the sequined make believe of Eddie's Tom Jones alter ego.

Director: Kerry Michael
Choreographer: Jason Pennycooke
Musical Director: Robert Hyman
Set and Costume Designer: Foxton
Lighting Designer: Paul Anderson
Sound Designer: John Leonard
Photographer: Robert Day

3/
RICHARD FOXTON
SET AND COSTUME DESIGN

SLEEPING BEAUTY
Jonathon Petherbridge (2000)

Mercury Theatre, Colchester
Dec 2013

RF: The traditional pantomime story was reimagined with a timeline from the mid 20th to the mid 21st century. The design opened in a heightened, stylised England of the 1940's and 1950's, including a fairy godmothers' common room lined with portraits of famous fairy godmothers through history, ranging from Cleopatra and Elizabeth I to Marie Curie and Amelia Earhart. As the story moved on 100 years into the mid 21st century the location designs were informed by a mid 20th century notion of what the future would look like, influenced by popular TV such as the Jetsons and Lost in Space.

Director: Tony Casement
Choreographer: Sally Rapier
Musical Director: Richard Reeday
Set and Costume Designer: Foxton
Lighting Designer: Mark Dymock
Sound Designer: Marcus Christensen
Photographer: Robert Day

Image 1
Chicago

Images 2 & 3
Takeaway

Image 4
Sleeping Beauty

LIZZIE FRENCH AND CADI LANE
SET AND COSTUME DESIGN

BLACK STUFF

Volcano
The Iceland building, Swansea High Street
October 2014

LF & CL: Black Stuff gave a new purpose to a forgotten Iceland supermarket on Swansea High street. This original piece was inspired by Welsh mining and the physical actions and emotional strains of being underground. We set out with the vision of creating a space that would take certain elements of a coal mine, but create something gritty and contemporary, making references to the mines using materials like coal, rope and wood. We introduced these materials into rehearsals very early on in the creative process. Our aim was to create an unsettling atmosphere and adapt the space whilst embracing the buildings character and flaws. We designed a journey through the space that kept the audience alert and on edge throughout. Due to the exploratory nature of the production, the show was constantly changing as new concepts and themes led us deeper into a world of madness and surrealism.

Director: Paul Davies
Choreographer: Catherine Bennett
Set and Costume Designers:
Lizzie French and Cadi Lane
Lighting Designer: Ben Stimpson
Sound Designer: Adam Howell
Production Media Designer: Erin Rickard
Photographer: Cadi Lane

Images
Black Stuff

CHRIS GYLEE
SET AND COSTUME DESIGN

CHEESE
Nikki Schreiber (2013)

fanSHEN
29-31 Oxford Street
September 2013

CG: We find ourselves in a drab office at the seedy end of Oxford Street; piles of removal crates, striplighting, carpet tiles. Three redundant office workers, casualties of the financial meltdown, tell us a story of a man living in a giant cheese, where cheese is the only currency and the only measure of wealth. Stationery is redeployed as props, the audience perches on filing cabinets, drinks are served over the fax machine. The office workers' narrative takes hold, and the seemingly trustworthy space opens up, layer by layer, revealing hidden landscapes. Vistas shift and flicker, light washes over us, the horizon creeps ever further away. We sink into an alternate reality until we are confronted with a vast cracked dam, ready to give way. In the aftermath of the disaster, our shared fantasy recedes to a silhouette as reality and the sodium glare of the streetlights outside seep back into the space.

Director: Dan Barnard & Rachel Briscoe

Set and Costume Designer: Chris Gylee

Lighting Designer: Joshua Pharo

Sound Designer: Richard Hammarton

Photographer: Paul Blakemore

Images
Cheese

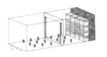

PAUL HALGARTH
LIGHTING DESIGN

FLIGHT PATHS
Adam Strickson and
Steve Kilpatrick (2011)

Wingbeats
The Spa, Bridlington and stage@
leeds, University of Leeds, 2011

PH: Flight Paths was a collaborative performance commissioned by iMove and formed part of the Cultural Olympiad programme in Yorkshire. Through opera and dance, a story of hope is told.

On a walk between Bempton Cliffs and Flamborough, Erin, a 'despondent female' experiences two journeys; an inner journey of self-discovery and an outer journey along an amazing coast.

My design was inspired by the colour families that resonate with the natural light of the Flamborough skies at different times of the day. I used light and texture to convey the spatial and temporal elements of the narrative. As the piece progressed the colours intensified, becoming bolder, darker, more saturated, creating a rich palette to communicate Erin's emotional journey. Very low, intense lighting angles were slowly introduced, providing long shadows and movement, augmenting the luminosity of the translucent projection sphere.

Director: Adam Strickson
Choreographer: Balbir Singh
Set and Costume Designer:
Jane Robinson
Lighting Designer: Paul Halgarth
Musical Director: Jonathan Lo
Media Designer: Chris Squire
Photographer: Malcolm Johnson

Images
Flight Paths

1/
ABIGAIL HAMMOND
COSTUME DESIGN

....

PARK
Jasmin Vardimon: (2005, revived 2014)

Jasmin Vardomon Company
Sadler's Wells
November 2014

....

AH: Park "is an urban oasis, a place of refuge
from ordinary life where eight characters play,
fight, fall in love and learn to survive".

Jasmin Vardimon's work is defined as
dance theatre, and in this instance that means
highly developed characters who communicate
predominantly through movement of a
particularly physical nature. Originally created in
2005 with designs by Merle Hensel, what was
most interesting in redesigning the costumes for
this work was the significance of the individual
dancers (an all new cast). Performing ostensibly
the same choreography, through their own
personality, nationality and physicality, the
characters were redefined and the choreography
evolved with them. This design experience was
one of micro attention to detail. Over a period
of three months of rehearsal each costume idea
was worked in and scrutinised to ensure it did
its job of making the audience believe in the
characters as their stories unfold.

Director and Choreographer: Jasmin Vardimon
Set Designer: Merle Hensel,
with adaptation by Guy Bar-Amotz
Costume Designer: Abigail Hammond
Lighting Designer: Chahine Yavroyan
Sound Designer: Ohad Fishof
with adaptation by Jasmin Vardimon
Digital Designer: Dan Shorten
Photographer: Danilo Moroni

Images
Park

2 /
ABIGAIL HAMMOND
COSTUME DESIGN

Images
Riot Offspring

RIOT OFFSPRING
Creative Producer: Jane Hackett (2012)

RIOT Company
Sadler's Wells
June 2012

AH: The key attractions of working on RIOT Offspring included
the performers, ranging from babies with their young mothers
to the Company of Elders (92 is the eldest), with children,
teenagers and young 'emerging artists' in between. In addition,
there was Sadler's Wells commitment to professional
production values for this community based work, and finally
that there were five choreographers, a strategic decision by
Creative Producer Jane Hackett. This necessitated a sharing of
ideas, not just one person's vision, reflecting the values in some
of the positive responses to the riots in London and the UK in
August 2011; this was in contrast to the riots that the Rite of
Spring ballet incited over 100 years ago.

This job required precision and organisation. There
were numerous costume changes, progressing from colour
to all white; mass shopping for 100 dancers, with five
different group 'looks' and speed fittings. Above all, the
costumes had to meet with the approval of the performers
to support their sharing of imagination and experiences.

Creative Producer: Jane Hackett

Choreographers: Ivan Blackstock, Mafalda Deville,
Pascal Merighi, Simeon Qsyea, Sebastien Ramirez

Set Designer: Creative team

Costume Designer: Abigail Hammond

Lighting Designer: Adam Carree

Composer: Igor Stravinsky: The Rite of Spring
(Le sacre du printemps)

Orchestra: Southbank Sinfonia,

Conductor: Gerry Cornelius

Writer: Yemisi Blake

Photographer: Bettina Strenske

1/
AMELIA JANE HANKIN
SET AND COSTUME DESIGN

MOTHER COURAGE AND HER CHILDREN
Bertolt Brecht (1939)

Drama Centre
Platform Theatre
June 2014

AJH: Mother Courage and her Children was designed and performed at The Platform Theatre in King's Cross. Drama Centre, an acting school merged with Central Saint Martins in 1999, now resides in their stunning newly restored Granary Building. This creative warehouse encourages collaboration between students and staff of different disciplines and houses studios, workshops, an interior street, exhibition spaces, lecture halls and the 350 seat Platform Theatre. The new theatre is used for professional showcases of student's work and also hosts independent events like dance and music festivals, which stretch to all corners of the local community. The theatre itself (also known as 'The Barn') is a huge studio space with dynamic seating and fly tower. I aimed to design a set, which reflected the epic nature of the play and the space itself. The play's 12metre diameter circular floor spans almost the entire width of the stage and is created from recycled floorboards, as was the creaky patchworked cart. The exposed 8 metre high scaffolding structures, which allowed the actors diverse preforming spaces, are symbolic of the harsh, cold power of Brecht's mammoth anti war play. I collaborated with CSM student and projection designer Shawn Soh in making projection a subtle backdrop to the action. At moments the scenes were injected with images of war throughout history to the present, and these became reminders that this play is as relevant today as it was in 1939.

Director: Annie Tyson
Choreographer: Shona Morris
Set and Costume Designer: Amelia Jane Hankin
Lighting Designer: Mike Robertson
Projection Designer: Shawn Soh
Sound Designer: Phillip Matejtschuk
Photographer: Richard Davenport

2/
AMELIA JANE HANKIN
SET AND COSTUME DESIGN

THE ITINERANT MUSIC HALL
Jessica Edwards and James Rowland (2014)

Flipping the Bird
Lyric Square, Greenwich and Docklands International Festival,
Watford Palace Theatre, Latitude Festival
June 2014

AJH: "I think all of us that are assembled here today can agree that it's an incontrovertible fact some people in this life have suffered more than others". The Itinerant Music Hall houses a rag tag troupe of three delightful miscreants in the world's smallest travelling music hall outfit: a honky tonk piano and tumbledown stage strapped to a bicycle on which they are trying to find their way back home to 1898.

This production was commissioned by the Lyric, Hammersmith and has toured to several festivals (as above). The Music Hall built of recycled pallets and props finds itself broken down in wildernesses, the cycling that's meant to start the cogs results in mists of smoke until the troupe have no choice but to perform on it, in promenade style, where it has landed. Young and old have enjoyed the somewhat intimate story telling and cabaret of three lost, down and out souls singing their tales of woe.

Director: Jessica Edwards
Set and Costume Designer: Amelia Jane Hankin
Photographer: Dave Flynn

Image 1
Mother Courage

Image 2 & 3
The Itinerant Music Hall

1/
EXHIBITION AND LIGHTING DESIGN

SENSING SPACES
Royal Academy of Arts
January 2014

SH: The exhibition design transforms and re-envisions the existing historical architecture of the Royal Academy of Arts. The lighting effects in Gallery IX and Lecture Room for Grafton's Installation allow visitors to wonder at the relationship between time, space, texture and weight.

My role was to produce a lighting effect that presented the movement of natural sunlight on a winters day in London, to ultimately enhance the intensity of the light. I wanted to create the light of four different winter days in London: warm/cold/strong/moonlight. One moment the visitor can feel the winter sun, the next a snowy morning, all programmed in a 20 minute loop.

Critical responses to the lighting design for Grafton and the installation in the Lecture Hall included:

"Great grey slabs plunge down from the ceiling, forming an interlocking play of cubic volumes, filtering fine shafts of light down across their faces into the ethereal gloom. Like entering some Blade Runner cathedral, the composition makes the room appear to soar upwards, way beyond its actual height."
O. Wainwright, The Guardian, 21/1/2014.

Exhibition Curation: Kate Goodwin
Architectural Installation: Grafton Architects (Diébédo Francis Kéré, Kengo Kuma, Li Xiaodong, Pezo von Ellrichshausen, Álvaro Siza, Eduardo Souto de Moura)
Exhibition and Lighting Design: Shizuka Hariu/SHSH Architecture+Scenography
Photographer: SHSH Architecture+Scenography

2/
SET DESIGN

A TIME THERE WAS
Benjamin Britten (various)
Jubilee Opera
Jubilee Hall, Aldeburgh
October 2013

SH: Scenes from Benjamin Britten's operas and his other vocal works were seamlessly linked together to create the production, A Time There Was. It was devised to celebrate Britten's Centenary at the historical Jubilee Hall in Aldeburgh. The cast including thirty five children from local schools performed in the imaginary space of seaside, while Britten's office at the front of the stage appeared much closer to reality. The use of abstract and concrete imagery in the scenography echoes my current academic research on the subject.

Conductor: Stuart Bedford
Director: Frederic Wake-Walker
Set Designer: Shizuka Hariu
Costume Designer: Kitty Callister
Lighting Designer: Cis O'Boyle
Photographer: SHSH Architecture+Scenography

3/
SET DESIGN

LUNCHMEAT FESTIVAL
Lunchmeat Festival
National Gallery, Prague
April 2014

SH: Lunchmeat Festival is a cutting edge music and visual festival that is held in the urban looking theatre space at the National Gallery in Prague. I collaborated with a VVVV artist and lighting designers to create a scenography for DJ performances. During a seven day limited time period, a light yet large scale scenography was created by combining translucent textile and wire. 3D mapping visuals were projected onto the scenography structure throughout the performance.

Director: Jakub Pešek
Set Designer: Shizuka Hariu
Lighting Designer: Dmitri Berzon and Petr Pufler
Sound Designer: DJ by Tim Exile
Media Designer: Desaxismundi
Photographer: Dita Havrankova

Image 2
A Time There Was

Image 1
Sensing spaces

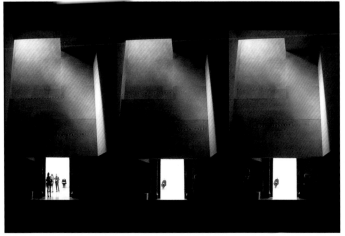

Image 3
Lunchmeat Festival

1/
KEN HARRISON
SET AND COSTUME DESIGN

OUTLYING ISLANDS
David Greig (2002)

Firebrand Theatre
Heart of Hawick/touring
September 2014

KH: An isolated scrap of land far out in the Atlantic Ocean: 1939. A survey of bird life by two young ornithologists soon becomes a study of human desires and impulses. In this production, which toured the Scottish Borders, the staging was pared back and intimate, a sense of place suggested by rippling sealight on a rock face, eggshells lying in the crevices.

Director: Richard Baron
Set and Costume Designer: Ken Harrison
Lighting Designer: Matt Eagland
Sound Designer: Jon Beales
Photographers: Ken Harrison and Graham Riddell

2/
KEN HARRISON
SET AND COSTUME DESIGN

THE ADMIRABLE CRICHTON
J.M.Barrie (1902)

Pitlochry Festival Theatre
June 2014

KH: An aristocratic family is shipwrecked in the South Pacific, and the social order upturned. An Island settlement is created and administered by their butler, Crichton, its buildings made from marine salvage. In true British style, an exotic fantasy combines with social satire and a display of improvised technology.

Director: Richard Baron
Choreographer: Chris Stuart-Wilson
Set and Costume Designer: Ken Harrison
Lighting Designer: Mark Doubleday
Sound Designer: Jon Beales
Photographer: Douglas McBride

Images 1 & 2
Outying Islands

Image 3
The Admirable Crichton

1/
KATHARINE HEATH
SET AND COSTUME DESIGN

L'ORFEO
Claudio Monteverdi (1607)

Silent Opera
Trinity Buoy Wharf
February 2013

KH: The design concept for L'Orfeo echoes the mission statement of Silent Opera, refracting the traditional through our modern hi tech world. We set L'Orfeo in a fragile, volatile, electrical world, where the Court of Act One is refuge from the beautiful danger of the outside world. The characters are earthed, plugged in, glowing, but earthy; harnessing electricity to grow a conservatory, glass fishing buoys hang from the ceiling in a constellation. When the audience descend into the underworld the characters sing in Monteverdi's Italian and wear early baroque garb frayed and broken down through the centuries. The river is a glistening cascade of glowing jars in low fog which the audience gather around. Upon entering hell mortals must give all possessions over to Caronte, the ferryman, and he collects peoples memories, sealing trinkets in jars; photographs, childhood toys, jewellery. Hell is barren, sparse and snowed-in, church pews hang upside down from the ceiling, frosted and broken.

Director: Daisy Evans
Choreographer: Anjali Mehra
Set and Costume Designer: Katharine Heath
Lighting Designer: Ziggy Jacobs
Sound Designer: Louis D'Heudieres/ Helen Atkinson
Production Media Designer: Ziggy Jacobs
Photographer: Tristram Kenton

2/
KATHARINE HEATH
SET AND COSTUME DESIGN

HENRY V
William Shakespeare (c.1599)

Theatre Delicatessen
Marylebone Gardens
June 2012

KH: We set Theatre Delicatessen's 'Henry V' in the Falklands War, and threw the audience straight into the English Soldier's makeshift barracks in a burnt out radio station. The audience sat at a long central table amongst the soldiers, on their beds and on sandbags filled with cushions on the floor amongst their possessions – endless kit, photographs of loved ones, French dictionaries, Shakespeare's sonnets.

Director: Roland Smith
Choreographer: Alexandra Baybutt
Set and Costume Designer: Katharine Heath
Lighting Designer: William Reynolds
Sound Designer: Fergus Waldron
Photographer: Lorna Palmer

3/
KATHARINE HEATH
SET AND COSTUME DESIGN

MY HEART IS HITCHHIKING DOWN PEACHTREE STREET
J. Fergus Evans (2012)

Contact, Manchester and Touring
February 2012

KH: Fergus hasn't been back to his hometown in Atlanta for five years. The show explores what it's like to live far away from home. In a cleaners cupboard I recreated fractured memories of Fergus' tales of Georgia; patchwork curtains hanging from brooms, origami cicada, hurricane lamps, suitcases and secret boxes of the Atlanta skyline, crow feathers, rusty nails and juicy peaches.

Director: J. Fergus Evans
Set Designer: Katharine Heath
Lighting Designer: Andrew Crofts
Media Designer: Laura Richardson
Photographer: Roshanan Rubin-Mayhew

Image 1
L'Orfeo

Image 2
Henry V

Image 3
My heart Is Hitchhiking Down Peachtree Street

SUSANNAH HENRY
SET AND COSTUME DESIGN

GIANNI SCHICCHI
Giacomo Puccini (1917-18)

Opera Holland Park
June 2012

SH: Gianni Schicchi formed the second half of a double bill at Opera Holland Park, so the set design had to work for both this and the preceding piece, which was Zanetto by Pietro Mascagni. Gianni Schicchi was performed by two companies: one of professional opera singers, and one of young emerging artists. The colours of the set design were found in a photograph of an Italian palazzo at dusk, with the intention to let the existing architecture of the Opera Holland Park stage (incorporating the frontage of Holland House) be seen as part of the design. In the final moments of the piece, the set splits in two and reveals the young lovers on the Ponte Vecchio, while Gianni Schicchi sings in the room in which the opera takes place, where greedy relatives have created chaos searching for the will of the recently deceased Buoso Donati.

Director: Martin Lloyd Evans

Set and Costume Designer: Susannah Henry

Lighting Designer: Colin Grenfell

Photographer: Robert Workman

Images
Gianni Schicchi

1/
SCENOGRAPHY - INSTALLATION

AUDIO OBSCURA
Lavinia Greenlaw (2011)

Co-commissioned by Manchester International Festival and Artangel
Manchester Piccadilly station and St Pancras International station
2011

IH: "In Audio Obscura, equipped with headphones, you'd enter the crowd and overhear voices around you. What did that woman mean? Did he really say that? Does she realise what she is saying? You might wish you hadn't listened or you might want to know more. You will look for stories and you might even find them..."

Co-commissioned by Artangel and Manchester International Festival, Audio Obscura is a sound work by award winning poet and novelist Lavinia Greenlaw. In an aural equivalent to the camera obscura, the audience experiences the project in a solitary way – hearing fragments of individual narratives, glimpses of interior worlds drawn from monologues that glance off one another, hovering between speech and unconscious thought.

The design of the kiosk is inspired by the geometry of a seashell – a common reference to sound and hearing – and camera obscura. It is a temporary sculpture as well as a functional information point where 42 headsets are stored and distributed to the public. It is designed to adapt to two different locations and create a memorable presence with equally interesting front and back. In Piccadilly Station, the kiosk appears to penetrate the glazed concourse, drawing attention from the train platforms. In St Pancras International, the kiosk is located in the middle of the arcade, visible from all sides and from the second floor.

Director: Lavinia Greenlaw
Sound Designer: Tim Barker
Kiosk Design: Ingrid Hu
Photographer: James Whitaker

Image 1   Images 2 & 3
Audio Obscura   Longplayer

2/
SCENOGRAPHY - INSTALLATION

LONGPLAYER DISPLAY
Jem Finer (2000)

Commissioned by Longplayer Trust
Lighthouse, Trinity Buoy Wharf, London
2013

IH: Longplayer is a 1000 year long musical composition conceived and composed by Jem Finer. It began playing at midnight on the 31st of December 1999, and will continue to play without repetition until the last moment of 2999, at which point it will complete its cycle and begin again.

I was commissioned to design a display and storage system for the 234 singing bowls that are part of the 66 foot wide orchestral instrument used to perform Longplayer Live. The design is based on a circular form evoking the movement of the Longplayer Live instrument and of the cycle of the music itself.

Each tier of the structure, containing 39 bowls positioned sequentially, corresponds to one of the six concentric rings of the Longplayer Live instrument. The curvatures are derived from the diameter of each bowl, allowing the handmade bowls to stand out.

The display is located at the Lighthouse, Trinity Buoy Wharf – home of Longplayer listening post. The singing bowls represent the reliance of human performance as one of the several 'survival strategies'. As a 'temporary' space relative to the entire lifespan of the project, the material presence of the bowls provides a powerful reminder of the transience of our own existence.

Scenographer: Ingrid Hu
Photographer: James Whitaker

Image 1
Das Rheingold

Image 2
Die Walkure

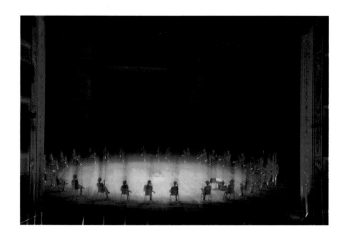

1/
RICHARD HUDSON
SET AND COSTUME DESIGN

DAS RHEINGOLD
Richard Wagner (1869)

Fondazione Teatro Massimo
Teatro Massimo, Palermo, Sicily
January 2013

RH: This is Nibelheim. We had forty actors playing the Nibelungs, dressed like Wall Street bankers. The atmosphere was of menacing evil and avarice.

Director: Graham Vick
Choreographer: Ron Howell
Set and Costume Designer:
Richard Hudson
Lighting Designer: Giuseppe Di Iorio
Photographer: Teatro Massimo

2/
RICHARD HUDSON
SET AND COSTUME DESIGN

DIE WALKURE
Richard Wagner (1870)

Fondazione Teatro Massimo
Teatro Massimo, Palermo, Sicily
February 2013

RH: This is the end of Die Walkure - Brünnhilde's Rock. The forty actors are now playing the fire that surrounds her. They are on a very large, slow revolve.

Director: Graham Vick
Choreographer: Ron Howell
Set and Costume Designer:
Richard Hudson
Lighting Designer: Giuseppe Di Iorio
Photographer: Teatro Massimo

JACOB HUGHES
SET AND COSTUME DESIGN

THE AENEID
Virgil (19BC) adapted by Joanne Pearce
(2012)

Magdalen College School Theatre Academy
Oxford Playhouse
July 2012

JH: An adaptation of Virgil's epic poem, the two islands revolved throughout Aeneas's journey, becoming and revealing new locations throughout his adventure.

Director: Joanne Pearce
Set and Costume Designer: Jacob Hughes
Lighting Designer: Ashley Bale
Sound Designer: Costa Cambanakis
Backdrop Design: Morgan Large
Photographer: Ross Young

Image
Aeneid

REBECCA HURST

THE PARDONER'S TALE
Geoffrey Chaucer (1475)
Adapted, directed and composed by Lewis Gibson (2014)

Unicorn Theatre / Tangere
co-production
Unicorn Theatre, London
January 2014

RH: Based on The Pardoner's Tale by Geoffrey Chaucer this production revelled in letting the audience in on the tricks and illusions of theatre. Through simple storytelling 'The Pardoner' (Gary Lagden) conjured up a world in front of the audience's eyes. Rain and snow fell at the click of a finger. The musicians (Hannah Marshall and Chris Preece) underscored the performance, utilizing Foley sound effects created from everyday objects hung and arranged on the simple set. The audience was let into the mechanics of theatre by watching how the lights were manipulated to create shadow puppet sequences and the scenery rolled and repositioned around the space to create different landscapes. The production centred on the collaboration of the audience to make believe.

Director, Composer and Adaptation:
Lewis Gibson
Designer: Rebecca Hurst
Lighting Designer: Ben Pacey
Musicians: Hannah Marshall
& Christopher Preece
Actor: Gary Lagden
Producer: David Johnston
Photographer: Manuel Harlan

Images
Pardoner's Tale

1/

IDOMENEUS
Roland Schimmelpfennig (2014)

The Gate Theatre
June 2014

AIJP: The design process for Idomeneus has been quite unusual. The director and I agreed to meet in unconventional places. Our second 'date' was in the Science Museum at 10am. The main entrance was full of excited children waiting for the doors to open. In the museum there were some experiments and games that I wanted to show the director. Once the museum opened we went straight to the playground area where we end up Playing! This process really influenced the play's development.

The minimal design was a playground for adults. It was a dark space where actors helped the audience to create mental labyrinths through the storytelling, awakening the imagination of both audience and actors into becoming children again.

The space changed as the story did; a blank page waiting for a story to be written.

Director: Ellen McDougall
Dramaturg: Clare Slater
Set and Costume Designer: Ana Inés Jabares Pita
Lighting Designer: Lizzie Powell
Sound Designer: Jon Nicholls
Movement Director: Joe Wild
Translator: David Tushingham
Photographer: Bill Knight

2/

DOMESTICA. LOST IN THE FUN HOUSE. PART THREE
Sleepwalk Collective (2014)

Sleepwalk Collective
TNT Terrasa, Catalonia
September 2014

AIJP: Working with a devised theatre company such as Sleepwalk Collective will completely change anyone's mind about what theatre design means and what scenography is. After two years and three residencies around Spain (Espaciol Azala, Vitoria and Espacio Eszena, Bilbao) and the UK (Barbican, London) we have given shape to DOMESTICA.

This is the first time that Sleepwalk have integrated designers into their devising process. The first step was getting to know the company's language so we could develop a new one together.

The scenographic proposal for DOMESTICA is a revision of different artistic genres, but especially Fine Arts from the Baroque period. The concept was to create a strong contrast between environment and costume; a dark minimal design with excessively ornate and bright costumes inspired by Zurbaran paintings

Our goals as a group were discovering new ways of devising, exploring the concept of 'performative maximalism', and having a special emphasis on the visual composition building static images that will stay in the audiences' minds.

Director: Sammy Metcalfe
Text by Sammy Metcalfe and Performers
Set and Costume Designer: Ana Inés Jabares Pita
Lighting Designer: David Alcorta
Sound Designer: Sammy Metcalfe
Video designer: Ainara Pardal
Performers: Gloria March Chulvi, Iara Solano Arana, Malla Sofia Pessi.
Photographer: Sleepwalk Collective

Images 1 & 2
Idomeneus

Images 3 & 4
Domestica

Image 1
Cinderalla

Image 2
The Raree Man Peepshow

Image 3
The Boy Who Cried Wolf

1/
KELLY JAGO
SET AND PROPS DESIGN

CINDERELLA
Tony Lidington (2013)

The Georgian Theatre Royal, Richmond, Yorkshire
December 2013

KJ: To mark the 225th anniversary of The Georgian Theatre Royal, we created a pantomime that emphasised the Georgian origins of traditional pantomime and the story of Cinderella. We incorporated traditional methods in the set design, like the 'slots', a Georgian method of sliding scenery onto the stage. The theatre also has many challenges for a designer: a very limited amount of back stage space, a grid that can't accommodate flying the full height of cloths above the stage, a raked stage floor and not a single straight or symmetrical wall in the building.

My research focused on the history of traditional pantomime, Harlequinade, Arthur Rackham and Georgian architecture and interior details. As well as designing the set and props my role also included painting the set, cloths, legs and borders, and making all of the props.

Director: Tony Lidington
Choreographer: Kelly Allison
Musical Director: Daniel Bowater
Set and Props Designer: Kelly Jago
Costume Designer: Naomi Parker Blackburn
Lighting Designer: Tony Wilcox

2/
KELLY JAGO
SET AND COSTUME DESIGN

THE RAREE MAN PEEPSHOW
Tony Lidington (2013)

Prom Prom Productions
Exeter RAMM Museum and touring
September 2014

KJ: 'The Raree Man' is a vibrant piece of street theatre presented as a Georgian peepshow. Developing from pre-cinematic popular entertainments, the Raree Man updates the format with digital multimedia seamlessly blending traditional performance skills including puppetry, story telling and showmanship.

Working in collaboration with The Bill Douglas Cinema Museum, I gained a great insight into the changing dynamics of the moving image and the history of our relationship with it. Challenges I faced specific to this show included designing for the cart's movement and weather proofing, I wanted to create a world steeped in history with the appearance of a travelling show that has seen many storms, summers and winters. Many hours were spent creating bleached wood, cracked paint, decayed fabrics and rusted metals.

This project involved working closely with Steve Sowden who created the projected animations for the three acts, and Tony Liddington, whose writing and showmanship brought The Raree Man to life as an interruptive, intimate, familiar and unexpected piece of street Theatre.

Set Designer: Kelly Jago
Costume Designer: Naomi Parker Blackburn
Film Maker and Animation: Steve Sowden
Photographer: Ben Pugh

3/
KELLY JAGO
SET AND COSTUME DESIGN

THE BOY WHO CRIED WOLF
Mike Kenny

Tutti Frutti Theatre Company
York Theatre Royal
July 2013

KJ: Mike Kenny's 'The Boy Who Cried Wolf' is a beautiful adaptation of the classic Aesop's fable, about a young shepherd boy who is bored by his surroundings and seeks adventure.

There are three main locations in the story, 'up on the hill', 'down in the village' and 'the edge of the forest'. Silas, the shepherd boy, spends many days and nights on his own high up on the hill looking down at the village, listening to the village knitters enjoying themselves. He repeats the same journey everyday, just as his Grandfather did, up and down the same mountain. This repetition is evoked through a circular design, with a route around the perimeter of the set.

During the R & D I proposed the concept of the villagers as knitters, who knitted with wool from Silas' herd. The annual highlight in the village is the Christmas jumper competition. All the costumes feature elements of intricate knitting, handmade by Silas' mother, known to be the best knitter in the village. The set comprises wintery trees wrapped in white wool and vast hilly landscapes, created using knitted blankets swagged on a line between the forest trees. Twinkling fairy lights are seen at key points during the play to emphasise Silas' loneliness beneath a star studded sky. I'd like to acknowledge Tom Bennett's beautiful and wittily comedic performance as Silas' Grandfather, Tom very sadly and unexpectedly passed away shortly after the international tour in 2014.

Director: Wendy Harris
Composer: Dominic Sales
Choreographer: TC Howard
Set and Costume Designer: Kelly Jago
Lighting Designer: Nick Duncan
Photographer: Brian Slater

1/
SOPHIE JUMP
SET AND COSTUME DESIGN

UNCLE VANYA
Anton Chekhov (1897)

Belgrade Theatre, Coventry and Arcola Theatre, London
April 2011

SJ: Vanya was a co-production between the Belgrade and Arcola theatres. This was one of those processes in which I created many, many versions before we settled on the final design. The Arcola is a smaller and less flexible space than the Belgrade studio, having a thrust stage with iron pillars and beams across the playing area. I designed the set to incorporate these specifications, so we had to recreate the layout and the pillars in the Belgrade. The audience surrounded the stage on three sides, and at the Arcola they were within touching distance of the actors, although the configuration in both spaces was fairly intimate. The set acknowledged that it was in a theatre, using the back wall in each space: concrete at the Belgrade and brick at the Arcola. The room had elements that bled outside into the trees and onto the wall.

Director: Helena Kaut-Howson
Set and Costume Designer: Sophie Jump
Lighting Designer: Alex Wardle
Sound Designer: Paul Bull

2/
SOPHIE JUMP
SCENOGRAPHY

LIKE A FISH OUT OF WATER
Seven Sisters Group (2012)

Seven Sisters Group with English National Ballet
Hillingdon and Hampton Lidos
July 2012

SJ: Like a Fish out of Water presented an inspired new concept, developed by myself and Artistic Director Susanne Thomas, that blends site-specific performance and handheld video technology featuring artists, dancers, actors and design, leading audiences on a magical journey around London lidos.

Taking place during opening hours, the audience received an iPod with headphones to follow the route on the iPod screen and listen to the soundtrack, stopping to sit on deck chairs or picnic rugs, encountering live and pre-recorded performance, installation and the everyday users of the lido. A story unfolded based on the fictional heroine of Like a Fish out of Water, an elderly woman who has visited and swum in the lido since childhood. She is 'like a fish out of water' when on land and her fantasies and inner life are captured in a combination of beautiful underwater scenes in pre-filmed sequences and live performance. Myths and legends, mermaids and selkies, all were explored in this fascinating multi sensory experience.

Director: Susanne Thomas
Co-Director and Scenography: Sophie Jump
Composer and Sound Designer: Craig Vear
Writer: Richard Hurford
Film maker: Dan Farberoff
Photographer: Chris Nash

Image 1   Images 2 & 3
Uncle Vanya   Like a Fish Out Of Water

MONA KASTELL
COSTUME DESIGN, DIRECTION

L'EVEIL
devised (2012)

Mona Kastell
The Arches, Glasgow
2012

MK: Consistently questioning what is socially acceptable, L'Eveil deal with the themes of Growth, Transformation, Beauty and Disfigurement. The uniqueness of the piece arises from the indivisibility of performer, sculptural costume and movement, challenging the distortion of the body and its place in society. The costume is created not around a character or an idea but through the relationship between body, material, movement and observer, creating a strong visual dynamic. Atypically visually directed through a costume and theatre designer eye and not script led, this project is an inventive and inspiring way of looking at costume,

Shortlisted for the New Zealander international costume Art competition World of Wearable Art in 2010, the costume is entirely made of hemp and recycled fabric waste hand dyed using Shibori techniques.

Director and Costume Designer:
Mona Kastell

Lighting Designer:
Alberto Santos Bellido

Sound Designer: Guy Veale

Photographer: Anita Barron

Images
L'Eveil

1/
SIMON KENNY
SET AND COSTUME DESIGN

....

THE MACHINE GUNNERS
Ali Taylor (2011), from the novel by Robert Westall (1975)

Polka Theatre
February 2011

....

SK: Set during the Second World War, it felt important to suggest the reality of wartime childhood for our young audience in as vivid a way as possible, albeit theatricalised for a formally configured proscenium stage.

Using the existing theatre architecture as the starting point, we imagined how the building itself might appear after one of the many bombing raids depicted in the story. Stage detritus and building wreckage formed the physical language of the piece; the storytelling was infused with a make-do-and-mend aesthetic as the characters improvised with objects which apparently belonged in a damaged theatre environment. The elaborate ironwork roof structure running the length of the auditorium was replicated and continued over the stage, with struts crashing into the space at dangerous angles. Timbers and girders pierced the stage floor; recognisable front of house light fittings were strewn across the stage; false theatre walls were blown through with each successive air raid in the play, until finally we reach the open air beyond.

Director: Adam Penford
Set and Costume Designer: Simon Kenny
Lighting Designer: Emma Chapman
Sound Designer: Tom Gibbons
Photographer: Robert Workman

2/
SIMON KENNY
SET AND COSTUME DESIGN

....

SLEUTH
Anthony Shaffer (1970)

Watermill Theatre, Newbury
February 2013

....

SK: Set in a secluded, fading country pile, the play seemed uniquely suited to the venue – an old converted mill along a country lane. In keeping with the playful, tricksy spirit of the piece, the existing theatre space itself was animated, as much as a set was designed to fit within it.

Using the oak frame of the old mill as a starting point, the design was assembled so as to lose all perception of what was real and what was scenic. Existing timbers were incorporated, staircases were extended into the stage area, the spaces beneath the galleries were excavated and integrated, paint finishes were matched, and window designs referenced those seen around the exterior of the building; all elements playfully subverting the architecture of the theatre.

Into this were built various puzzles, secret doors, hatches, impossible crossovers, special effects and magic tricks, so the lines between real and theatrical, existing and specifically designed were truly blurred.

Director: Jessica Swale
Set and Costume Designer: Simon Kenny
Lighting Designer: Nick Richings
Sound Designer: Isobel Waller-Bridge
Photographer: Colin Willoughby

3/
SIMON KENNY
SET AND COSTUME DESIGN

THE MERCHANT OF VENICE
William Shakespeare (1596)

Shakespeare's Globe
March 2014

SK: The Globe is a space that announces itself loudly and the designer must embrace that. The challenge here was to acknowledge the building while also creating a strong, coherent playing space within it. Our solution was to make a few very bold design choices using the scale and proximity of the venue – a huge graphic neon sign, a fully working hot-tub in the yard, some highly caricatured costumes – but to support these with other more stealthy choices.

   Some elements were built and finished to tie in with the existing space, others were skeletal so the theatre building was always visible through and behind them. Liberal amounts of gold fabric and paint were used to tie the scenic elements to each other and to the existing décor. While many of these elements may not have been immediately apparent, they all served to enhance an overall design where the building itself played a featured role. In this particular case, many individual elements of the set were explicitly designed to go largely unnoticed.

Director: Bill Buckhurst

Choreographer: Georgina Lamb

Composer: Olly Fox

Set and Costume Designer: Simon Kenny

Photographer: Ellie Kurttz

EMMYLOU LAIRD
COSTUME DESIGN

THE FORTRESS
Danielle Corbishley & Liz Alum
(2014)

Beautiful Creatures
Caversham Festival
July 2014

Image
The Fortress

EL: The Fortress explores a community of characters inspired by birds who are under threat from predators in the form of a development company. The Fortress debuted at Caversham Festival 2014 and will tour in 2015. It is a dance based performance devised for an outside space and centres around five beautiful, enormous, hand made and bespoke chimes, played by the performers throughout the piece. The costumes were designed and developed to be light, flexible, non-constraining and robust as the performers have a lot of physical contact. They refer to birds in a similar way that the chimes reference a nest structure and are constructed from environmentally sustainable bamboo and viscose.

Director: Danielle Corbishley
Choreographer: John Darvell/
Nocturne Dance
Costume Designer: Emmylou Laird
Sound Designer: Tom Neill &
Alan Dicker
Photographer: Richard Fletcher

KATE LANE
SET, COSTUME AND DIRECTION

BRAVE NEW WORLD 1: UTOPIA
Brave New Worlds (2014)

Brave New Worlds
The Yard, London
July 2014

Image
Brave New World 1: Utopia

KL: BRAVE NEW WORLDS is a performance collective based in the South East of England and Lithuania. It is a collaboration between Lithuanian visual artist Guoda Jarusceviciute, Italian theatre maker and performer Valentina Ceschi (co-artistic director of Dancing Brick) and British costume designer Kate Lane. Our aim is to question the aesthetics of performance and its role in the creation process. Our work sits on the border of theatre and live arts; the driving principle is a fundamental belief that design should be the catalyst of the devising process.

'Brave New World 1: Utopia' was our first exploration into aesthetic-led performance. Our work starts with a conceptual premise which we explore using an intuitive approach, trying to understand the physical aesthetic form of a conceptual idea (for example: what does Utopia look like? what shape? colour?). Out of the forms we look to create movement, character and story. We invite other artists (writers, composers or sound artists, lighting designers) to respond to the aesthetic world we've created. Through creating visual responses to the idea of Utopia we started making different objects or 'forms' which were then explored through movement. This piece has developed from an end on theatre performance to a multi platformed work that exists live as a gallery piece and performance, and online as a series of films.

Directors: Valentina Ceschi,
Guoda Jarusceviciute, Kate Lane
Set and Costume Designers:
Valentina Ceschi, Guoda
Jarusceviciute, Kate Lane
Lighting Designer: Beatrice Rocchi
Sound Designer: Caroline Devine
Text: Thomas Eccleshare
Photographer: Jemima Yong

1/
MIKE LEES
SET AND COSTUME

SOMMER:14
Rolf Hochhuth
(German premiere 1994, English premiere 2014)
Cerberus Theatre
Finborough Theatre
August 2014

ML: To coincide with the centenary of the outbreak of
World War 1, Hochhuth's Sommer:14 (the first play
of its kind to deal with the war from a specifically
German perspective) sees Death return to explore
who is ultimately responsible. An epic examination of
history, following the structure of the Danse Macabre,
showing that all are equal in death, from the boys on the
battlefields, the victims onboard the Lusitania, Kaiser
Wilhelm and even Winston Churchill himself.

Director: Christopher Loscher
Set and Costume Designer: Mike Lees
Lighting Designer: Rob Mills
Projection Design: Mike Lees and Rob Mills
Photographer: Scott Rylander

2/
MIKE LEES
SET AND COSTUME

COUNT OEDERLAND
Max Frisch (1962)
Cerberus Theatre
Arcola Theatre
January 2013

ML: The British Premiere of Max Frisch's Count Oederland
was described as 'American Psycho meets V for
Vendetta'. A private act of revolt becomes an infectious
underground movement. A Swiss bank clerk commits the
seemingly senseless murder of a colleague. The public
prosecutor assigned to the case finds he understands the
murderer better than himself. Thousands join in and 'take
to the axe' as those in power struggle to understand and
contain the violence.

Director: Christopher Loscher
Set and Costume Designer: Mike Lees
Lighting Designer: Jethro Compton
Sound Designer: Philippa Herrick
Photographer: Mike Lees

Images 1 & 2   Images 3 & 4
Sommer: 14   Count Oederland

1/
MARIE-JEANNE LECCA
COSTUME DESIGN

THE MAGIC FLUTE
Wolfgang Amadeus Mozart
(1791)

Bregenz Lake Stage
Bregenzer Festspiele
July 2013 - July 2014

MJL: The lake stage in Bregenz is a very special location, a huge space, that requires big theatrical gestures, broad brush strokes and enormous clarity in telling the story. There are nearly 7000 audience every night. With these coordinates in mind, the choice of The Magic Flute as a piece meant enhancing the magic to a maximum.

David's brief was to create oversized characters which I translated into large scale puppets. I imagined the three ladies as Amazons, riding their archaeopteryx like birds, who could behave like flirting young girls, playful, clumsy, quite endearing but be threatening and aggressive at the same time.

Even when keeping to the human scale there were costume elements that were oversized, enhancing certain traits and giving the characters an extra dimension: the Queen of the Night's skirt of lights, Papagena's head dress, Papageno's bird catcher outfit.

Director: David Pountney

Conductor: Patrick Summers

Set Designer: Johan Engels

Costume and Puppets Designer: Marie-Jeanne Lecca

Lighting Designer: Fabrice Kebour

Stunt and Action Choreography: Ran Arthur Braun

Puppetry: Blind Summit

Birds, Three Ladies Puppets and Pappagena:
Robert Allsopp and Associates

The Two Knights Puppets: Puppet Players Stefan Fichert

Photographer: Karl Forster

Images
The Magic Flute

2/
MARIE-JEANNE LECCA
COSTUME DESIGN

MOSÉ IN EGITTO
Gioachino Rossini (1818)

Welsh National Opera
Wales Millennium Centre, Cardiff, and touring
October 2014

MJL: Rossini's opera is an 'azione tragico-sacra', an oratorio style piece that made us think of bold and simple solutions. It begins with a plague of darkness and ends with the crossing of the Red Sea. There is a monumental dimension to it all. It deals with national destiny and is based on the Old Testament. Marc Chagall made a series of illustrations and paintings for the Old Testament, including one entitled 'The Crossing of the Red Sea', a wonderful composition and powerful metaphoric image.

Out of the primeval darkness at the beginning of the show, the costumes should emerge colourful, strong and full of tension in their contrasts, defining the two sides - Egyptians and Hebrews.

Director: David Pountney
Conductor: Carlo Rizzi
Set Designer: Raimund Bauer
Costume Designer: Marie-Jeanne Lecca
Lighting Designer: Fabrice Kebour
Fabrics Printed By: Nicola Killeen Textiles
Photographer: Marie-Jeanne Lecca

Images
Mosé In Egitto

VERENA LEO
PERFORMANCE DESIGN

....

LIKE A COG IN THE WHEEL
Texts by Maria Lauber and Ueli Schmid
Music - 'Se Dió Vuelta Y Para Qué by Alfredo Del Rio

Abandoned Matchstick Factory, Switzerland
June 2012

....

Patrick Moore photography

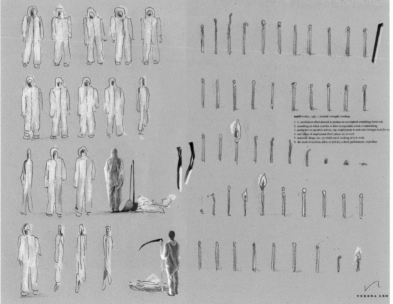

VL: The 'factory owner' meets the spectators at the train station and leads them quietly through the rural landscape to the abandoned factory. The windows are wide open, framing three figures looking silently into the far distance. Before the doors open the writer begins to read. Word by word, room by room, step by step, the spectators follow the traces of bygone days until the dark shadows of the past appear reflected in a silent dance performance. Only once - like a passing dream - a melody resounds from afar. Inside the walls soaked with sweat and memories of hardship, the audience is taken back to the time when machines were still running day and night. Ghosts are moving along the walls following their own patterns and rhythms, trapped and driven by the merciless beat of an endlessly pounding machine called time.

**Director, Choreographer,
Set and Costume Designer:** Verena Leo
....
Actor: Michel Allenbach
....
Reader: Ueli Schmid
....
Dancers: Anina Weber, Karin Iseli,
Laura Helena Stierli

Images
Like A Cog In The Wheel

1/
SARAH LEWIS
SET AND COSTUME DESIGN

BOLERO
Michael Pinchbeck (2014)

Nottingham Playhouse
May 2014

SL: Ravel's 1928 Bolero; Torvill and Dean's performance in Sarajevo set to his composition; the siege, eight years later, that saw the bombing of the stadium in which they performed; the assassination of Franz Ferdinand. All of these were narratives explored in the overlapping journey of the piece. I designed a simple space with an ever evolving (or devolving) wall that, importantly, the performers themselves would transform. They existed amidst the opulence of the Paris Opera House; the cardboard signed world of the siege; and finally the post war ruins of Sarajevo. Simple black costuming enabled the cast members' many roles, with mere hints at their various identities. The supporting shadowy ensemble wore faded grey imitations of the core cast's costume. Props were simple and symbolic.

The piece was toured to Sarajevo for the British Council's Connecting Creatively programme marking the anniversary of the start of the First World War.

Director: Michael Pinchbeck
Choreographer: Arianna Maiorani
Set and Costume Designer: Sarah Lewis
Photographer: Julian Hughes & Sarah Lewis

2/
SARAH LEWIS
SET AND COSTUME DESIGN

ENRON
Lucy Prebble (2009)

Nottingham Playhouse
Nottingham Playhouse Youth Theatre
August 2013

SL: Enron, a story of corruption and greed at the heart of American business was an exciting script to explore with the advanced youth theatre at Nottingham Playhouse. This was a fast paced, physical piece, investigating the rotten core at the centre of the outwardly shining American dream. In design terms, there was a lot to utilize in these themes.

I created a space that left no doubt of the hierarchy of power: two levels that allowed the bosses to lord it over their puppet like traders below; the back projection screens enabling them to be silhouetted like idols.

Projection was key in creating the moments of high energy – the flickering screens of the trade floor, the glossy world of magazine covers that Skilling, the CEO resided in, as well as Benjamin Franklin within his $100 bill, peering down on the whole charade, casting his judgement.

Director: Sarah Stephenson
Set, Costume and Projection Designer: Sarah Lewis
Lighting Designer: Stephanie Bartle
Sound Designer: Mark Di Martino Marriott
Photographer: Sarah Lewis

Images 1 & 2   Image 3
Bolero   Enron

FALSTAFF - LA OPERA - NOVEMBER 2013

FALSTAFF - LA OPERA   NOVEMBER 2013

FALSTAFF - LA OPERA   NOVEMBER 2013

1/
ADRIAN LINFORD
SET AND COSTUME DESIGN

FALSTAFF
Giuseppi Verdi (1893)

Los Angeles Opera
Dorothy Chandler Pavilion, Los Angeles
2013

Director: Lee Blakeley

Set and Costume Designer: Adrian Linford

Lighting Designer: Rick Fisher

Choreographer: Nicola Bowie

Photographer: Adrian Linford

2/
SET AND COSTUME DESIGN

THE WITCH OF EDMONTON
William Rowley, Thomas Dekker,
John Ford (1621)

RADA
Vanburgh Theatre, RADA, London
March 2014

Director: Philip Franks
Set and Costume Designer: Adrian Linford
Lighting Designer: Peter Small
Photographer: Adrian Linford

3/
SET AND COSTUME DESIGN

IL TURCO IN ITALIA
Gioachino Rossini (1814)

Angers Nantes Opera
Théâtre Graslin, Nantes, France
December 2013

Director: Lee Blakeley
Set and Costume Designer: Adrian Linford
Lighting Designer: Emma Chapman
Choreographer: Tess Gibbs
Photographer: Adrian Linford

Images 1-3
Falstaff

Image 4
The Witch of Edmonton

Images 5-7
Il Turco in Italia

SOPHIA LOVELL SMITH
SET AND COSTUME DESIGN

THE SNOW QUEEN
Anupama Chandrasekhar (2011)

Unicorn Theatre, London
November 2011

SLS: A journey from Northern Europe to South Asia, The Snow Queen was a re-imagining of the classic Andersen fairy tale in an Indian landscape. The Unicorn Theatre's commission from Anupama Chandrasekhar became a fantastical tale, going from coast to Bollywood, desert to mountain. The design needed to capture the vast scale and colour of an ancient subcontinent onto a stage in Southwark. This vivid production was then re-shaped by Trestle Theatre for a British Council excursion to Mumbai, Chennai and Bangalore, returning to the UK for a tour. A three year adventure!

With protagonists, Gowri (Gerda) and Kumar (Kai) the audience dip their toes in the warm seas at the southern tip of India, whilst looking up towards the icy mountains of the North and the forbidding silver and white palace of the Queen. To rescue her friend from the Queen's frozen heart, Gowri travels across hot and cold terrains, encounters a sea goddess, dallies in a lush garden beguiled by scents, is dazzled by Bollywood's palace of dreams and learns the art of Kalaripayattu from a bandit renegade.

Images
The Snow Queen

Director: Rosamunde Hutt
Choreographer: Ash Mukherjee
Set and Costume Designer: Sophia Lovell Smith
Lighting Designer: Phil Clarke
Composer: Arun Ghosh
Movement Director: Emily Gray
Photographer: Alistair Muir

Images
The Birthday Of The Infanta

RACHEL MACALLAN
SET AND COSTUME DESIGN

THE BIRTHDAY OF THE INFANTA
From a short story by Oscar Wilde (1891)

Solar Bear - Deaf Youth Theatre
Eastwood Park Theatre and The Tramway
August 2013

RM: Birthday of the Infanta is particularly special because it tackled the themes of 'difference' and 'what we have in common'. As many of our young Solar Bear performers are deaf, hard of hearing, or children of deaf adults, the group development of the individual characters in this piece really connected and responded to these themes.

The design of this highly intimate piece really built a multi sensory world for this story without language. We used bold colours, visible musicians playing live, projection and live flowers and branches to give as many entrances as possible for the audience into the world. It created an accessible piece which allowed deaf and hearing audiences to have an appreciation for the story of the Infanta.

Since the initial performance of this piece, it has never stopped developing. Recently a short adapted extract from the piece was performed as part of a production created by Indepen-dance at the Tramway theatre. Our hope is that Infanta can continue to develop, bringing this story to new audiences.

Director: Gerry Ramage

Set and Costume Designer: Rachel Macallan

Lighting Designer: Alexander Ridgers

Sound Designer: Ian Bustard

Photographer: Stephanie Gibson

1/
GARANCE MARNEUR
SET AND COSTUME DESIGN

THE LEGEND OF CAPTAIN CROW'S TEETH
Matthew Lenton and the company (2012),
original book by Eoin Colfer (2007)

Unicorn Theatre
March 2012

2/
GARANCE MARNEUR
SET AND COSTUME DESIGN

DARK WOODS DEEP SNOW
Chris Thorpe (2013)

Northernstage Theatre Company
Northernstage, Newcastle-upon-Tyne
December 2013

GM: Full of excitement after reading Eoin Colfer's children book,
my first meeting with the director started like this:

MATT LENTON: It is about darkness, childhood fears, how we
latch onto one thing and let it grow in our minds. It should be scary,
and also a lot of fun!

ME: Brilliant, let's physicalise and personify darkness on stage!
What would darkness look like, feel like? What does fear look like?
Let's create a highly atmospheric playground for a lot of 'shiver-me-
timbers-tastic fun'.

For the set I created a huge porthole that dominated the stage of the
Unicorn theatre. I think that the frontier between children's perception
of reality and their relation to their own imagination is a blurred space
at times. I chose to portray this through a wide open frame allowing for
characters from both worlds to come through and merge. Dark wools,
and various fish nets filled the space beyond the porthole, densifying
darkness from which spooky characters could suddenly appear, but
also creating a nurturing and cocooned feeling to this dark world. The
porthole morphed to become a moon, a sea landscape, a pirate ship, a
cradle, a cliff, a playful slope for the children to skate on and climb, and
the ominous black hole of our deepest fears.

Director: Matthew Lenton
Adaptation: Matthew Lenton and the company
Set and Costume Designer: Garance Marneur
Lighting Designer: James Mackenzie
Photographer: Ludovic Des Cognets

GM: In Chris Thorpe's first draft, we met the central character, a young
boy, lost in a forest. Was the forest real or part of his psyche as he
journeyed into manhood? I asked myself, "If I were little again, a mini-
me, closing my eyes, walking into that forest… what would I see?

'An endless forest of gigantic flying trees… a cute little tree house that
magically appears and disappears…iridescent blue shifting of darkness for
the dark spirits coming from a crack in the floor (leading to the centre of
the Earth)… candy striped trees, giant hair plates, huge snowflakes falling
upside down and glowing constellations… I see calligraphies appearing
on the trees as the story unfolds, fantastic creatures emerging from those
trees, people disappearing… and a talking pig!"

So we did just that!

We wanted to create an epic landscape; an uncompromising,
unpatronising space fantasy everywhere, with true magic. I flooded
the set with innovative projections that were a mixture of my own
drawings and abstract paintings. These, animated along with other
video footage, allowed me to constantly change and animate the
texture on the trees to create all these worlds.

A Christmas show is the best opportunity to offer visual treats
and magic to an audience of all ages. I believe the darkness of our
subconscious is an exciting, beautiful, scary and fun place. This was
the perfect playground to root our show.

Director: Lorne Campbell
Set and Costume Designer: Garance Marneur
Lighting Designer: James Mackenzie
Projections: Garance Marneur
Sound Designer: Rebecca Wilkie
Photographer: Garance Marneur

Image 1
The Legend Of Captain
Crow's Teeth

Image 2
Dark Woods Deep Snow

Images 3 & 4
Comfort Zone

3/
GARANCE MARNEUR
DRAMATURGY AND PRODUCTION DESIGN

COMFORT ZONE
Benjamin Levy (2013)

LevyDance
The Exploratorium Museum, San Francisco
October 2013

GM: What if I had an avatar which is individual to me that I could grow and interact with? A better version of myself that could challenge me, push me beyond my comfort zone both emotionally and physically, and connect me with others in social environments?

Our bodies are our vehicles for experiencing the world and the other people who inhabit it. We physically lean for comfort on those we love; we scoot away from those whom we perceive as a threat. We use our bodies to navigate a whole host of unspoken social parameters, and those parameters in turn help shape who we are and how we act.

Comfort Zone is a new participatory installation which integrates choreography into a virtual, interactive experience. "Visitors will have an opportunity to step into a hyper real, virtual world where their actions and choices will affect their surroundings. It's like stepping into a video game." (Director, Benjamin Levy).

At the centre of the experience is a virtual, responsive 'avatar' which interacts with visitors through movement, encouraging them to investigate choice in social situations. "This installation is about trust and breaking down the barriers between the performers and the watchers," says Pam Winfrey, co-curator of the West Gallery. "It's about making people more spatially aware, more tuned in to their bodies in space."

Director and Choreographer: Benjamin Levy
Sound Designer: Ben Juodvalkis
Dramaturge and Visual Designer: Garance Marneur
Product Designer: Paul Marneur
Interaction Design & Software Development:
Anticlockwise Arts
Photographer: Amy Snyder @ Exploratorium

Image 1
Disco Babies

Image 2
Baroque Box

Image 3
Julius

1/
NADIA MALIK
COSTUME DESIGN

DISCO BABIES
Silversmith Dance Theatre (2014)

*Oxford House (London) and U.K. Tour
April 2014*

NM: Disco Babies is a contemporary dance-theatre production which looks at the world of children's freestyle disco dancing to investigate themes of pressure, failure, friendship and child-parent relationships through the eyes of four competitors.

Costuming adult bodies representing children who present themselves as adults has many layers of complexity. My costume designs aim to make these clear. Their extreme and playful nature reflects the reality of the sexualisation, superficiality and intense physicality apparent in competitive freestyle disco. It also allows the performers to reveal the feelings of exposure, vulnerability and other delicate intricacies of human nature that can arise from highly pressured environments and high level competing. In a wider sense, through the costume design in synthesis with the performance, the audience is asked to reflect on their own childhood experiences in comparison with those that children have in society today. What kinds of environments and behaviours do we expect for and of our children?

Director: Lorraine Smith
Choreographer: Lorraine Smith with performers Gina Biggs, Morena De Leonardis, Chris Mead, Lauren Okadigbo
Costume Designer: Nadia Malik
Sound Designer: Patrick Furness
Filmmaker: Will Huntley
Photographer: Alex Traylen

2/
NADIA MALIK
SET AND COSTUME DESIGN

BAROQUE BOX
Concept, Text and Artistic Direction:
Jacek Ludwig Scarso (2011)

*Elastic Theatre
Greenwich and Docklands International Festival
(London)
June 2011*

NM: Baroque Box, inspired by the aesthetics and inquiry within Caravaggio's paintings, looks at the time when the blood circulation system was discovered and ideas about the body, religion, science and art were all diverging. Echoing this complicated period in history, Baroque Box is a site specific, devised, performer-guided, promenade dance-opera, with two stories being told at any one time to the audience at both ends of the two double corridors running the inside length of the box. The space inside, on top of and all around the 'box' was used with several visual surprises along the way, re-envisioning the grounds of the Baroque Royal Naval College performance space.

Designing the costumes and set was part of developing the voice, movement, characterisation, music, lighting and staging in collaboration with the interdisciplinary and multi-skilled company (a contemporary dancer, opera singers, a circus performer, a commedia expert, video artists, live musicians, a director and me, the designer). Specifically, the costumes fused historical and contemporary cut and construction techniques with contemporary design and textiles. This experimentation created a visually cohesive modern day peep into the imagination of a Baroque artist exploring his sacred, scientific, sensual and superstitious visions.

Director: Jacek Ludwig Scarso
Composer: Ivan Hussey
Set and Costume Designer: Nadia Malik
Video and Direction of Filmography:
Savage Mills
Production Manager: Greg Piggot
Photographer: Ludovic des Cognets

3/
NADIA MALIK
COSTUME AND ILLUSTRATION

JULIUS
Concept, Text and Artistic Direction:
Jacek Ludwig Scarso

*Elastic Theatre
Spitalfields Music Festival (London)
+ U.K., E.U. and U.S.A. Tour
June 2013*

NM: JULIUS is a multi-format theatrical film experience which focuses on subconsciously triggered 'intrusive thoughts' which can lead to Obsessive Compulsive Disorder (OCD). Julius is an adolescent boy who, provoked by the overbearing characters in his life, performs increasingly complex rituals in order to erase the recurring, intrusive thought of seeing himself as Julius Caesar.

Inspired by Fellini film sequences a minimalist design approach enables colour in the costumes to chart the protagonist's journey. The set was reduced mainly to overlaying illustrations within the film sequences so that the final performance format could be as flexible and experimental as possible. The storytelling/action is interwoven across three projection screens which can be shown at any scale and in any configuration, or all three strands can be viewed as part of one screen. Screenings have also been combined with live performance interaction and 'structured improvisations'.

Director: Jacek Ludwig Scarso
in collaboration with Savage Mills
Costume and Illustration Designer: Nadia Malik
Composer and Sound Designer: Ivan Hussey
Sound Designer: Ernest Mills
Photographer: Ludovic des Cognets

THOMASIN MARSHALL
SET AND COSTUME DESIGN

THE LAST POLAR BEARS
Harry Horse (1996),
adapted by Joe Douglas

*National Theatre of
Scotland Tour
May 2012*

TM: The Last Polar Bears tells the story of an old man and his dog, Roo, on a quest to the North Pole to see the polar bears before all the ice melts. The Company undertook the four week tour in the summer of 2012 on bicycles, visiting primary schools in Ayrshire, Dumfries and Galloway, the Borders, East Lothian and Edinburgh.

On tour, the play was followed by a workshop for pupils which explored the production, as well as issues of climate change and cycling. As part of the production's legacy towards climate change and to safeguard the future of polar bears, the National Theatre of Scotland adopted 17 Svalbard Polar Bears with the World Wildlife Fund for Nature to give to each of the primary schools on the tour.

The play was performed in the natural light of school halls using puppetry and live music. The world of ice sculptures, snow storms and igloos was created from the lightweight, portable and frequently recycled objects; one bike, its back wheel propped up, created the sounds of the snow storm, a cycle helmet with ears became a wolf costume, balled up pairs of socks were used as

snowballs. The colourful patchwork backcloth was suspended between two giant golf clubs, held in place by a pair of bicycles which marked out the performance area.

The cast and crew cycled the three hundred mile round trip to venues, on custom-built reclaimed bikes, carrying all costumes, set, props and personal belongings in their recycled bike panniers and on two trailers.

Director: Joe Douglas
Set and Costume Designer: Thomasin Marshall
Puppet Designer: Ross Mackay
Photographer: Johnny McLauchlan

Images
The Last Polar Bears

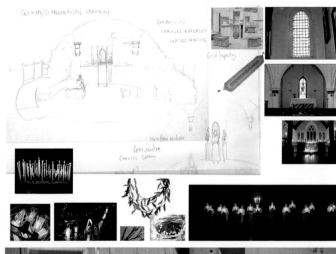

1/
LOIS MASKELL
SET AND COSTUME DESIGN

WOLF RED
Devised by the Company & Chris Fittock
Original Score by Meike Holzmann (2011)

Tmesis Theatre
The Unity Theatre, Liverpool
2012

LM: The stimulus for this original piece of physical theatre was a series of reports of kidnap and abduction; the idea of the long term prisoner became central to our explorations of captivity, uncovering complex human behaviour and dark primal instincts. Influences included: the psychological state, Stockholm syndrome; Angela Carter's text, The Bloody Chamber; folklore and fairytales such as Blue Beard's Castle. Seeking ways to explore physicality in the themes of desire and sexuality; identity and habitat; nature versus nurture, the crux of the design became about control (taming), boundaries and mortality. The solo performer is apparently held within a small square space, though there is little to prevent her from stepping outside it. The design has echoes of the foundations of a room; it may also be read as an exposed shallow grave. Nature is omnipresent. Outside the 'room' is a forest floor of earth and bark. A suspended sapling hovers, lost in half light whilst the stump of an old oak tree stands by the edge of the space. Inside the 'room', every object (particularly the manmade) has been scrutinised before inclusion.

Director: Yorgos Karamalegos
Choreographer: Beverley Edmunds
Set and Costume Designer: Lois Maskell
Lighting Designer: Arek Chrusciel
Sound Designer: Xenia Bayer
Dramaturgical Input: Lorna Marshall and Fin Walker
Photographer: Mark Loudon and First Take

2/
LOIS MASKELL
SET AND COSTUME DESIGN

A WONDROUS PLACE
Alison Carr, Sarah McDonald Hughes, Matt Hartley,
Luke Barnes (2013)

Northern Spirit
The Studio, Royal Exchange Manchester; Crucible Studio
Theatre, Sheffield; Unity Theatre, Liverpool; Northern Stage, Newcastle
May 2013

LM: A Wondrous Place was a very special theatre making project by Northern Spirit that celebrated all that is unique, inspiring and unsaid about the North of England. The venture began life on a website that invited multi-disciplinary artists, writers and bloggers to contribute perspectives and ideas about the region in which they live. From this nutritious mix, four brilliant writers took on the challenge of creating a play that would show their home towns in an unexpected and fresh way.

The design had to become a playground of opportunities for the fast paced storytelling staged by director Chris Meads. I took inspiration from the endeavour itself - a collage of thoughts and voices. Works by artists such as Hockney, Blake and Cornell (his boxes in particular) fed into the final form which was likened to 'an arching advent calendar, with props and treasures hiding behind each window'. Projection mapping was used on the entire set to integrate video and animation.

Director: Chris Meads
Set and Costume Designer: Lois Maskell
Lighting Designer: Phil Saunders
Sound Designer: Caroline Churchill
Production Media Designer: Sam Meech
Animation: Kate Jessop
Dramaturg: Suzanne Bell
Photographer: Sam Freeman (Unity Theatre)

Image 1   Image 2 & 3
Wolf Red   A Wondrous Place

1/
TUPAC MARTIR
PERFORMANCE DESIGN, DIRECTION AND CHOREOGRAPHY

LOTERIA
Tupac Martir (2012)

Satore Studio
Morelia Film Festival / Morelia Mexico
July 2012

TM: Loteria channels performance and technology to tell the story of Mexican cinema. The project began as a projection outside the Rich Mix in London for the Mexican film festival, then progressed to the Film festival in Morelia, Mexico.

At Rich Mix, it meant that people could find out what was happening inside the festival space but in a more dynamic and digital manner. In order to realise this idea we used the facade as a framework for projection. The panels rotate, generating a kind of frame, that is visible during the day. When the sun goes down the images projected onto the facade can gradually be appreciated, and the space comes alive as night falls. At Rich Mix it was a merge of digital visual arts within the concept of film, the incorporation of the piece itself with the music being streamed to the audience headphones. For the second part in Morelia, we exchanged the streaming for live performance and an audio installation of 150 musicians moving across the city, converging all together to make a grand band.

Loteria is based on the game (Loteria), from the way the cards are shown, to the singing of the game and the characters that have become archetypes used by directors and writers in movies. It is a part of Mexican-imagery with cultural values and identities that may be unfamiliar to many. Using these archetypal characters, we build the different histories of Mexican cinema.

Director and Choreographer: Tupac Martir
Set Designer: Tupac Martir and Kenji Ikenaga
Costume Designer: Aztecas Marching Band
Lighting Designer: Tupac Martir and Muly Yechezkel
Sound Designer: Tupac Martir and Austin TV
Media Designer: Tupac Martir and Kenji Ikenaga
Michoacan University Marching Band
Photographer: Darrell Berry

2/
TUPAC MARTIR
PERFORMANCE DESIGN, DIRECTION AND CHOREOGRAPHY

NIERKA
Tupac Martir (2012)

Satore Studio Productions
Peacock Theatre, London
January 2012

TM: Nierka is a multidisciplinary production that combines music, contemporary dance, puppetry, video and lighting with both traditional and new technologies. The show creates an environment in which ideas from post modernism, avant-garde and expressionism combine with more modern trends to create a fluid performance piece. Although presented in a proscenium theatre, the stage environment extends into the audience but is reconfigured throughout the performance using automation, video and video tracking.

The performance consists of three acts depicting an autobiographical rite of passage. The narrative develops in the imagination of the protagonist, as a dialogue between his conscious and subconscious mind, the imagery portraying his emotions.

The first act reflects upon how society has jaded the person by falling into a spiral of monotony of which he is unaware. In the second act the protagonist is confronted with his own mortality and sense of being. His monsters and demons from the unconscious become real as he has to accept his flaws and the repercussions of his previous actions. The third act is about the reconciliation of his soul, body and mind; understanding the challenges and the beauties of the world, he is becoming one with the universe and its laws.

The show is influenced by Wassily Kandinsky's The Yellow Sound, also Artaud and Craig's philosophies. Music is used to tell the story in a more intimate way; voices from a soprano and choir are abstract vocalisations of emotion, allowing each spectator to make their own individual connections and interpretation.

Director: Tupac Martir
Producer: Tom O'Donnell
Choreographer: Fernando Hernando Magadan and Zoran Markovic
Set Designer: Tupac Martir
Costume Designer: Gabriela Gower, Jenny Christoph and Diane Rawoski
Lighting Designer: Tupac Martir and Muly Yechezkel
Composers: Austin TV, NSM PSM, Nicole Robson
Media Designer: Kenji Ikenaga, Ben Sheppe, Hudson Viana, Daniel Florencio, Pablo Fernandez and Tupac Martir
Photographer: Darrell Berry

1/
GARY McCANN
SET AND COSTUME DESIGN

DIE FLEDERMAUS
Johann Strauss II (1874)

Norwegian National Opera
December 2012

GM: The hypercritical, style-obsessed Viennese society in Strauss' operetta is transposed to a modern day New York fashion/art crossover scene – where the competition to look good is so fierce that the ball's guests become grotesque casualties from an avant-garde catwalk show.

The Act II ballroom scene is conceived as a large white Neo-Classical space overwhelmed by a tangle of coloured plastic flumes. Video mapping projection occasionally suggests these tubes are filled with champagne.

Director: Laurence Dale
Conductor: Alexander Joel
Choreographer: Mark Smith
Set and Costume Designer: Gary McCann
Lighting Designer: Dominique Borrini
Production Media Designer: Eric Holmberg
Photography: Erik Berg

2/
GARY McCANN
SET AND COSTUME DESIGN

Images 1-3
Die Fledermaus

Images 4-6
The Barber of Seville

THE BARBER OF SEVILLE
Gioachino Rossini
Date of Origin (1816)

Nationale Reisopera
Netherlands tour
November 2013

GM: The set for the Barber of Seville provided an ever changing, kaleidoscopic world clad in colossal, Gaudi-esque tiles, which featured a mixture of Baroque and Moorish motifs. Each tile was carefully hand painted and glazed, set at subtly different angles and surrounded with outsize grout. The surface provided an appropriate background for both interior and exterior spaces, the definition of which was assisted by mobile, cobalt blue palm trees and inset chambers within the periactoid structures.

Costumes combined 18th century and contemporary elements. Characters were defined by elaborately coiffured wigs.

Director: Laurence Dale
Conductor: Antonino Fogliani
Set and Costume Designer: Gary McCann
Lighting Designer: Richard ten Hof
Photography: Marco Borggreve

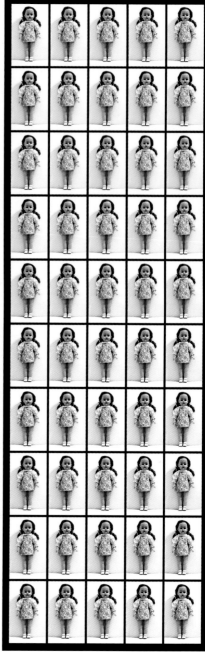

HOLLY McCARTHY
SET AND COSTUME DESIGN

THE KILLING OF SISTER GEORGE
Frank Marcus (1964)

Theatr Pena
Touring
March 2014

HM: Stories of gay relationships, alcohol abuse and the private lives of celebrities have almost become passé in the minds of modern audiences. However, a story that featured a much loved radio actress with a penchant for gin and abusing nuns in taxis was certainly considered shocking in 1964. At the heart of the story is a difficult and fragile relationship, one defined by a pattern of domination, abuse and submission.

This play is typical of its era, intended for a traditional theatre space, with an array of essential scenic elements and a multitude of integral props, so interpreting it for an intimate studio tour was certainly challenging. Early on we decided that we needed to retain a sense of period in order to contextualise the story for a modern audience. Certain things had to be present for the dialogue to work, including elements like doors, city skylines, and a

collection of dolls and horse brasses. I chose to represent some of these in a more abstract form; to both enhance the conflicting, surreal relationship of the lead characters and the changing popular culture of the 60s.

Director: Erica Eirian
Set and Costume Designer: Holly McCarthy
Lighting Designer: Ian Buchanan
Sound Designer: Gruffydd Johnston
Photographer: Holly McCarthy

Images
The Killing Of Sister George

IONA McLEISH
SET AND COSTUME DESIGN

SONS WITHOUT FATHERS
A new version of Anton Chekhov's
Platonov (1923) by Helena
Kaut-Howson (2013)

*Belgrade Theatre Coventry,
Arcola Theatre and KP Productions
B2 Belgrade Theatre Coventry
April 2013*

IM: During one of the early telephone conversations with the director of 'Sons Without Fathers' we discussed the disintegration and stagnation of Platonov's world, a place which is described as remote and little known. In another conversation the idea of the 'Ship of Fools' was touched on, where man's ignorance leads to his disaster and where the madman possesses forbidden knowledge which predicts the end of the world. Linking with this I felt there was something about the brooding, cynical and destructive character of Mikhail Platonov that had a corrosive, toxic nature. Those people he came into contact with were damaged, destroyed or eaten away by him.

I was also really interested in the relevance of this early Chekhov play in the 21st century and the combination of these thoughts led me to search for information on environmental disasters and toxic spills. I came across the devastating catastrophe in Hungary in 2010 where a torrent of toxic waste from the Ajka aluminium factory flooded several small towns and over fifteen square miles of countryside. The images I found of the noxious rust red slurry and the desperate attempts to clean and decontaminate the landscape really resonated with me and I found parallels with Platonov's world. I realised that until I had begun this line of research I had not heard about this disaster, for us perhaps Ajka was too remote to have registered on the general UK news. Further research led me to the photographs of Palíndromo Mészáros, who captured the event in a series of photographs called 'The Line'. These were particularly evocative because they illustrated the beauty in the devastation; equally we can see the attraction in the compelling character of Mikhail Platonov. My design process developed both the idea of the red stain left by the Ajka toxic spill on people's homes and the intensive aluminium production from the factory. The real people whose lives had been scarred by the events, both in Ajka and in the play are very close to us and the contemporary costumes used in this production enable this recognition. The concept of the 'Ship of Fools' still resonates, where madness is triumphant while the world is destroyed.

Director: Helena Kaut-Howson

Set and Costume Designer: Iona McLeish

Lighting Designer: Alex Wardle

Sound Designer: Paul Bull

Media Designer: Iona McLeish

Photographers: Simon Annand & Iona McLeish

Images:
Sons Without Fathers

1/
ANNE MINORS
PERFORMANCE CONSULTANTS

Bishopsgate Institute, London
June 2011

AM: Bishopsgate Institute has been a hub for culture and learning since opening in 1895. The recent renewal programme (2009-2011) has transformed the building and facilities to the highest standards, while remaining sympathetic to Charles Townsend's original designs and restoring the historic features of the Grade II* listed building.

Already well known as a rehearsal facility and adult education centre, AMPC helped the client expand their use of the impressive Great Hall to accommodate dance performances, recitals and examinations in addition to their past repertoire. In addition to flexible seating layouts, AMPC developed a production lighting scheme that enables any part of the Great Hall to be the stage and collaborated on the design of the acoustic canopy above the stage.

Client: Bishopsgate Institute
Photographer: Paul Riddle
Theatre Consultants: Anne Minors Performance Consultants
Architects: Sheppard Architects
Building Services Engineers: Michael Popper Associates
Structural Engineers: Adrian Cox Associates
Quantity Surveyor: Bristow, Johnson + Partners
Acoustics Consultants: Adrian James Acoustics

2/
ANNE MINORS
PERFORMANCE CONSULTANTS

The Ruddock Performing Arts Centre
April 2012

AM: The Ruddock Performing Arts Centre is the result of collaboration between King Edward's School and King Edward VI High School for Girls and is designed to support the high quality of both their music and drama departments.

After the school's initial scheme became too costly AMPC were brought on board to look at ways of improving efficiency while reducing costs in order to realise the project. Liaising closely with the heads of drama and music, AMPC used models and sketches to explore potential ideas before seeing these through to completion.

The 500 seat concert hall caters for soloists, small orchestras, choirs and larger symphony orchestras while the adjustable stage area and production facilities also allow the space to transform into an end-on theatre space for drama, dance and musical theatre. A 140 seat drama studio, a dance rehearsal space and 12 music practice rooms complete the centre.

Client: King Edward's School, Birmingham
Theatre Consultants: Anne Minors Performance Consultants
Architects: ADP Architects (Design development & Completion)
Design Concept: Haworth Tompkins Architects
Acoustics Consultants: Sound Space Design

3/
ANNE MINORS
PERFORMANCE CONSULTANTS

Zorlu Center, Istanbul
October 2013

AM: AMPC worked closely with acoustics sister company SSD on the cultural offer of this large complex in central Istanbul, incorporating shopping, hotel and residential as well as two theatres, recording studio and cinema. Hosting world-renowned artists, the Zorlu Performing Arts Center (PSM) includes a 2,300 seat Main Theatre for amplified musicals, Turkish music and dance, and occasional classical concerts. The smaller 750 seat Drama Theatre is intentionally compact to create an intimate relationship between audience and performer and is suitable for anything from recitals and spoken word to small chamber concerts, dance and conferences.

AMPC developed the brief for the centre setting out the form of both theatres along with the associated support spaces and undertaking consultation with production companies and potential operators to ensure their needs would be met.

The comprehensive stage engineering design enables a variable proscenium width and other automated stage elements to accommodate the range of uses.

Theatre Company: Nederlander Theatre
Client: Zorlu Group
Theatre Consultants: Anne Minors Performance Consultants
Architects: Emre Arolat Architects & Tabanlioglu Architects
Acoustics Consultants: Sound Space Design

Image 1
Bishopsgate Institute

Image 2 & 3
The Ruddock Performing
Arts Centre

Image 4 & 5
Zorlu Center

Images
White Gold

1/
BECKY MINTO
SET AND COSTUME DESIGN

WHITE GOLD
Originally conceived by Mark Murphy (2014)
Iron-Oxide, Glasgow 2014 Cultural Programme
The Sugar Sheds, Greenock
June 2014

BM: White Gold took the audience on a transformational journey through Greenock's iconic Sugar Sheds. As they walked through an immersive and surreal landscape, stories that have been gathered from across Inverclyde were brought to life by musicians, actors and aerialists with a cast of over 100 professionals and volunteers.

From the metal girders and columns of the shed we suspended the set, lighting and sound rigs, aerial constructions, trussing and people. The audience were led into spaces that constantly shifted from small rooms to wide open space, changing their perspective of their environment. The cast, whose costume was inspired from the original Sugar Shed workers, were involved in all scene changes and counter balancing within the performance. The vision was to create a show that has the power to transform: to find the extraordinary in the everyday; to confound expectations of what a group of people with a united intention could achieve.

Director: Simone Jenkinson and Joseph Traynor, Cuerda Producciones
Composer: Nathaniel Reed
Set and Costume Designer: Becky Minto
Lighting Designer: Lizzie Powell
Aerial Consultant: Jennifer Paterson
Head Rigger: Alex Palmer, Cold Mountain Kit.
Assistant Director: Brigid McCarthy
Photographer: Iron-Oxide

Images
Ignition

2/
BECKY MINTO
SET AND COSTUME DESIGN

IGNITION

National Theatre of Scotland in Association with Shetland Arts Trust. Car Parks, Ferry Terminals and Village Halls of the Shetland Isles March 2013

BM: Over the course of six months, all 23,000 inhabitants of Shetland were invited by National Theatre of Scotland, to explore their bittersweet relationship with the automobile – how it shapes us, defines us, supports us, frees us, and sometimes, kills us. The stories and design were unmistakably Shetland inspired; a hitcher, The White Wife collected stories in unsuspecting Islanders cars, her cape creating the landscape on its hem as she travelled. In Yakking and Makking sessions held in Village Halls locals recounted stories whilst knitting pieces that would eventually create a cover for our touring and performance car. We travelled all over the Shetland Isles locating sites for workshops and the performances. It became apparent due to the diverse weather conditions that the vehicle would become our auditorium. The audience and vehicle drove to Car Parks, Ferry Terminals and Village halls, whilst outside the landscape of Shetland became our stages and theatrical backdrop.

Director: Wils Wilson
Dramaturg and Text: Rob Evans
Associate Director: John Haswell
Choreographer: Janice Parker
Parkour Director: Chris Grant
Set and Costume Designer: Becky Minto
Lighting Designer: Ross Corbett
Sound Designer: Hugh Nankivell and JJ Jamieson
Associate Artists: Lowri Evans and Jacqui Clarke
Photographer: National Theatre of Scotland and Simon Murphy

Images
Once Upon A Castle

BILL MITCHELL
DIRECTION AND DESIGN

ONCE UPON A CASTLE
WildWorks
Kasteel Van Gaasbeek – Belgium
2014

BM: I set up WildWorks in 2005 to explore the thrill of making theatre in unconventional places. Being a design led company we begin every new journey with site and route, not scripts. We spend time talking to the people who belong to the place. We search for memories, values, passion and meaning. We look for the genius loci. We are told stories of wonder and the work grows from here.

Once we have a feel of the context, our team of artists/makers, musicians and performers make their work, inspired by and alongside local people. We enable people to inhabit the world they've helped us create.

In Kasteel Van Gaasbeek we saw the castle as a time machine. We used objects and people to develop a narrative – running workshops with the castle team and delving deep into the archives. The research and development process led to a 22 room installation that travels emotionally and sensually through the last 500 years; and which is animated through performance by the castle team and volunteers.

Director: Bill Mitchell

Writer and Researcher: Mercedes Kemp

Designers: Bill Mitchell, Myriddin Wannell, Ellie Williams, Sue Hill

Collaborating Designer: Tim Van Steenbergen

Costume Design: Myriddin Wannell

Composer: Jeroen D'hoe

Sound Designer: Helen Atkinson, Emma Laxton

Lighting Designer: Lucy Gaskell

Photographer: Steve Tanner

WILDWORKS

IT STARTS AND IT ENDS WITH PLACE AND PEOPLE.........

WildWorks is an art led international theatre company from Cornwall, founded in 2005 by Bill Mitchell to focus on site-specific events. WildWorkers are site-specific theatre makers – they create large scale spectacular productions and artworks that grow out of their locations, both inside and out: quarries, cliffs, derelict industrial sites, castles, empty department stores, shipyards, occupied zones. The work is developed alongside the people who belong to a place. A community is essential to the building of a narrative of site – by telling their stories and memories, and by contributing their skills and passions. The design process is firmly grounded on what the site offers – its topography, the traces that history has left upon it – and the narratives that people attach to the place.

Our work has taken us to many different locations. For the Make/Believe exhibition Myriddin Wannell (Associate Designer) chose The Passion of Port Talbot whilst Bill Mitchell (Artistic Director) presented Kasteel Van Gaasbeek's Once Upon a Castle. These two productions define the range of the work: The Passion was a massive scale event occupying an entire town and involving more than 1,000 community performers. It follows the strand of work that started with A Very Old Man with Enormous Wings and Souterrain, sited in locations and with communities often facing dramatic change – finding new purpose after the collapse of traditional industry, post-conflict, or on the brink of radical development.

Once Upon a Castle followed on from Enchanted Palace (Kensington Palace), transforming Kasteel van Gaasbeek, an important heritage site in Belgium, through design and performance. Although the projects are very different they both rely on the same set of principles. As a company we are drawn to stories that are both epic and intimate, human stories that can touch and resonate

with audiences across barriers of language, age and nationality.

The WILDWORKS approach to place and community is distinctive.
The meaning of the work develops from research, from chance encounters, from probing the feelings, thoughts, stories and memories of people. This is the creative heartbeat, found by attending carefully to the place, the genius loci, and working in a spirit of mutual hospitality with the people who inhabit the physical space.

The Passion of Port Talbot (WILDWORKS and NATIONAL THEATRE WALES with Michael Sheen, 2011) was designed as a three-day non stop event that would take place over the entire town and its surroundings. We used the beach and promenade, the Civic square, a mountaintop overlooking the town, the shopping centre, motorway underpasses, a prison cell, cemeteries, a terrace of miner's cottages, a working man's club, a housing estate, a procession route along several miles of streets which culminated in a strangely fitting Golgotha set in the middle of a roundabout. For a year we had immersed ourselves in the life of the town, explored its spaces and non-places, got lost in a dérive punctuated by conversations that threw light into its troubled geography. The beach, a long stretch of sand and sea flanked on either side by the Babylon of smoke and lights of the steel works and chemical factory. The town straddled by the massive concrete infrastructure of the M4, its pillars cutting through residential streets, churchyards, green spaces; creating dead ends and darkened tunnels and strangely lopsided urban features.

The place posed questions which we explored in conversations with its inhabitants. What emerged was a tale of post industrial decay, brutal planning and enforced evictions to make way for the motorway. In one particular location an entire side of the street, made up of workers terraces, had been demolished, leaving the other side intact and inhabited. The evictions had not been forgotten and the remaining residents held strong memories of their neighbours and the vibrant community that once was. A man showed us a collection of home made films documenting the demolition of houses, pubs and shops and other significant buildings. The sense of loss was really palpable.

The story of The Passion is a story of occupation and insurgency. This translated into Port Talbot as a community besieged by corporations eager to force the people out of their houses and take control of the land. Myriddin's design emerged out of this narrative. House doors, both as objects and as metaphors for the idea of home, became central to the design scheme: At the beginning of the show, when corporation members and their security forces arrive from the sea, a door appeared in the middle of the beach and the figure of the Stranger (based on John the Baptist) made his entrance through this unlikely, surreal threshold. At the end, the scaffold for the crucifixion is constructed out of the doors ripped out of homes to make the houses vulnerable and uninhabitable. The town was filled with makeshift camps, the people become refugees in their own home. Another element that became very important was the collections of personal photographs and home movies that had been brought to us by community members, documenting a way of life and a memory of place that was clearly mourned by the people of the town. This found material was projected, at the end of the show, onto a 15 meter tall water jet fanning behind the crucifixion, a hypnotic and spectacular finale commemorating the memory of the everyday, of disappeared neighbours and family members.

In Kasteel van Gaasbeek (Belgium 2014/15) the challenge was to transform 24 rooms through design and performance. Four designers were involved in creating Once

Upon a Castle, and it was Bill's role to create the overall visual narrative and design the rooms that linked the narrative together.

Bill imagined the castle as a character, extending a warm welcome to visitors and making it clear it wants to communicate with them. Throughout the centuries both major and minor historical events had taken place here. The castle walls are steeped with them. What if the walls could talk? What if this ancient building was trying to remember how it all happened? There are many ways of understanding history and many paths to the interpretation of the traces left by human lives. Our way is to search for human emotion. Our treatment of history seeks a poetic vision that is grounded in documentation, but undergoes a series of transformations through visual art forms, performance, poetry, music, sound.

Once again we returned to our research methodology, starting with community and their emotional relationship to the place. Here the community was composed of the people who care for the castle: Curators, archivists, guides, gardeners, cleaners, admin staff. For several months we worked with the staff, their role to introduce us to the castle's narratives and former inhabitants.

We asked our hosts to show us the castle. We asked for very specific tours: A tour of romance, A tour of violence, A tour of domesticity...

Our hosts, who would become the performers in Once Upon a Castle, acted as clever guides, and we witnessed the castle waking up. We explored its rooms from the cellars to the attics. We wandered its secret passages and its grand staircases. Our guides told us stories, anecdotes, showed us their favourite objects and rooms, deciphered the significance of the traces left by history. The most recent memory was that of the Marquesina Arconati Visconti, a hugely important figure in the history of Gaasbeek. But we could sense that there were deeper layers, that the castle's memory went much further. The next step was to explore the castle's extensive archives, covering 800 years of history. In the end we were captured

by three characters: Lamoral, Count of Egmont, the 16th century hero; Paul Arconati Visconti, the Enlightenment visionary; and Marie Peyrat, Marquesina Arconati Visconti, the early 20th century collector and cultural patron. There were traces of their lives everywhere: boxes and boxes of correspondence, diaries and journals, maps, photographs (or, in the case of Egmont, contemporary cartoons of his execution). There were key discoveries that provided the foundations for Once upon a Castle. Finding the text of Egmont's passionate last letter to his wife Sabine, and the cold, cynical correspondence between Philip II and the Duke of Alba after taking Egmont to the scaffold. Paul Arconati Visconti's astounding notebook "Culture et Recettes" where he reveals himself as a practical visionary, his correspondence with world leaders proposing a plan for world peace and the densely hand-written journals where, at the end of his life, he begs a Higher Being for the salvation of his soul. Marie Peyrat's extensive correspondence, lively and opinionated in her prime, and reflecting the sadness of her decline after the death of the love of her life. Working in the archives was like holding conversations with ghosts.

Bill's vision, to give voice to the castle and bring its emotional memory to life, held the visual narrative together and ensured that all design elements cohered, transforming Gaasbeek into a kind of time machine where all times coexisted in the memory of the castle.

Taking part in the SBTD exhibition has been really important for the work that we do, which is hard to describe and harder to capture. Having the work included in a theatre design exhibition widens the definition of 'theatre' and what theatre designers do. The work escapes the conventional boundaries of the theatre space. It starts and it ends with place and people.

Mercedes Kemp
WildWorks Associate Director –
Research and Community

MYRIDDIN WANNELL
PRODUCTION DESIGN

THE PASSION
WildWorks & National Theatre Wales

Port Talbot
2011

MW: Port Talbot had so much to share with us. In the social clubs and shopping malls, in sitting rooms and on beaches we unearthed memories of the place. Over 1200 community members took part as musicians, singers, performers, makers, stewards, angels and demons. We found powerful locations where the story could unfold; we walked the beach against the backdrop of the massive, smoke belching steelworks, found lost memories in underpasses and searched for the ghosts of displaced neighbours under the M4. The whole town became a stage and the people our cast and heroes, telling their story through one of the defining narratives of our time.

The Passion was a three day nonstop theatrical celebration that started at dawn on Good Friday and concluded on the night of Easter Sunday. Michael Sheen had come home to star in this one off, groundbreaking theatrical event and he led the people of Port Talbot on this epic, explosive and emotional journey.

With a final procession through the streets to a seafront roundabout (The Crucifixion) we amassed a gathering audience. This was no flash mob - this was ownership and pride. We lost count at 25,000.

Co Directors: Michael Sheen & Bill Mitchell

Writer: Owen Sheers

Production Designer: Myriddin Wannell

Musical Director: Claire Ingleheart

Sound Designer: Mike Beer

Photographer: Ian Kingsnorth

Image 1
The Final Procession

Image 2
Procession route daytime

Image 3
They Wait for the Teacher to Arrive

Image 4
Beach Baptism

Image 5
The Crucifixion

Image 6
ICU Soldiers

Image 7
The Last Supper

CATHERINE MORGAN
SET AND COSTUME DESIGN

OTHELLO
William Shakespeare (1603)

Bussey Building, Peckham, London
February 2013

CM: Shakespeare's character, Othello the Moor, is a renowned
mercenary soldier, so in our updated production we set the play
within the booming yet mysterious world of western military security
companies, the private armies of today. Against this backdrop of cut
throat competition for military contracts, the production explored
the more personal battle of Othello against his own instincts, as Iago
tragically undermines his adoration of Desdemona. I reconfigured the
long warehouse theatre space of the Bussey Building into traverse
as I felt this would allow for a more dynamic staging, with the actors
travelling long distances up and down and making strong entrances at
either end of the space. I designed a sparse set to accommodate our
carefully choreographed moments.

Director: Anthony Green
Set and Costume Designer: Catherine Morgan
Lighting Designer: Richard Williamson
Photographer: Adam Levy

Images
King Lear

RUARI MURCHISON
SET AND COSTUME DESIGN

KING LEAR
William Shakespeare (1606)

Quarry Theatre
West Yorkshire Playhouse
September 2011

RM: Our production was created through many meetings with Ian Brown and also our Lear - Tim Pigott-Smith. As Tim is incredibly fit it became possible to design a structure that he could scale at times and use physically. We imagined the world of King Lear as a brutalist concrete space on which a huge gilded box had sunk, mired in vanity, corruption and politics. When the box revolved, it showed the back structure pulled up from the floor. This became the space where Lear, Gloucester, the Fool and Edgar shelter from the storm. The storm scene was played with the box revolving, carrying Lear around on a scaling ladder six metres up in the air. After the storm, literal locations were dispensed with and the empty concrete stage was left. The world stripped away to nothing, King Lear has lost everything and only then comes to the realisation of what his life has been and what he has done.

Director: Ian Brown
Set and Costume Designer: Ruari Murchison
Lighting Designer: Chris Davey
Sound Designer: Mic Poole
Photographer: Ruari Murchison/ Keith Patterson

Images 1-3
Lohengrin

Images 4 & 5
La Bohème

Images 6 & 7
I Puritani

1/
CONOR MURPHY
SET AND COSTUME DESIGN

LOHENGRIN
Richard Wagner (1846-48)

Royal Swedish Opera
April 2012

CM: The opera 'Lohengrin' takes place on the war-torn banks of the river Scheldt, in and around the castle grounds, in Lohengrin and Elsa's bridal chamber and finally back to the river banks. The action moves from heightened reality to myth as Lohengrin himself becomes manifest from a dream. The design aimed to create a magical space where light was both integral to the dramatic action and to the reorientation of the space during the three acts. Lohengrin first appears from the light, emerging from water in the form of a reversed video image of a drowning man before he becomes 'real'. He also departs the space in this way to make way for the entrance of the child, Gottfried, thought to have been drowned at the beginning of the piece.

Director: Stephen Langridge

Set and Costume Designer: Conor Murphy

Lighting Designer: Fabrice Kebour

Production Media Designers: Thomas Bergmann & Willem Bramsche

Photographers: Erik Dahlberg & Alexander Kenney

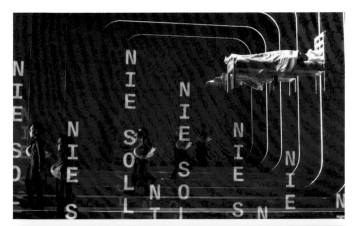

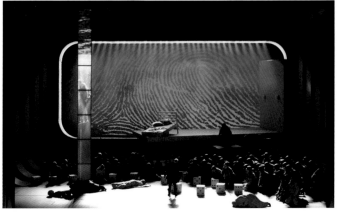

 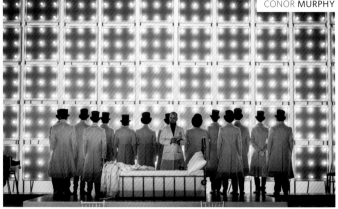

2/
CONOR MURPHY
SET AND COSTUME DESIGN

LA BOHÈME
Giacomo Puccini (1896)

Nationale Reisopera, Holland
May 2011

CM: In La Bohème we updated the action so that the artists' garret became a damp cellar set within an abstracted blue space covered in text from Henri Murger's original novel; or perhaps the text which Rodolfo is typing at the beginning of the piece. In Act 2 the space expanded to become an illusory shopping complex built from oversized Christmas presents, and in Act 3 the Barrière d'Enfer became the wasteland at the back of a nightclub which seems to have broken through the walls. When we return to the garret in Act 4, the destruction of the space continues as the room appears to have come through the floor. It is now seen from above, and we are made aware of the chaos of their lives in more detail.

Director: Stephen Langridge
Choreographer: Natalie Ayton
Set and Costume Designer: Conor Murphy
Lighting Designer: Paul Keogan
Photographers: Conor Murphy, Jef Rabillon, Hermann & Clärchen Baus

3/
CONOR MURPHY
SET AND COSTUME DESIGN

I PURITANI
Vincenzo Bellini (1834)

Grange Park Opera Company
Grange Park Opera, Alresford
May 2013

CM: 'I Puritani' centres around Elvira's famous mad scenes and the director and I used these as the starting point to design a production focusing on the study of madness and hysteria which was popular in the first half of the 19th century. We used a low-resolution video wall created from LED lightbulbs which could be used facing upstage against a white backdrop and facing downstage to reflect the world of shadows, dreams and hallucinations which are evoked by the piece.

Director: Stephen Langridge
Choreographer: Anjali Mehra
Set and Costume Designer: Conor Murphy
Lighting Designer: Paul Keogan
Production Media Designers: Thomas Bergmann & Willem Bramsche
Photographer: Robert Workman

1/
NEIL MURRAY
SET AND COSTUME DESIGN

THE THREEPENNY OPERA
Bertold Brecht: Composer: Kurt Weill
(1928)

*Co-production between Nottingham and
Birmingham Rep/New Wolsey, Ipswich and
Graeae 2014*

Images 1-3
The Threepenny Opera

NM: The design premise was that a group of vagrant, troublesome and dangerously political performing beggars had taken over an abandoned warehouse that had been, until recently, used for recycling old clothes – maybe for Oxfam. This seemed to link nicely with Peachum's Emporium for creating fake beggars' outfits. We wanted something timeless but contemporary - something sordid yet epic and operatic. We also wanted the entire 20 piece orchestra of actor musicians onstage, throughout, on either side of the acting space.

Within this warehouse the beggars created their theatre which included a magnificent front cloth - a huge patchwork of old rags, ancient lace curtains and underwear which was Kabuki dropped at the top of the show to reveal the entire cast playing Weill's overture while, centre 'stage', a beggar is dressed as Macheath.

Co directors: Jenny Sealey and Peter Rowe
Set and Costume Designer: Neil Murray
Musical Director and Arranger: Robert Hyman
Movement Director: Mark Smith
Projections Designer: Mark Haig
Lighting Designer: Malcolm Rippeth
Sound Designer: Dew Baumohl
Photographer: Patrick Baldwin

2/
SET AND COSTUME DESIGN

STEPTOE AND SON
Original TV scripts: Ray Galton and Alan Simpson (1962-74)
Adaptation: Emma Rice (2012)

Co-produced by Kneehigh Theatre and West Yorkshire Playhouse
Courtyard Theatre: West Yorkshire Playhouse
August 2012

NM: Our first task was to create the world of the scrap merchants in a new and distinctly different way to the television series, one that was theatrical rather than naturalistic.

From the opening description of a huge pile of junk in Emma Rice's adaptation, we gradually, through a process of elimination, developed the idea of a cart which was big enough to contain all the furniture and props needed in the performance but light enough to be pulled manually as part of the action. Onto the side of the cart were placed two doors advertising the scrap yard which opened up to allow the interior of their house to spill out into the action.

Behind it hung a huge sky made from a rough and ragged collage of torn and worn out scrap clothes. A large moon hung to one side on to which, when required, was projected a huge clock.

Director: Emma Rice
Set and Costume Designer: Neil Murray
Lighting Designer: Malcolm Rippeth
Score and Sound Designer: Simon Baker
Projection Designer: Mic Pool
Choreographer: Etta Murphitt
Assistant Director: Simon Harvey
Photographer: Steve Tanner

Images 1 & 2
Steptoe & Son

Images 3-5
Mary Queen Of Scots Got
Her Head Chopped Off

3/
SET AND COSTUME DESIGN

MARY QUEEN OF SCOTS GOT HER HEAD CHOPPED OFF
Liz Lochhead, Edinburgh Festival (1987)

Royal Lyceum Theatre, Edinburgh
2011

NM: As a response to Liz Lochhead's telling of this historical piece we wanted to create a radical and expressionistic world within a surreal and anarchic urban wasteland - with an abandoned, torched car, crucifix dumped in a skip, statue of John Knox wearing a traffic cone like a dunce's cap and a 'phone box wearing a crown of thorns. Within this disturbing ambience of dumped and rusting elements the characters played out their story in a ragbag assortment of clothes - like children playing at dressing up.

Director: Tony Cownie
Set and Costume Designer: Neil Murray
Lighting Designer: Charles Balfour
Composer: Philip Pinsky
Co-composer: Morna Young
Photographer: Douglas McBride

1/
KIMIE NAKANO
SET AND COSTUME DESIGN

....

ITMOI (IN THE MIND OF IGOR)
Nitin Sawhney, Jocelyn Pook and Ben Frost (2013)

Akram Khan Company
MC2 Grenoble and Sadler's Wells London – World Tour
May 2013

....

Image 1	Images 2 & 3	Images 4 & 5
iTMOI	The Little Prince	Dust

KN: iTMOi- in The Mind Of igor - was inspired by Igor
Stravinsky's 'Rite of Spring' and three key words, Rupture,
Death and Birth. Costume fabrics' textures and colours
allude to the world around Stravinsky. He lived very close
to nature and was inspired by its sounds, such as breaking
ice. Characters are inspired by Stravinsky's traditional
dance and ritualistic music themes.

Director and Choreographer: Akram Khan
Set Designer: Matt Deely
Costume Designer: Kimie Nakano
Lighting Designer: Fabiana Piccioli
Photographer: Jean Louis Fernandez

2/
KIMIE NAKANO
SET AND COSTUME DESIGN

THE LITTLE PRINCE / LE PETIT PRINCE
Antoine de Saint-Exupéry (1943) Philip Feeney (2012)

Les Grands Ballets Canadiens de Montréal
Place des Arts (Montréal) and tour
May 2012

KN: The Little Prince is as relevant today as it was when first published almost 70 years ago. The aim was to remain true to the poetry, philosophy of life and generous universal spirit of Saint-Exupéry, to explore the characters of our street life and in our society.

We used video art, enhanced by a giant two way mirror, which gave an illusion of depth and space.

The clever use of a wind blown, fine silver voile (using motors), gave both a feeling of a desert mirage and the northern lights in a night sky. The video images (sunset, sand storm, growing roots and megalopolis) are simple abstract and mainly in slow motion. The hats, the box, the papers and the lamp connect us with the story of 'The Little Prince'.

Director and Choreographer: Didy Veldman
Set and Costume Designer: Kimie Nakano
Lighting Designer: Marc Parent
Video Artist: Matt Deely
Music composition and arrangements: Philip Feeney
Photographer: Richard Champagne

3/
KIMIE NAKANO
SET AND COSTUME DESIGN

DUST - LEST WE FORGET
Jocelyn Pook (2014)

English National Ballet
Barbican Centre and tour
April 2014

KN: The piece is inspired by two things; firstly, the concept of a trench, of the young men and old men all going into trenches, and disappearing. The other substantial part was inspired by the women. In World War 1 there was a huge social shift involving women. Weapons and a huge workforce were needed for the war. Women knew they would be letting go of fathers, husbands, and sons; they might lose them. Yet they were making weapons that would kill others' fathers, husbands, and sons. It didn't matter which side you were on – they both felt loss and death. But in order for someone to live, someone else was putting their life on the line. That cyclical thing was what I wanted to explore.

Director and Choreographer: Akram Khan
Costume Designer: Kimie Nakano
Lighting Designer: Fabiana Piccioli
Photographer: Gabriel Corcuera Zubillaga

1/
FRANCIS O'CONNOR
SET AND COSTUME DESIGN

DER FLIEGENDE HOLLANDER
Richard Wagner (1840)

Oper Bern
Stadtheater Bern
September 2011

FO'C: The design aimed to make a tangible dark world for Wagner's extraordinary opera, a vivid space in which Senta's story could be told. The stage machinery was used to reveal the ships through the floor of the stage. We saw the image of Senta drowning during the overture, this was repeated at the end of the opera. We set the second Act in a fish factory so that the women were seen working within the context of a community of fisherfolk. The whole was played without an interval to maintain the intensity of the story. The scene changes moved seamlessly and without pause.

Director: Dieter Kiaegi
Set and Costume Designer: Francis O'Connor
Lighting Designer: Jacques Batocletti
Photographer: Annette Boutellier

Images 1-3
Der Fliegende Hollander

Images 4-6
Druid Murphy:
Conversations on a Homecoming
Famine
Whistle in the Dark

2/
FRANCIS O'CONNOR
SET AND COSTUME DESIGN

DRUID MURPHY - PLAYS BY TOM MURPHY
Tom Murphy (2012)

Druid Theatre Galway Ireland
Galway then World Tour
May 2012

FO'C: Druid Murphy was a work composed of three plays by Tom Murphy. They were performed consecutively in one day, in around six hours plus of theatre. The plays were originally conceived individually, but by playing them together with an ensemble company common connections and themes could be explored. The design was born out of deciding the sequence of performance. We started the evening with Conversations on a Homecoming, set in a bar in the early 1980s, this demanded the most naturalistic of the settings. The next play Whistle In The Dark was set in the 1960s in a house in Coventry. I was able to reduce this to scenic elements essential to performance of the piece. Gradually the set was being stripped back to expose the final play Famine, set during the Irish Famine of the 19th century. This was when the landscape that had surrounded all the plays was finally revealed. I used rusting corrugated sheets at an angle to give the impression of tilled fields or driving rain. The image seemed apt for all three plays. The wooden floor was broken within the action of the play and earth was exposed beneath the boards.

Director: Garry Hynes
Associate Directors: David Bolger and Francis O'Connor
Set Designer: Francis O'Connor
Costume Designer: Joan O'Clery
Lighting Designer: Chris Davey
Sound Designer: Greg Clarke
Composer: Sam Jackson
Photographer: Francis O'Connor

1/
ALISON NEIGHBOUR
SET AND COSTUME DESIGN

FOLLOWERS
Stewart Melton (2014)

Southwark Playhouse, London
January 2014

AN: Followers is an exploration of Shakespeare's Julius Caesar from the perspective of the crowd, written for schoolchildren and aiming to help them understand the power of the crowd in the play and the parallels to today's social and political climate of protest and unrest. Our playing space was a tiny room at the top of Southwark Playhouse, never previously used for performance. I was immediately struck by the quirky features of the space that suggested a potential performance environment. We chose to accentuate these features and take inspiration from recent news events, setting the performance in an occupied school – a space recognisable to our young audience, and yet filled with unsettling imagery – lightbulbs trailing cables from an emergency generator; a cabinet filled with animal skulls and insects in jars; protest banners covering windows; toy soldiers on guard on every surface. The audience sat on the floor in the centre of the space, as the performance happened around, over, and amongst them.

Director: Thomas Martin
Set and Costume Designer: Alison Neighbour
Lighting Designer: Derek Anderson
Sound Designer: Jon Mcleod
Photographer: Marcos Avlonitis

2/
ALISON NEIGHBOUR
SET AND COSTUME DESIGN

THE EYES HAVE IT
Stewart Melton (2014)

Bread & Goose
Watford Town Centre
July 2014

AN: The Eyes Have It was devised by the company in response to an open-call by Watford Palace Theatre for performances to animate the new town centre. We wanted to explore the moments we might miss when we blink, and take the audience on a journey into a magical world of surreal possibility. We chose locations that intrigued us, and built a story around the site and the characters who might inhabit it. We also worked with a magician to create real moments of magic. The show moved between moments of intimate encounter with individual audience members, and the epic spectacle of a hot air balloon rising over the high street.

Director: Marianne Badrichani
Choreographer: Sinead O'Keeffe
Set and Costume Designer: Alison Neighbour
Sound Designer: Jon Mcleod
Photographer: Alison Neighbour

Image 1
Followers

Images 2 & 3
The Eyes Have It

1 /
BEK PALMER
SET DESIGN

....

BETRAYAL
Harold Pinter (1978)

London Classic Theatre
National Tour
September 2013

....

2 /
BEK PALMER
SET, COSTUME AND PUPPETRY DESIGN

....

THE ELVES AND THE SHOEMAKERS
Mike Kenny (2010)

The Berry Theatre, Hampshire & Theatre Hullabaloo
National Tour
November 2012

....

BP: Betrayal begins at the end of an affair and presents the disintegration and decay that has resulted from the character's actions. I wanted this to be reflected in the set.

Pinter chose to select very short but specific episodes from within the time period that the events of Betrayal occur. It is as if we are peeling away the layers, dipping in and pulling out snapshots of particular moments.

Rooms and objects registered with me as being important, how they can be so closely associated with an emotion and another person, but over the passage of time, as feelings and circumstances change, they can become trivial, meaningless or intolerable.

With these initial impressions in mind, my first response was that we should see resonances of the past materialising in a space that once had vitality and life, but was now a shell holding only traces of memories.

I looked at how buildings deteriorate naturally over time leaving physical hints of the period styles and people who occupied the space; how nature takes over decaying spaces, reflecting renewal and the cyclical nature of relationships. Using this I created disintegrated fragments of spaces where the peeling and crumbling surfaces show glimpses of what used to be, with characters that bring them back to life as they return, like ghosts, to the places they once inhabited.

Director: Michael Cabot

Set Designer: Bek Palmer

Costume Designer: Katja Krzesinska

Lighting Designer: Andy Grange

Photographer: Sheila Burnett

BP: The Elves and the Shoemakers was a touring Christmas production for young audiences. We wanted to conjure a traditional festive, fairytale world but also make the plight of the poor shoemakers, with their failing business, believable.

I looked at traditional decoration of Norwegian houses for inspiration because of the nation's history of trolls and fairies in folklore, and designed a space that was a slightly off-kilter version of this. The play opened looking into the front window of the shoe shop, which then swung open to reveal the interior of the shop.

The elves were played by both table-top puppets, when in the presence of the shoemakers and then the puppeteers themselves, when alone, to run wild in the shop at night.

Director: Sarah Brigham

Set, Costume and Puppetry Designer: Bek Palmer

Photographer: Farrows Creative

Image 1
Betrayal

Images 2-4
The Elves And
The Shoemakers

ROMA PATEL
SET DESIGN

ROMEO AND JULIET
William Shakespeare (1591-1596)

Corcadorca Theatre Company
Cork Opera House
October 2012

RP: My early discussions with director Pat Kieran centred on creating a neutral setting that was not specific to any era as we felt the play was universal and timeless. The team worked collaboratively at a very early conceptual stage, allowing for more exploration and sharing of ideas.

We discovered people still pay homage to the lovers by sticking declarations of love on the stone walls of Juliet's house in Verona. Inspired by this, Corcadorca collected declarations of love from the people of Cork on the weeks leading up to the opening. These progressively fell from a tree on the stage, like leaves flying in the wind as well as fluttering down onto the audience at the end of every show. The make believe had come full circle.

The design accommodated fight sequences using water, climbing and jumping from platforms, quick flowing scenes, live fire, projections on the vertical surfaces and a stage that extended into the audience.

Director: Pat Kiernan

Set Designer: Roma Patel

Costume Designer: Catherine Fay

Lighting Designer: Paul Keogan

Sound Designer: Fergus O'Hare

Media Designer: Michael Hurley

Dramaturg: Dr. Ger Fitzgibbon

Composer: Maurice Seezer

Photographer: Roma Patel

Images
Romeo And Juliet

MICHAEL PAVELKA
SET AND COSTUME DESIGN

TWELVE ANGRY MEN
Reginald Rose (1957)

Bill Kenwright Ltd.
Garrick Theatre, London
November 2013

MP: Twelve Angry Men presents themes of justice, libertarian thought and ignorance. My design aimed to reflect the play as a carefully constructed parable: a fable, not a work of naturalism.

The ensemble of jurors have no names, only numbers. They represent 'ethical positions', not people, and in that sense the play is Shakespearean. There are many ritualistic and spatial aspects of a trial that mirror theatrical performance. They both formalise social interaction: creating hierarchies, and structuring both social and material space. My design disrupted the audience's relationship with the fixed Jury Room and mixed this with the shifting ideas in the play.

I deconstructed the room's architectural elements and represented them metaphorically as an unstable, transparent, storytelling 'machine' - notions that I had developed with the all male ensemble company Propeller Theatre and using the three principles of 'Action Design': function, collaboration and fluidity.

I designed the central table to revolve imperceptibly slowly, 180° in each act. Many of the audience hadn't realised it had spun full circle by the end of the performance.

Director: Christopher Haydon
Set and Costume Designer: Michael Pavelka
Lighting Designer: Mark Howland
Sound Designer: Dan Hoole
Photographer: Robert Day

Images
Twelve Angry Men

1/
XRISTINA PENNA
PERFORMANCE INSTALLATION

UNCOVERED
Xristina Penna (2013)

aswespeakproject
The Bluecoat, Liverpool
April 2013

XP: Can clothes tell stories? This interactive installation piece is based on a simple yet complex performance system which uses the audience's own clothes as a springboard for devising material for the show ad hoc. The performance space works as a composing device: For five hours the team of three (performer, sound designer and the artist) collect information (images, sounds and stories) related to the audience's clothes. Multimedia, direct audience participation, sound and a sewing machine are employed to uncover stories related to the clothes and to build up a patchwork of memories, words and responses.

Performer: Vanio Papadelli
Set Designer: Xristina Penna
Sound Designer: Michael Picknett
Photographer: Jody Leach

2/
XRISTINA PENNA
PERFORMANCE INSTALLATION

I KNOW THIS, I DO THIS ALL THE TIME (I DON'T LIKE IT THOUGH)
Xristina Penna (2009)

aswespeakproject at the Currents Santa Fe International New Media Festival.
Museo Cultural de Santa Fe, New Mexico.
2013

XP: This performance installation is an investigation of the manifold faces, masks and skins of our individuality and identity in relation to the 'Other'. With the use of projection, direct audience participation and the performer's body, the piece unearths the patterns that shape the space of the self, the messages and images that invade, embed and collude on our encounter with the Other.

The scenography refers to the mind and its processes, especially focusing on how information is represented (audience's drawings), processed (performer's drawings on the paper), and transformed (performer's drawings on the wall).

Set Designer: Xristina Penna
Performer: Kate Kita
Photographer: Xristina Penna

Images 1 & 2
Uncovered

Image 3
I Know This, I Do This
All The Time
(I Don't Like It Though)

1/
ANTONELLA PETRACCARO
COSTUME DESIGN

WE ARE FREE
Fabian Reimair (2014)

English National Ballet
The Pit, Barbican London
May 2014

AP: From the very beginning this dance piece was meant to have a strong visual impact. Although I was only briefed on the dancers' movements and the symbolism in the piece, it soon became clear that this performance would be centred on its costumes. 'We Are Free' is a short dance performance commemorating the centenary of World War 1. The choreography is inspired by Siegfried Sassoon's poem 'Absolution' from which the line 'time's but a golden wind that shakes the grass' gave me the inspiration for the designs. Designing for the body in movement is always a challenge, and in return I like to challenge the moving body, which here is attached to strings as part of the costume. My graphic style of designing fits well with this piece. The costumes deliberately illustrate a picturesque idyll and naivety of the characters, but the destruction of youth's romantic view on war is imminent.

Choreographer: Fabian Reimair

Costume Designer: Antonella Petraccaro

Lighting Designer: Fabian Reimair

Sound Designer: Stephan Hodel

Dancers: Adela Ramirez, Angela Wood, Francisco Bosch, Jeanette Kakareka & Laurent Liotardo

Costume Makers: Antonella & Thomas Petraccaro

Costume Dyeing: Symone Frost
Supported by the English National Ballet's Costume Department

Photographer: Josh Brandao

2/
ANTONELLA PETRACCARO
COSTUME DESIGN

THE BEAUTIFUL
Petar Miloshevski (2013)

Petar Miloshevski
Tristan Bates Theatre, London
August 2013

AP: The costume for The Beautiful came into being in close collaboration with the director. It needed to contribute to the choreography and was created for specific sequences of this physical theatre piece.

This multi layered costume depicts a peculiar character trapped in a world of his own. Whilst on a quest for a state of heightened beauty, his appearance suggests an emotionally wounded and physically disfigured creature. The costume is a cluttering of unidentifiable items and a layering of odd garments that have lost their beauty long ago. My work focuses on the theatrical aspect of costume design. I like costumes to interact with the artists, to evolve during a performance and have narrative qualities. The costume here plays a pivotal role in the development of the storyline, it also substitutes for the set design.

Director and Choreographer: Petar Miloshevski

Costume Designer: Antonella Petraccaro

Lighting, Sound and Media Designer: Petar Miloshevski

Costume Makers: Antonella & Thomas Petraccaro

Photographer: Josh Brandao

Image 1 & 2
We Are Free

Image 3
The Beautiful

Images 1 & 4
The Winterling

Images 2 & 3
Seeing The Lights

1/
ANNA PILCHER DUNN
SET AND COSTUME DESIGN

THE WINTERLING
Jez Butterworth (2006)

Studio Theatre, Theatre by the Lake, Keswick
May 2014

APD: It's winter on Dartmoor, and in a derelict farmhouse West waits for former associates from the city. This could be his chance to get back in the game: a reunion and a return from exile. But there's a mysterious girl upstairs, an axe by the door, and the dog is missing. Nothing is quite what it seems and going home will come at a price.

Director: Jez Pike
Set and Costume Designer: Anna Pilcher Dunn
Lighting Designer: Jo Dawson
Sound Designer: Maura Guthrie
Photographer: David Dunn

2/
ANNA PILCHER DUNN
SET AND COSTUME DESIGN

SEEING THE LIGHTS
Brendan Murray (2014)

Studio Theatre, Theatre by the Lake, Keswick.
June 2014

APD: A new comedy about family relationships, rivalries and responsibilities. Terry is a nurse by day and full time carer for his mum. As her 75th birthday approaches, the family descends and the siblings start to bicker. Terry wants things to stay as they are, but his sister Marion has other ideas. And then there's the will... As the pressure builds and her favourite son Kenneth still hasn't arrived for the party, mum's left wondering if she'll ever get to see the Blackpool Illuminations just one more time.

Director: Stefan Escreet
Set and Costume Designer: Anna Pilcher Dunn
Lighting Designer: Jo Dawson
Sound Designer: Maura Guthrie
Photographer: David Dunn

1/
TOM PIPER
INSTALLATION DESIGN

BLOOD SWEPT LANDS AND SEAS OF RED
Tower of London Poppy Memorial
Paul Cummins and Tom Piper (2013)

Historic Royal Palaces
The Tower Of London
August 2014

TP: Inspired by the words of an unknown WWI soldier Paul approached the Tower of London with his bold vision of creating 888,246 ceramic poppies, one for each allied fatality in World War 1. I was commissioned to realise and dramatise this vision in this iconic location. We wanted the poppies to be organic and flow out of and around the Tower, evoking the blood and lost life force of all those young lives. The scale of the project was such that we had to plan for a three month period to make and plant the poppies once my sculptural elements were installed. We had no idea that it would become such a phenomenon and that over 21,000 people would volunteer to plant, share stories of their family histories and come together to reflect. Over five million more have come to watch and the online postings and debate has gone global. Thousands watch the roll of honour each night as the names of 180 nominated fallen are read from the middle of the poppy field. All the poppies have been sold, raising nearly £10 million for charity and giving the installation a second fragmented life as each poppy is planted in new locations scattered around the world. It has been humbling to be involved in such a symbolic project that seems to have touched and moved so many.

Collaboration between Ceramic Artist Paul Cummins and Designer Tom Piper
Photographer: Tom Piper

2/
TOM PIPER
SET AND COSTUME DESIGN

CARMEN JONES IN CUBA

Oscar Hammerstein / Georges Bizet orchestrated by
Robert Russell Bennett (1943)

Carmen in Cuba
Havana Old Docks
June 2014

TP: A workshop production of this iconic musical
relocated to Cuba. We worked in a found space, an old
dockside building open to the sea on three sides with
crumbling concrete pillars. I worked closely with the
Cuban construction team, adapting ideas to what was
possible as raw materials are so hard to get. Much of
the set was created using found bits of old doors etc on
site and rusty nails picked off the ground. I painted the
space with chalk water and pigment, paint was just too
expensive! A production of rough raw passion.

Director: Christopher Renshaw

Book and Lyrics: Norge Espinosa

Choreographer: Roclan Gonzales Chavez

Set Designer: Tom Piper

Costume Designer: Elio Vives with Tom Piper

Lighting Designer: Willem Metz & Manolo Garriga

Photographers: Tom Piper/Willem Metz

Images 1-3
Blood Swept Lands
And Seas Of Red

Images 4-7
Carmen Jones in Cuba

1/
KATHERINA RADEVA
SET AND COSTUME DESIGN

FALLING IN LOVE WITH FRIDA
Caroline Bowditch (2014)

Caroline Bowditch/Dance4
Lakeside Nottingham and national tour
May 2014

KR: Designing for Falling in Love with Frida was a real joy. Not least because I was designing a show about a painter that I admired so much. A pivotal point in my process was a research trip to Paris to see Frida Kahlo's paintings live. Also a long conversation with Caroline Bowditch about colour, and designing a show which was also going to be a moving painting. And that is what we did!

I spent a lot of time painting as part of the design process so it wasn't just designing the environment, but it became more of a study of her work through my own process of painting.

Choreographer: Caroline Bowditch
Set and Costume Designer: Katherina Radeva
Lighting Designer: Emma Jones
Sound Designer: Dan Beats
Photographer: Anthony Hopwood

2/
KATHERINA RADEVA
SET AND COSTUME DESIGN

NEAR GONE
Two Destination Language (2013)

Two Destination Language
UK and international tour
October 2013

KR: Near Gone was a tough show to design. For the first time I felt that colour had to be as minimal as possible because we are were dealing with a very tragic story. So, I started to paint the stage in grey, variations of which actually became very rich. Then we discovered the flowers, the fresh white carnations which painted the stage in the most beautiful and simple way.

And that was it: simple, bare and beautiful. This design is one of my own favourites for its boldness in allowing space for the show. The 400 fresh carnations that we used for each show allowed the audience to paint and colour the monochrome picture that I had created.

Directors: Alister Lownie and Katherina Radeva
Additional direction: Charlotte Vincent
Choreographer: Two Destination Language
Set and Costume Designer: Katherina Radeva
Lighting Designer: Two Destination Language
Sound Designer: Tim Blazdell
Photographers: Alma Haser, Tamsin Drury

Images 1 & 2
Falling In Love With Frida

Images 3 & 4
Near Gone

COLIN RICHMOND
SET AND COSTUME DESIGN

Images
Wendy And Peter Pan

WENDY AND PETER PAN
Ella Hickson (2013), Based on the novel Peter Pan and Wendy by JM Barrie (1911)

Royal Shakespeare Company
The Royal Shakespeare Theatre, Stratford-upon-Avon
December 2013, returning November 2015

CR: Ella Hickson's brilliantly fresh re working of Peter Pan through the eyes and ears of Wendy Darling, gave us a chance to look at an old classic equally afresh. Ella's version centred on finding your 'happy thought', in this instance after the untimely death of the Darling children's poorly brother Tom, with a healthy dose of Girl Power.

Everything derived from the confines of the Darling's attic nursery, allowing us the chance to play with lots of visual metaphors to create the world of Neverland in a fun and thrilling way. As the wall of the nursery breathed out to allow a huge toy ship to sail onto stage, vines of children's books hung from the space, with suspended beds and bedside tables, rocking horses and prams. From the void between the floorboards, the home under the ground was created. The planked floor hinged up to allow a lost boys world of childhood chaos and mayhem to burst through into the nursery. The design used every inch of the expansive RST stage. A huge hanging mobile structure circled the air above the initial scenes and allowed us to deliver Peter, the children and Tink to Neverland to find Tom, the Darling household's 'lost boy'.

Director: Jonathan Munby
Choreographer: Mike Ashcroft
Set and Costume Designer: Colin Richmond
Lighting Designer: Oliver Fenwick
Sound Designer: Christopher Shutt
Production Media Designer: Ian William Galloway
Photographers: Lucy Barriball and Zuleika Henry

Image 1
Set Fire to the Stars
Image 2
Blood Wedding
Image 3
Coronation Festival Gala

1/
FRANCISCO RODRIGUEZ-WEIL
COSTUME DESIGN

SET FIRE TO THE STARS
Celyn Jones and Andy Goddard

Mad as Birds
Cinemas
April 2014

FRW: This wonderful feature film sheds light onto the first visit of Dylan Thomas to the USA. Set in 1950, the period costumes had to be as precise and period accurate as possible. All the design was made for digital filming in colour, while keeping in mind that the end product was to be presented in black and white. A great level of research was done into B&W filming techniques and period film making, as well as the period itself.

The film, shot in Wales, was made with a high level of community involvement that helped with the making, maintenance and organisation of the costumes. We were also supported by different local institutions dedicated to researching the life and work of Dylan Thomas.

Actors came from all over the world and were only available a few days or even just one day before filming, which meant having many doubles and the same costumes in many sizes so that they could be fitted on locations the day before.

Director: Andy Goddard
Cinematographer: Chris Seager
Set Designer: Edward Thomas
Costume Designer: Francisco Rodriguez-Weil
Photographer: Francisco Rodriguez-Weil

2/
FRANCISCO RODRIGUEZ-WEIL
SET AND COSTUME DESIGN

BLOOD WEDDING
Federico Garcia Lorca (1932)
Translation Tanya Ronder

Aria Entertainment and SOT Stage
The Courtyard Theatre, London
October 2013

FRW: Vintage doors opened on to the town square and defined the space. I played with the idea that behind every door there is a drama and a particular life situation. The action that was being played could be true to any of the inhabitants behind any of the doors. The doors not only defined the space but gave enormous flexibility to the director for entrances and exits, while also providing great hiding places for "Death" and "Moon".

Director: Bronagh Lagan
Set and Costume Designer:
Francisco Rodriguez-Weil
Composer: Lewis Greenslade
Producer: Katy Lipson
Photographer: Francisco Rodriguez-Weil

3/
FRANCISCO RODRIGUEZ-WEIL
SET AND COSTUME DESIGN

CORONATION FESTIVAL GALA
Summer 2013

Raymond Gubbay Ltd
Buckingham Palace, London

FRW: The show comprised a very diverse number of acts, performed by a large number of people on a 44 metres wide set. It was a huge task to design and coordinate the costumes for all the acts that included dancers from Matthew Bourne's New Adventures, to individual singers, bands, children, and an orchestra. There were around 450 costumes in total. The design and colour of the set was carefully planned to work well with the Palace and to suit digital filming. The design had elements in large and small scale so that it could be appreciated by the both the live and TV audience. The event took place over three days in the garden of the Palace but only one night was filmed.

Director: Luc Mollinger
Set and Costume Designer:
Francisco Rodriguez-Weil
Lighting Designer: Vince Foster
Musical Director: Ian Masterson
Photographers: T. Cohen and B. Tulga

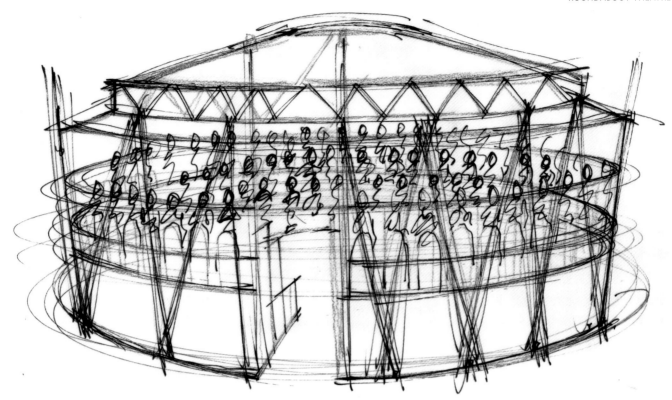

ROUNDABOUT THEATRE

Lucy Osborne, Emma Chapman,
Howard Eaton
developed between 2010-2014

Commissioned by Paines Plough
Touring nationally
August 2014

Image 1
Sketch: Lucy Osborne

Image 2
Image of venue: Paul Zanre

Image 3
Image with audience: Sarah Rushton-Read

LO. EC. HE: We were commissioned by Paines Plough to design and build a pop-up theatre. They were looking for a self-contained, in the round structure which put the writing at the heart of its architecture. It needed to be put up as quickly as possible by just a handful of people, be able to travel anywhere and fulfill a stringent environmental remit, with a sensitivity towards materials and sustainability. Critically they wanted an audience to see the same show with the same high standard of production values, regardless of where in the country they are.

Following four years of development, we launched the ROUNDABOUT in August 2014.

ROUNDABOUT pops-up in a day with a team of 8 people only 1 with prior knowledge. It requires no tools other than an allen key and a mallet and is constructed at ground level with the ceiling winched into position from below, so that there is no working at height needed. Our aspiration is that it is a democratic space, where everyone has a clear view and is encouraged to participate. We wanted to get as far away as possible from a conventional neutral black box theatre space, and instead have chosen to utilise a bold archi- tecture which takes Paines Plough's personality as a company with it on the road - we wanted it to feel dynamic, new, open and inviting.

ROUNDABOUT is a holistically designed space, in which the technical requirements of the auditorium were not separate from the architecture. The lighting and sound panels are integrated into the architecture meaning that no units hang within the space.

There are three voms which intersect in the centre of a playing space 4.6 metres in diameter. Opposite each vom is an audience staircase. The overall footprint is 11.1 metres diameter with an apex height of 5 metres. Overhead we use LED panels utilising a mixture of RGBW and 'tuneable' white, with minimal power consumption. The RGBW pixels allow for any colour to be selected, whilst the 'tuneable' white are capable of creating a tungsten feel through to HMI. With 627 pre-focused LEDs at 13 degrees each it is possible to light an actor from a variety of angles wherever they stand within the playing area. In collaboration with Avolites the lighting system is able to pixel map to create movement effects, patterns and images.

Paines Plough's vision is for ROUNDABOUT to tour the country for at least the next ten years allowing everyone to see the work as it was originally designed and conceived. Currently requiring an external marquee to sit outside, the next stage is to design a bespoke tent which will allow ROUNDABOUT to sit anywhere as a self contained unit.

Roundabout Auditorium Design:
Lucy Osborne and Emma Chapman in collaboration with Charcoalblue and Howard Eaton

Auditorium built by: Factory Settings

Lighting System designed and built by:
Howard Eaton Lighting Ltd

Ceiling Structure built by: Total Solutions

Acoustic Consultation: Gillieron Scott Acoustic Design

Lighting Control System: Avolites

Auditorium layout: Will Bowen

Project Manager: Bernd Fauler

Sound Designer: Tom Gibbons

1/
ALEXANDER RUTH
SET AND COSTUME DESIGN

ROOM
Commissioned by V&A at Dundee and Scottish Dance Theatre

2013 Linbury Prize for Stage Design
National Theatre Linbury Exhibition, London
November 2013

AR: The design was commissioned by Scottish Dance theatre in connection with V&A at Dundee for the 2013 Linbury Prize for Stage Design.

This was a design led speculative project to create a performance area that can be set up quickly in a variety of locations (initially City Square Dundee) to make performance accessible to the public, to potentially reach new audiences and generate interest in contemporary performance and design. It is a transformable and sustainable performance area, made from recycled carpet and textiles, that comments on the architecture around it. The inspirations were game boards and the notion of 'play' in performance. The piece developed from ideas of social design, audience participation and the questions: what is a performance environment, and, how we can experience performance on our own body through participation?

The costume concept is an experimental and playful approach to join performers and spectators in an experience with the idea of 'play' in performance. It is based around the thought that the spectator perceives dance on their own body through being linked with the performers.

Choreographer: Fleur Darkin
Set and Costume Designer: Alexander Ruth
Performers: Students at Dundee College BA Contemporary Dance
Video from R&D session: Alexander Ruth

2/
ALEXANDER RUTH
SET AND COSTUME DESIGN

MIANN (GAELIC: LONGING)
Fleur Darkin (2014)

Scottish Dance Theatre
Carid Hall Dundee and Edinburgh Fringe Festival, Summerhall
August 2014

AR: The piece was a development of the original prize winning collaboration between Scottish Dance Theatre and myself. It naturally evolved from the Linbury Prize and was performed in Dundee as part of the 2014 Commonwealth Games, under the title Human Scale, as part of Scottish Dance Theatre's progressive artistic projects around Dundee. It was also performed at the 2014 Edinburgh Fringe Festival.

At the beginning was an enquiry into intimacy, nature and transformation. The observations and artistic development made in the initial collaboration process became the foundation for a venture into new aesthetic and dramaturgical directions. During its creation I made a number of costume experiments based around ideas of rituals, initiation, transformation, covering and vulnerability.

The spatial concept stayed similar to the initial design development. Arranging the performance space in a circle was based on research into circles as ritualistic and ceremonial places. The notion of time as a narrative and performative inspiration was important to the artistic team so that both stage and costume design developed fluidly during the creation of Miann. The stage design (inspired by a sundial) and the transformative nature of the costume designs comment on this.

The original and live music by the One Ensemble gave the piece a beautiful eeriness and sensuality.

Choreographer and Artistic Director: Fleur Darkin
Lighting Designer: Emma Jones
Music: The One Ensemble
Costume Designer: Alexander Ruth
Set Design: Alexander Ruth/ Scottish Dance Theatre
Photographer: Brian Hartley

Images 1 & 2   Images 3 & 4
Room   Miann

1/
HANSJORG SCHMIDT
LIGHTING DESIGN

ABOVE ME THE WIDE BLUE SKY
Fevered Sleep (2013)

Fevered Sleep
Young Vic Theatre, London
March 2013

HS: Fevered Sleep's work is always devised and channeled through an extensive research and development phase. To enable the devising process there are often some set rules at the start, in this case the presence of a 360° screen for projection.

Above Me The Wide Blue Sky became a performance installation that explores our profound connectedness to the natural world. An actress, Laura Cubitt, delivers a collage of texts that respond to nature and the process of change. The challenge for the lighting was two-fold: on a practical level, not to interfere with the projection; and on a dramaturgical level, to connect Laura with the projections to help maintain a strong presence within the very powerful mise-en-scene of the screens. Quite early on we found that conventional theatre lights felt wrong. The disembodied light from the theatre spotlights seemed too disconnected from the physical presence and qualities of the performer and set. So we moved towards having light sources on set, first as a range of found lights such as anglepoises and 8mm film projectors. These were eventually too specific and disconnected from the abstraction of the text and set. So, we made our own lights, very simple designs made from metal rods, a lamp holder, and a diffuser. These instruments allowed me to light Laura as and when required, but equally to create a very animated and textured layer of light that rooted Laura within the eye level of the audience, whilst also responding to text and movement with light and providing its own narrative texture.

Director: David Harradine
Set Designers: David Harradine,
Sam Butler, Ali Beale
Lighting Designer: Hansjorg Schmidt
Sound Designer: Charles Webber
Production Media Designer: Will Duke
Photographer: Matthew Andrews

Images 1-3
Above Me The Wide
Blue Sky

Image 4
Krapp's Last Tape

2/
HANSJORG SCHMIDT
LIGHTING DESIGN

KRAPP'S LAST TAPE
Samuel Beckett (1958)

Sheffield Theatres
Crucible Theatre, Sheffield
June 2014

HS: As with Above Me The Wide Blue Sky, this production was driven by a shared intent to create a performance experience deriving from notions of installation (thereby freeing the audience from the confines of their seats). Krapp was placed inside an acoustically sealed shed which turned very slowly and continuously on a revolve, providing multiple points of view to an audience in the round. This allowed the Sound Designer, Dan Jones, to experiment with the way the sound from inside the shed (Krapp's voice both recorded and live) reached the audience. To achieve this there was a complex array of speakers, creating a sound dome that allowed every audience member to hear what Krapp hears, to be both inside the shed and inside his head. The lighting for the production needed to bridge the gap between the physical reality of the set and actor - Richard Wilson's presence inside it - and the immaterial quality of the sound. I wanted the light to enable the audience to follow and trust the disembodied voice floating through space. The light, in brief, needed to provide dramaturgy: to make meaning of a series of powerful but intentionally disconnected layers. This was achieved by aiming for three things: to make the performance space itself into a some kind of unheimlich 'other place' through replacing all the conventional house-lighting with an array of bulkhead and fluorescent lamps; also by lighting the shed itself with a single bulkhead and a single fluorescent tube; finally, by using theatre lights to carefully illuminate the structure of the mise-en-scene: the skin of the shed and the speakers.

Director: Polly Findlay
Set Designer: Alex Lowde
Lighting Designer: Hansjorg Schmidt
Composer and Sound Designer: Dan Jones
Photographer: Mark Douet

Image 1 & 2
The Only Way Is
Chelsea's

Image 3 & 4
Queen Of The Nile

1/
MILA SANDERS
SET AND COSTUME DESIGN

THE ONLY WAY IS CHELSEA'S
Frazer Flintham (2013)

Root Theatre
York Theatre Royal / Touring
October 2013

MS: Based on research with young people in York, the show toured to small thrust studio spaces. The play was set entirely in a garage filled with clutter including a large television. Teenager Chelsea and her friends construct a reality show of their own. I wanted the audience to feel as if they were part of the gang. The structure of the garage was a fragmented wooden framework allowing the audience to peer through the walls. During choreographed scene transitions actors stepped through the structure, boxes were thrown, props and costumes appeared and disappeared from boxes, all lit by the glow of the television screen. At the climax the characters transformed the garage into their idea of a glamorous nightclub using Christmas decorations and the contents of the garage.

Director: Jane Fallowfield
Choreographer: Ibrahim Shote
Set and Costume Designer: Mila Sanders
Lighting Designer: Ziggy Jacobs
Sound Designer: Becky Smith
Photographer: Mila Sanders

2/
MILA SANDERS
SET AND COSTUME DESIGN

QUEEN OF THE NILE
Tim Fountain (2012)

Hull Truck Theatre, Hull
April 2013

MS: Set in Luxor against the backdrop of the Arab spring, the action moves quickly between a restaurant, a felucca and many other locations. A chaotic over developed streetscape is crisscrossed with wiring and washing lines and peppered with satellite dishes. Faded billboards and street signs provide surfaces for projections that use a combination of designed images and photographic stills taken on location.

The felucca - made of a flown sail that provides another surface for projections – is accompanied by a simple boat truck on the thrust stage. Luxor's ancient Egyptian heritage is reflected in the hieroglyphs bordering the proscenium arch, the red stone floor and the skyline of the Valley of the Kings that appears in the distance.

Director: Mike Bradwell
Set and Costume Designer: Mila Sanders
Lighting Designer: Jason Taylor
Sound Designer: Mic Pool
Production Media Designer: Mic Pool
Photographer: Mila Sanders

NETTIE SCRIVEN
SET AND COSTUME DESIGN

INSIDE OUT OF MIND
Tanya Myers (2013)

Meeting Ground and Lakeside Arts Centre
Lakeside Arts Centre Theatre Company
June 2013

NS: Subterfuge is a powerful theme running through this play, which takes a disquieting look at caring for patients with dementia, and at dementia itself. Responding to a strategy of care, called ˈbaffling', which supports patients to remain safe inside, we created a door at the apex of the design which is covered with wallpaper shaped as a tree, concealing its exit. All sculptural lines are drawn to this point, as is the character of Mr P, in a constant search for a way out of his forest of subterfuge. The director and I worked closely with the digital media designer to create a visual landscape working on many levels- the ward with no name, Mr P's forest, and a hidden world of burning synapses and neurons no longer connecting in the brain.

Director: Tanya Myers
Set and Costume Designer: Nettie Scriven
Lighting Designer: Richard Statham
Sound Designer: David Wilson
Media Designer: Barret Hodgson
Object Theatre: Sean Myatt
Photographer: Alan Fletcher and Lakeside Arts Centre

Images
Inside Out Of Mind

DRAGON BREATH THEATRE

GULLIVER'S TRAVELS BY JONATHAN SWIFT (1726) / PETER RUMNEY (2012)
DRAGON BREATH THEATRE, CURVE STUDIO AND TOURING, APRIL 2011 - MAY 2012

Over a period of 18 months the Dragon Breath collaborators explored ways to realise this epic story's vision, depth and fantasy into a poetic narrative. At each stage of its development this challenging adult political satire was tested and researched with the children who were to be its audience. Discovering different theatrical ways to play with scale called for a fusion of forms: Gulliver as a giant in the little world of Lilliput, peering through the Palace window at the Emperor, his eye projected large scale at the door; Gulliver as the tiny puppet at the hands of Glumdalclitch his giant protectoress. Visual moments were created from overlaps of imagination and disciplines - Gulliver sweeping tiny boats in a vast ocean tied around his waist - a moment created by choreographer and puppetry director at the very beginning of our long process.

APRIL 2011

I make
a space full
of objects, materials
available for play.

A question posed...
Why Gulliver now?

Choreographer.
Puppetry Director.
Blue cloth, paper boats
drawn across the Studio floor,
a diagonal...

Designer as Mrs Gulliver
At a long table
Strawberry platter
Knife
What is her story?

Man giant
Gulliver drags
Blefuscan fleet
across the sea
towards its doom...

Writer juxtaposes
iconic image
with Swiftian text

The idea is made.
Gulliver Impro # 3, R&D Artist's Lab 1, Curve Leicester.

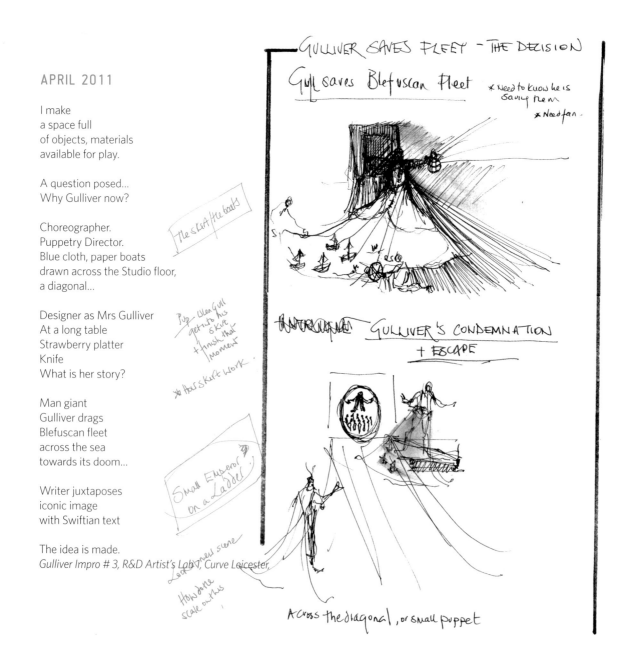

Like Lemuel Gulliver's perceptions of the bizarre and changing worlds he encounters, my design process shifted and transformed as the months went by. I constantly sketched and doodled, read and researched, modelled and re modelled. From the collective on the rehearsal floor, and alone in my studio, responding to, feeding back into, the process. I was a harvester ….collecting the ripe fruits of each and every collaborator on our journey to create fantastical, recognisable worlds for each of the books we adapted from Swift's Gulliver's Travels.

JULY 2011

Summer heat.
A school playground.
A question asked…
Glumdalclitch loses tiny Gulliver.
What is her fate?
The children improvise…

Wire fence.
A girl tied,
held down,
restrained,
tortured,
by two others
aged 11…
 "You are in our power"

This is Glumdalclitch.
A new scene is created,
Not Swift, but Swiftian…
*Gulliver Impro # 12, R&D Lab 2,
South Wigston High School*

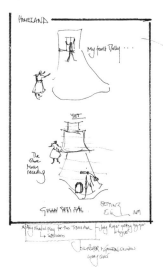

What was the story we wanted to tell. How could we explore its grandeur and epic sweep? How could we ensure a C18th satire had meaning for young people in the C21st, on the threshold, in transition to secondary school?

We returned to the children we were working with, over a period of months, to test their responses to both the actor's text and the visual narrative. We explored shadow puppetry and the shifts in scale from world to world, informing our creative process through their eyes and understanding.

The children affirmed the efficacy of our characterisations and theatrical gestures, discussing how the evolving scenario and imagery reflected their own lives and experiences. Some ideas created through school workshops weren't realised on stage, such as the giant eagle that carries Gulliver across the sea - here the young people's work was reflected in the power of the actor's voice in soliloquy, rather then through design.

At the heart of the piece is the disintegration of Gulliver, psychologically and physically, as he encounters the fall of a civilised world. How does this apocalyptic and jaundiced C18th vision of the world relate to the lives of our audience, young people living today…how does it reflect their experiences of and relationships to adults…and how can the act of theatre affirm and give hope as they think towards the future?...

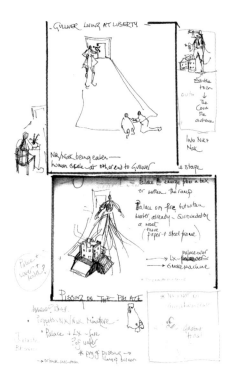

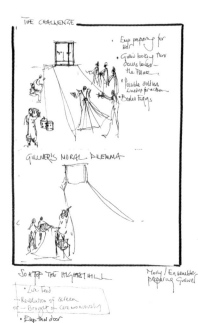

THE TEXTURE OF
THE DESIGN IS RICH
AND MANY PATTERNED
BECAUSE OF ALL THE
COLLABORATIONS
INVOLVED

DECEMBER 2011

We play with swathes of white material
cascading through a palace door
exploring scale.
Lilliputian egg and tin soldiers.
Composer in corner
playing on piano.
Film makers'
live-feed experiment...
Sail-actor-puppet-model palace.

Composer says
"Let's see Gulliver's eye at the door"

Scale established,
the form emerges
a compendium of ideas.
Writer, Designer, Director
Develop, underscore, refine...
*Gulliver Impro # 23, R&D Artist's Lab 2,
Curve Leicester,*

Since 2004 Dragon Breath have made epic,
visual, poetic theatre for young people, in a
variety of performance spaces, ranging from
traditional auditoria and flexible studios, to
immersive events in underground sites and
school halls.

Unusually for such a small company,
Dragon Breath make large-scale work, often in
partnership with bigger cultural organisations.
The process is driven by myself as Designer
and Writer Peter Rumney. We work as
co-authors of the visual and verbal text,
responding to a core group of collaborators
who bring filmic, puppetry, choreographic,
music, performer and directorial vision to the
development of a theatre language embracing
both traditional and new theatre technologies.

Productions grow from extensive research
and development phases, spanning up to
two years. The R&D process includes artist
laboratories, and involves collaboration
with research scientists, academics, school
teachers and undergraduates. Core to
the process of creation are R&D projects
which draw on the input of young people
as 'performance researchers'. Working
alongside children and young people enables
the company to engage with and reflect their
experiences, and challenge the audience's
perceptions of the world, on a personal and
political level.

The texture of the design is rich and many
patterned because of all the collaborations
involved - at some moments in the process,
the creation of a visual idea can be pinpointed
to be an image offered by, say, the composer,
as happened with Duncan Chave in Gulliver's
Travels. At others, the witnessing or
enabling of a child's powerful vision, through
improvisation, sculpture or drawing, generates
a new thread in the script, as advocated by
the designer.

The Designer, and the visual team as a whole, contribute profoundly to the development of the spoken text, as well as the mise en scene and visual events indicated in the script. In our first Gulliver's Travels Artist Lab at Curve in 2011, Nettie created and improvised the character of (Swift's almost invisible) Mrs Gulliver. Exploring Mrs Gulliver's madness in response to the complete breakdown of Gulliver on his return to the world of humans, Nettie generated both character and a narrative device for establishing the world at the beginning of the play. Three months later, our workshops with children translated 'Gulliver's wife' into 'Gulliver's daughter' Molly, as created by the 10 year olds we were working with, as the best window for a young audience to step into the world of Swift's classic story"
Peter Rumney, Writer Gulliver's Travels

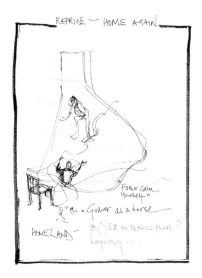

GULLIVER

Molly...
Molly, I am broken
Molly, like a Horse. I am broken. Everything is broken...

GULLIVER SHAKES
LIKE A HORSE.
MOLLY SHAKES LIKE
A HORSE.

MOLLY

Look at me Father. I am your child...and I am not broken. My spirit will never be broken, I'll be strong and brave like you Father, you sailed across the sea, and you returned, I will grow up, and I will be free, and you will un-break with me, father, we'll be free together, just you see, just you see..

Director: Adel Al-Salloum
Choreographer: Liz Clark
Set and Costume Designer: Nettie Scriven
Lighting Designer: Arnim Friess
Sound Designer: Composer Duncan Chave
Media Designer: Creative Forum
Puppetry Director: Sue Pycroft
Photographer: Pamela Raith

JOANNA SCOTCHER

WHISPER MACHINES

QUEEN ANNE   MARY & WILLIAM   LITTLE WILLIAM

JOANNA SCOTCHER
SET DESIGN

....

HOUSE OF CARDS

Coney
Commissioned by Historic Royal Palaces for Kensington Palace
March 2012

....

JS: House of Cards gave us the unique opportunity to re-imagine the rich history of this space in the same way we are inspired to breath new emotional life into a text on stage. The piece was designed to pull the threads of intrigue from playful minds and ask the viewer to interact and make connections within the experience. Though rooted in meticulously researched historic facts, this multi-layered transformation asked the viewer to consider the emotional journeys of the characters and discover a new narrative exploring the aspirations and imagining of a young Prince William, the last generations of the Stuarts. Our chosen protagonist, who's short life is often overlooked, became our frame to re-tell his story of a fragile family at the very heart of political change.

"LONDON'S KENSINGTON PALACE NOW IMPRESSIVELY BLENDS BOTH OLD AND NEW... CONEY AND SCOTCHER'S TEAMWORK IS MORE ABOUT THOUGHT-PROVOKING PLAYFULNESS THAN IT IS ABOUT ARTIFACTS IN GLASS CASES".
ARCHITECTURAL DIGEST

Director: Annette Mees
Set Designer: Joanna Scotcher
Lighting Designer: Natasha Chivers
Photographer: Ludovic Des Cognets

Images
House Of Cards

ASHLEY SHAIRP
SET AND COSTUME DESIGN

THE SOLOTORIA
Ashley Shairp (2014)

Planning a Trifle
World Museum, Liverpool
November 2014

AS: The Solotoria is pop-up theatre for one - truly immersive miniature entertainment. Like many designers, Pollock's toy theatres have delighted and inspired me since childhood. This project has built on those memories, magnified by my constant wonder and excitement upon entering a new theatre or opera house for the first time; particularly those that are historic and ornate.

These tiny theatres provide an environment to host a repertory of concentrated performances. The auditoria are based on observed versions of iconic venues mixed with a touch of fantasy, and not to any exact scale. Initially there are two (The Royal Opera House and Blackpool Grand Theatre) but my ambition is to have a large group of tents containing a diverse range of theatres, concert halls and even the odd cinema from across the world.

Rather than being solely used as a tool within the design and production process I am interested in putting models and miniaturisation at the centre of the event. In previous UK design exhibitions I have created installations/exhibits based on already realised projects that became works in their own right. The natural progression for this exhibition was to bring an actual project and perform it live throughout the entire residency. To my surprise there is even a social media element to the performance devised by Sam Heath.

As with all performance design work, The Solotoria is a collaboration of rich and vital contributions from a wide range of makers and artists. The project has been developed using a grant from Arts Council England.

Director: Tony Lidington and the company
Set and Costume Designer: Ashley Shairp
Lighting and Sound Designer: Sam Heath
Makers: Nina Patel-Grainger, Colin Eccleston
Photographer: Sam Heath

Image:
The Solotoria

RAJHA SHAKIRY
SET AND COSTUME

I STAND CORRECTED
Collaboration: Mojisola Adebayo
and Mamela Nyamza

*Artscape, Cape Town, Oval House,
London and SIFA
August 2012*

RS: First conceived in April 2012, by writer/director Mojisola Adebayo and choreographer/dancer Mamela Nyamza. I Stand Corrected tackles the alarming phenomenon of 'corrective' hate rape in current South Africa. It has since played in various locations across South Africa, UK and more recently at the Singapore International Festival of Arts (SIFA), 2014.

The piece shifts between several worlds that entwine and run parallel within the narrative. Taking audiences through juxtaposing locations, the pre-wedding preparations and the murder scene, the wedding turning into a memorial service, flowing between real to supernatural worlds. The brutality and horror of the subject matter, had to be balanced by the beauty and celebration of the lives lost. The materials used became integral in shaping the narrative and visual concepts through out the piece.

For this project, we embarked on an early collaborative dialogue, alongside the use of creative processes and tools. This enabled the design to be an integral part of the production, to serve it best, not to take away or distract. The uncluttered design aesthetic was shaped by subject matter, context and use of space, whilst responding and bearing in mind its internationally diverse audiences. The stark creative choices made throughout my design process, were made to extract and amplify the tragic consequences of these acts.

Director: Mojisola Adebayo
Choreographer: Mamela Nyamza
Set and Costume Designer: Rajha Shakiry
Lighting Designer: Mannie Manim
Sound Designer: Mix 'n' Sync
Photographer: Kong Chong Yew

Images
I Stand Corrected

1/
NICKY SHAW
SET AND COSTUME DESIGN

DON QUICHOTTE
Jules Massenet (1910)

Danish National Opera / Den Jyske Opera
Musikhuset Aarhus, Denmark
August 2014

NS: Don Quichotte is a French opera by Massenet. It is called a comédie-heroïque and is based on the story of the mad knight Don Quixote from the great Spanish novel of that name by Miguel de Cervantes.

It is the story of an old, idealistic, lovelorn knight who lives in the world of his imagination and is mocked for doing so by all around him. The world laughs at him because of his age and old-fashioned ideas, but he has access to a world of honour and imagination.

From the start I saw a world of shadow play and images in stark relief coming from the memory of Don Quichotte. I wished to use cut cloths with projection screens and dramatic lighting in addition to some 3-dimensional elements. We wanted to make exciting scene changes in seconds; to go from a completely empty stage to an enormous town wall to magical forests full of mist, then to hidden windmills in the distance to the giant windmill that Don Quichotte famously fights, then back again to the town, returning in death to the forest at the end.

It is not often possible, even in a large opera house, to use the entire flying grid for one production, but for this show we were able to and all scenery was flown in and out behind a black iris in seconds.

Director: Annilese Miskimmon
Set and Costume Designer: Nicky Shaw
Lighting Designer: Mark Jonathan
Photographer: Kaare Viemose

2/
NICKY SHAW
SET AND COSTUME DESIGN

ACIS & GALATEA
George Frederic Handel (1739)

Mid Wales Opera
RWCMD Theatre, Cardiff and Tour
January 2014

NS: Acis & Galtea is a pastoral opera by George Frederic Handel, with words by poet John Gay.

It tells an enchanting story from ancient mythology: Acis is the son of the spirit Pan, Galatea a nymph of the sea. They fall in love, only to be thwarted by the monstrous Cyclops, Polyphemus. In a jealous rage he murders Acis, leaving Galatea bereft. In her despair, she turns the blood of her dead lover into a river, forever flowing into the sea.

The production toured to small theatres, churches and festivals with temporary stages. Not only did the set need to be compact, but also to work in different configurations and look good with the minimal lighting in some venues.

We wanted to play with the ideas of a court masque and set our production when it was composed. Starting with a bare plywood box on the outside, there were many traditionally painted layers of scenery within that could be opened in various ways, by the cast, to reveal different aspects and hidden elements all contained inside.

Director: Annilese Miskimmon
Set and Costume Designer: Nicky Shaw
Lighting Designer: Declan Randall
Photographer: Robert Workman

Image 1 & 2
Don Quichotte

Image 3 & 4
Acis Galatea

1/
DAVID SHEARING
INSTALLATION

....

...AND IT ALL COMES DOWN TO THIS...
Kamal Kaan (2012)

stage@leeds
September 2012

....

DS: ...and it all comes down to this... was an intimate, design-led performance without actors. The installation placed the audience at the heart of the action. Wearing headphones, they were immersed in a visual landscape created from thousands of glass jars, three-screen video projection and surround-sound. Guided via subtle instructions, audience members were invited to connect with the unfolding environment; with light, sound and each other. As the landscape shifted, the audience become absorbed into the fiction, and, slowly, they became the protagonists of their own fables. The intention was to create an immersive performance that could tour.

Director and Set Designer: David Shearing
Sound Designer: James Bulley
Design Assistants: Chloë Jayne Oldridge, Laura Price
Photographer: David Shearing

2/
DAVID SHEARING
INSTALLATION

....

IF ANYONE WONDER WHY ROCKS BREAKDOWN
Kamal Kaan (2011)

stage@leeds
October 2011

....

DS: If anyone wonders why rocks breakdown was a performance installation designed to encourage audience interaction with design and movement around the space. Designed as an immersive experience, the piece consisted of two large panoramic projector screens and surround-sound. The audience listened to and read the performance text, which was delivered via headphones, a booklet (handed to them on entry) and projected on the screens along with images of a cityscape. Covering the floor were thousands of tiny 1:50 scale model figures and torches, which the audience could manipulate. The aim was to place the audience in a city landscape that encouraged mindful reflection.

Set and Media Designer: David Shearing
Photographer: David Shearing

Images 1 & 2   Images 3 & 4
And It All Comes Down   If Anyone Wonders Why
To This   Rocks Breakdown

SET AND COSTUME DESIGN

THE BUTTERFLY LION
Michael Morpurgo (2004)
adapted by Daniel Buckroyd

*Mercury Theatre, Colchester by arrangement
with Bill Kenwright Ltd
Mercury Theatre and National Tour
August 2013*

JS: The adaptation of Morpurgo's book began
as a small scale tour and when the tour moved
to larger venues we chose to keep the same
simple concept. An Aga in a Wiltshire kitchen
takes centre stage. Seventy year old Millie tells
her story to young Michael, who is playing
truant from boarding school, using objects
from her past which she pulls from boxes piled
around the stove. There is a stylised green
landscape and a pair of iron gates. Through
artful choreography of the gates we explore the
theme of confinement; the school in England;
the compound in Africa; the trenches in France;
the unfortunate lion's cage.

The growth of the lion is portrayed by
a series of rag puppets as if from Millie's
washing basket and there are hyenas, a snake
and blue butterflies. We finish with a sky full
of fluttering blue butterflies.

Director: Daniel Buckroyd

Set and Costume Designer: Juliet Shillingford

Lighting Designer: Mark Dymock

Composer: Carlton Edwards

Sound Designer: Adam McCready

Associate/Movement Director:
Matthew Cullum

Puppetry Director/Maker: Sue Pyecroft

Photographer: Robert Day

Images:
The Butterfly Lion

AMANDA STOODLEY
SET. COSTUME. INSTALLATION

MANCHESTER LINES
Wils Wilson / Errollyn Wallen

Library Theatre Company (HOME)
Number One First Street, Manchester
2012

AS: The Library Theatre has been finding performance spaces in and around the city whilst waiting for its new HOME. Manchester Lines, one of its first itinerant productions, took place on the fifth floor of a new glass-encased office block at Number One, First Street – a huge, empty, soulless room, but with a view that Wils, Jackie and I fell in love with, from which trams, trains, roads, canals and pedestrians can be seen, all revealing the 'lines of Manchester'.

Audience members arrived in groups and were transported by lifts to the Lost & Found Reception. They made their way along a winding, 'underground' corridor, leading to the Lost Property Office - an intimate space encircled by floor-to-ceiling metal racks, stuffed with everything that could, or had been lost, labelled and filed on the shelves. Before taking a seat, they could look at and listen to the hundreds of items, each with its own tale to tell - the everyday and the surreal sitting side by side, with their significance gradually emerging as each story was told. Seven characters in search of themselves, who all connect through the office where they meet the Keeper of Lost Things (and souls) – lines, strands that link our day-to-day encounters, whether through chance or design.

Finally, a hidden door opened up to reveal the vista, and the 'Alphabet Song' performed with the community choir high above the city.

Director: Wils Wilson
Set and Costume Designer: Amanda Stoodley
Lighting Designer: Anna Barrett
Sound Designer: Pete Rice
Photographer: Sam Heath

Images
Manchester Lines

ANDREAS SKOURTIS
SCENOGRAPHY

"02 ACADEMIC STAFF / COMMUNNI-TY-CATION"

Olive Grove in Corinth,
Room D-Royal Central School of Speech and Drama,
Several Undefined Spaces in UK
September 2013

AS: ...a Scenography led performance/installation in three parts; three different spaces and times, two different countries, one maker, eighty five members of a Specific 'audience', and (my) olive grove, names that become physical memory, bottles of (my) olive oil, summer sound and light, Room D, plywood signs on olive trees somewhere far yet nearby, a new job, a bit of me, a bit of home and a bit of 'home', natural and constructed landscapes in dialogue, a permanent marker, time and reality to be explored, scenography to be continued...

Scenographer and Photographer: Andreas Skourtis

Images
Communi-ty-cation

SUMMER HARVEST
ANDREAS SKOURTIS

...when I was a child, I often visited the site – the building: a busy warehouse of a local Forest and Agricultural Cooperative build in the 60's, abandoned in the 80's; I remember myself shaping ideas about re-using that space; many years later, in 2007, that theatre collective was born, and since then the space lives again in a different way as the found part of a scenography each summer...

...six years, six summer productions around the same one building - 'Summer Harvest' was the sixth time exploring the scenography of the same space, creating a new theatrical Topos...

My collaboration with Theatriki Skini Chiliomodiou has taken the shape of a full and long research project: it is about exploring and using as much and in as many different ways the same architecture, landscape, earth, real natural material, new and old plants and a previously abandoned building; each year's summer sunsets behind the surrounding mountains, the financial crisis that broke and the need of local people to re-define their everyday life, to speak through theatre – "theatre FROM the community" as Peter Farley said one day I was describing the project to him; and it is also about me re-defining a part of my scenographic practice and motivation to make theatre.

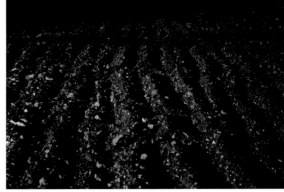

This year 2014, 'Summer Harvest', written in 1946, was staged on a 2000 square metres 'stage' made of real-only materials, carefully planned and planted (literally) – we used the plinths of an old demolished house nearby to construct part of the set, original objects-props given from members of the team, pieces of old wood found in yards, a tree moved from another field, and of course the same building 'performed' again, together with the fields and the soil around it. Drawings were sent from my London desk to Greece, seeds were put in in March so that the plants reach the desirable height for July performances.

It feels like a different-each-year scenographic up-cycling of the same site; a use / re-use of the same actual materiality to create scenography and 'tell' stories of the past that somehow mirror current thoughts and debates; that directly respond to the contemporary lives of local people that are the company and the audience of the performances. During the ten days of 'Summer Harvest' 2014, 2500 people walked through a field to take a seat and watch a play about people of a similar town trying, united, to save their fields 60 years ago. Material, 'materials', matters...

MUSIC is the sound and the feeling of a mild wind towards a sunset – passing through an audience and a scenographic landscape, travelling time.

Summer is the best WEATHER to reflect on past, present and future winters.

People responding to a real need and shaping a hybrid bespoke 'theatrical prod-action' practice is a way to think about POLITICS without politicians or policies involved.

I was born in Chiliomodi.

Alexis Damianos (1921 - 2006) was a theatre, film and television director, known especially for films: Until the Ship Sails (1966), Evdokia (1971) and Eniochos the Charioteer (1995). He founded and directed many plays for Experimental Theatre and Theatre Poreia.

'Summer Harvest' (To Kalokairi Tha Therisoume) is his first theatrical play written in 1946 and has been staged only a few times. It is set in a Greek small village community that is trying to recover from the deconstruction after World War II and a dramatic civil war that followed. Literally and metaphorically locals are trying to transform a marsh to cultivated fields, fighting against nature and death. Is fighting for a new world and a better society just a Utopia? Is there going to be a Summer Harvest?

SUMMER HARVEST
Alexis Damianos (1946)

*Theatriki Skini Chiliomodiou
Co-Operative Warehouse, Chiliomodi, Corinth, Greece
July 2014*

Director: Christos Tsirtsis

Scenographer: Andreas Skourtis

Costume Designer: Dimitris Andrianos

Photographers: Michalis Andrianos, Andreas Skourtis

RAE SMITH
SET AND COSTUME DESIGN

THE PRINCE OF THE PAGODAS
Benjamin Britten (1957)

*National Ballet of Japan and Birmingham Royal Ballet
New National Theatre, Tokyo; The Lowry Salford, Birmingham
Hippodrome, Coliseum London, Theatre Royal Plymouth
Japan 2011, UK January 2014*

RS: At the beginning of our fairy tale, Princess Sakura
flees the Japanese Court after her Father is overthrown
by her evil Step Mother. Her dead brother, transformed
in to a Salamander, rescues her and guides her through
the elements of earth, air, fire and water to his magical
kingdom. She is accompanied on this perilous journey by
four supernatural, mischievous frog monsters, the Yokai.
The Yokai are inspired by fantastical Japanese monsters
which can be viewed as a child would, both with a mixture
of laughter and horror.

In Utagawa Kuniyoshi's pictures, monsters can
represent fears, or a specific group of people in society.
They all have roles to play and traditionally have a very
specific purpose. Here, they have the job of leading the
Princess on her dream journey to her brother's land.

Director and Choreographer: David Bintley

Set and Costume Designer: Rae Smith

Lighting Designer: Peter Teigen

Photographers: Seto Hidemi, Roy Smiljanic, Bill Cooper

Images
The Prince Of The Pagodas

1/
JASON SOUTHGATE
SET AND COSTUME DESIGN

TROJAN WOMEN
Caroline Bird (2012)

The Gate Theatre London
November 2012

JS: Caroline Bird's adaptation was set in a modern day women's prison, Hecuba is being held in the maternity ward awaiting her fate. The problem...to fit three hospital beds, a transit van and 70 seats in the very small but adaptable Gate Theatre in Notting Hill.

I wanted a 360 degree immersive design, so the audience was pushed right back against the three walls of the theatre. The effect of this is that the action is right in the audiences faces, they become another chorus watching and judging the events as they unfold. Childish murals juxtapose the white clinical space. When the dead baby Astyanax is brought onstage the audiences response was palpable.

Director: Christopher Haydon

Set and Costume Designer: Jason Southgate

Lighting Designer: Mark Howland

Sound Designer: Gareth Fry

Production Media Designer: Iona Firouzabadi

Photographer: Iona Firouzabadi

2/
JASON SOUTHGATE
SET AND COSTUME DESIGN

THE TYRANT
Paul Dresher (2005)

Teatro Comunale Bolzano, Italy
February 2012

JS: The opera is based on a short story by Italo Calvino called The King Listens. A king is paranoid that he will be overthrown due to his tyrannical rule, he sits on his thrown listening to any sound that's might be his downfall.

My idea was for the singer to be trapped in a void, the kings head space an abstract space with oval ear apertures. The king can be seen listen and it would also help light the inside of the box. The space outside is divided into two spaces, the front with the real musicians and the rear divided by a black silk that drops at the most dramatic section of music...it reveals a no mans land of destruction with a broken orchestra.

Director: Michael Hunt

Set and Costume Designer: Jason Southgate

Lighting Designer: Michael Hunt

Production Media Designer: Armin Ferrari and Mauro Merlino

Photographer: Franco Tutino

Images 1 & 2
The Trojan Women

Images 3 & 4
The Tyrant

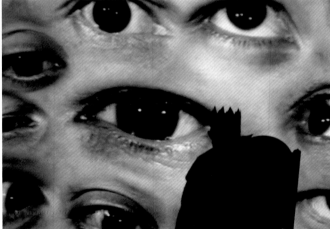

1/
GABRIELLA SLADE
SET AND COSTUME DESIGN

HOW DO YOU EAT AN ELEPHANT
Devised (2014)

National Youth Theatre Wales
Aberystwyth Arts Centre, Dowlais Engine House & Cardiff City Hall
September 2014

GS: National Youth Theatre Wales' devised production focused on verbatim theatre and the presenting, solving and answering of life's most probing, trivial and sometimes bizarre questions like 'Why don't birds get electrocuted on phone lines?', 'What's the point of Made In Chelsea?' and 'What time is it on the moon?'

The main stimulus to the questions was the use of social media – Facebook, Twitter and recording people's responses at street interviews. It was important that the design could facilitate experimental ways to present information as there needed to be constant connections between performers and audience members. The space needed to feel interactive.

Inspiration came from the set up and themes of Adam Buxton's 'Bug' and the 90s children's science programme 'How 2'. The neon and UV reactive Rubik's cubic pod setting represented a contemporary /retro approach to a TV game show. The adaptable, multi-functional structure was a representation of the puzzling issues in the play. Large scale grids incorporating the questions in both Welsh and English added a technological dimension and perspective to the space. They provided the transition between questions and the physical change of performance space. In collaboration with the lighting, the set could transform into an otherworldly space for demonstrations. The design process involved the incorporation of AV, live sound and film making.

Director: Jude Christian
Set and Costume Designer: Gabriella Slade
Lighting Designer: Joshua Pharo
Sound Designer: Joe White
Film Makers: Isolde Godfrey & Claire Nolan
Photographer: Robert Workman

2/
GABRIELLA SLADE
COSTUME DESIGN

IN THE HEIGHTS
Lin-Manuel Miranda & Quiara Algeria Hudes (1999)

Runaway Entertainment
Southwark Playhouse
May 2014

GS: The main aim of the costume design for In The Heights was to encompass and express the environment and culture of Washington Heights. The musical hits on the dreams and desires of the residents. The racial make-up of the neighbourhood is predominately of Dominican origin but also with denizens of Puerto Rican, Cuban and Hispanic descent.

The score is a blast of rap, hip hop and salsa and represents the simmering passions of the locals. This was a huge reference point in the design process. I focused on the fusion between urban American street style and the authentic cultural taste and fashion of the characters' personality and heritage. However, the costumes also had to style together as I wanted the characters to show a strong sense of community as they referenced, blended and juxtaposed with takis's split level set design. The set was an industrial combination of metal, scaffolding, bodega signage and rust, allowing for an abundance of colour and energy to come from the costumes.

I referenced local street art, graffiti and the colours of the train lines with a strong theme of high energy and intense heat, which is so vividly present in the script. I wanted the costumes to feel contemporary but with a sun-bleached, acid wash texture; to represent the run-down environment and the lack of money, as well as a deep rooted vibrancy and diversity. In some cases I chose edgy neon accessories or pieces to enhance and contradict the distressed garments.

Director: Luke Sheppard
Choreographer: Drew McOnie
Set Designer: takis
Costume Designer: Gabriella Slade
Lighting Designer: Howard Hudson
Sound Designer: Gareth Owen
Photographer: Robert Workman

3/
GABRIELLA SLADE
SET AND COSTUME DESIGN

DEAD BORN GROW
Frantic Assembly

Frantic Assembly & National Youth Theatre Wales
Aberwyswth Arts Centre, Galeri Caernarfon,
Taliesen
Swansea & Blue Room WMC
August 2013

GS: Dead Born Grow was a collaboration between Frantic Assembly and National Youth Theatre Wales. Based on ensemble work this devised piece explored the themes and trials of the young and adolescent in society and social situations. Because the production was heavily based in physical theatre, space was integral to the design. Flats attached to trolleys, could alter and change the bare space in dramatically choreographed movements, not reflecting a physical or recognisable place but abandoned surreal places or wasteland.

My key inspiration for the use of clothes lines came from looking at the work of installation artists Kaarina Kaikkonen and Guerra del la Paz. Their sculptural installations consist entirely of clothing and explore the manifestation of memories, presence, identity, modern conflict and consumerism, which seemed entirely relevant to what we were trying to express through 'Dead Born Grow'.

The clothes gauze and piles of clothes provided a density of textural colour with a simplicity that worked well with the lighting and the AV providing a very telling, unsettling and controlled method of portraying the desires of/for social adhesion and unstable, constantly changing emotions. A wardrobe through which members could disappear enhanced a sense of loss and abandonment, while the sofa enabled domestic issues to be raised. Because the space didn't have an era or identity, it enabled strange and alternative choices of lighting and eclectic music, which helped the performers to be figurative, show character defamation and the social concerns of teenage life.

Director: Eddie Kay & Jessica Williams
Choreographer: Eddie Kay & Jessica Williams
Set and Costume Designer: Gabriella Slade
Lighting Designer: Andy Purves
Sound Designer: Ethan Forde
AV designer: Ethan Forde
Photographer: Kirsten McTernan

Images 1 & 2
How Do You Eat
An Elephant

Image 3
In The Heights

Images 4-6
Dead Born Grow

Image 1
Father Christmas

Image 2 & 3
Glengarry Glen Ross

1/
ZOE SQUIRE
SET AND COSTUME DESIGN

FATHER CHRISTMAS
Raymond Briggs (1973),
Pins and Needles (2012)

Pins and Needles and Lyric Hammersmith
Co-production
Lyric Hammersmith / West Yorkshire Playhouse
November 2013

ZS: Adapting the much-loved children's book Father Christmas by Raymond Briggs for the stage for the first time has been one of the biggest and most exciting challenges of my career so far. How do you bring one of the world's most famous characters to life; take the audience on a journey around the entire world in 45 minutes; and make this all believable to a 4 year old?

The design process started on day one of the Pins and Needles adaptation. Finding the right balance of story, characters and inventive design to take your audience on a journey through sunset, rain, fog, snow, sunrise and travel around the world all in one space! Where else do you get to create such a memorable and magical encounter: a close up of Father Christmas' sleigh taking off, pulled by puppeteered galloping reindeer.

Director: Emma Earle

Set and Costume Designer: Zoe Squire

Lighting Designer: George Ogilvie

Sound Designer: Lucy Rivers

Puppet Designer: Max Humphries

Photographers: Lyric Hammersmith: Simon Annand;
West Yorkshire Playhouse: Keith Pattison

2/
ZOE SQUIRE
SET AND COSTUME DESIGN

GLENGARRY GLEN ROSS
David Mamet (1983)

Engage and Pins and Needles Productions
Theatre Royal Bath/Ustinov Studio
May/2013

ZS: Four salesmen are locked in a cut-throat competition to sell real-estate – the winner gets a Cadillac, the loser gets the sack. David Mamet's classic is a masterpiece of tight, taut dialogue with a searing emotional kick.

I wanted to create a visual interpretation of Mamet's script that would challenge the all-male cast of professional and non-professional actors from the theatre's engage program.

The set was designed to paint a glossy picture of the American real-estate business, but then allowed the audience to see the reality; its fakeness and its cracks; rubbish towering around the edges, hidden behind posters idealising the American dream. The cage-like walls and dirt seeping through the office carpet tiles seemed to trap the actors like animals.

Changing the locations where events take place allowed me to create a more interesting and versatile design: a restaurant; a burger trailer; a crowded commuter train; the back streets; a bar. Adding these visual transitions allowed us to introduce surreal physical movement into an otherwise static piece and create a filmic feel.

Director: Emma Earle

Choreographer: Paul and Rae Chantry

Set and Costume Designer: Zoe Squire

Lighting Designer: Paul Green

Sound Designer: Sam Halmarack

Photographer: Paul Blakemore

1/
TAKIS
SET AND COSTUME DESIGN

THE JUNGLE BOOK
Rudyard Kipling (1894),
Stage adaptation by Stuart Paterson (2008)

Citizens Theatre, Glasgow
November 2013

T: The motivation behind the design was to create a modern, urban jungle by using recycled materials, strong florescent colours, concrete blocks, animal print tires and other elements. In this stage environment the performers were able to act, perform acrobatics, play instruments, create sounds by using recycled materials, climb up ropes and into the boxes. The animal costumes were inspired by pop culture, for example in the monkeys' knitted balaclavas and sports wear, for Balloo a knitted onesie and for Baghira a Geek chic look.

Director: Nikolai Foster
Choreographer: Cressida Carré
Set and Costume Designer: takis
Lighting Designer: James Whiteside
Music: BB Cooper
Lyrics: Rudyard Kipling and Barb Jungr
Orchestration: Sarah Travis
Photographer: Tim Morozzo

2/
TAKIS
SET AND COSTUME DESIGN

WEST SIDE STORY
Based on a conception of Jerome Robbins,
Book by Arthur Laurents
Music by Leonard Bernstein,
Lyrics by Stephen Sondheim (1957)

National Youth Music Theatre
Victoria Warehouse, Manchester
August 2013

T: The vast space of the Victoria Warehouse empowered this site specific design, the red brick walls in conjunction with the use of five reclaimed shipping containers, staircases and ladders transported us to NYC. The different coloured containers created microcosms for specific scenes, but also macrocosms creating a modern and evocative approach to the Manhattan neighbourhood. The live 30 piece orchestra was incorporated and accommodated within the set. Playing with colour and 1950's patterns, the costumes had a contemporary feel. Colour, shapes and architecture were used conceptually to support the visual dramaturgy of this iconic musical.

Director: Nikolai Foster
Choreographer: Drew McOnie
Musical Director: Tom Deering
Set and Costume Designer: takis
Lighting Designer: Ben Cracknell
Sound Designer: Tom Marshall
Photographer: Matt Hargraves

3/
TAKIS
SET AND COSTUME DESIGN

OTTONE
George Friederic Handel (1719)

English Touring Opera
Hackney Empire & National Tour
October 2014

T: The design is inspired by Byzantine art and architecture. The set comprises three sections of Byzantine apses. The interiors are hand painted with golden mosaics inspired by Ravenna & Agia Sophia (Istanbul). Their exteriors are an amalgamation of metals, mainly copper with verdigris and lichen accents creating structures that set the battlefield scenes. The apses rotate into a number of different configurations creating new compositions, reflecting the emotional landscapes of the opera. They are enclosed by a brooding blue clouded landscape. Light and shadow, absence and presence support the psychological journey of each character on their path towards their destiny.

Director: James Conway
Conductor: Jonathan Peter Kenny
Libretto by Nicola Francesco Haym
English Translation by Andrew Porter & James Conway
Set and Costume Designer: takis
Lighting Designer: Lee Curran
Photographer: Robert Workman

Images 1 & 2
The Jungle Book

Images 3 & 4
West Side Story

Images 5 & 6
Ottone

LAURA JANE STANFIELD
SET, COSTUME,
PRODUCTION/MEDIA DESIGN

PARALLEL LIVES
(2012)

Claque Theatre
Parish Church, Hartfield, Sussex
July 2012

LJS: Parallel Lives was a community play written for the residents of Hartfield village in Sussex by Jon Oram. The play, performed in promenade, jumped between Edwardian Hartfield, the 1930s and present day. I created a simple abstract set comprising four permanent stages and four portable stages. We used projection and shadow puppetry to recreate anything from elaborate ballrooms, the trees of Ashdown Forest to the trenches of the first world war. The costumes were essential markers of the period and sometimes became part of the set to create magical jumps in time. We also created a medieval 'play-within-a-play' with hand painted costumes inspired by the stained glass windows of the 16th century church in which we were performing.

Director: Jon Oram
Set and Costume Designer:
Laura Jane Stanfield
Lighting Designer: Jack Kelly
Production Media Designer:
Laura Jane Stanfield

Images
Parallel Lives

SHEREE TAMS
COSTUME DESIGN

IMPRINTS
Michael Spence (2011)

Theatre Gargantua
Factory Theatre Studio
November 2011

ST: We imagine our ancestors through a window called genetic memory and visualization. Imprints is a play about the thousands and thousands of strangers that make up our lineage and how their experiences are manifested in our instincts, fears and dreams.

Director: Jacquie P.A. Thomas
Set Designer: Michael Spence
Costume Designer: Sheree Tams
Lighting Designer: Laird Macdonald
Photographers: Michael Cooper/Sheree Tams

Images
Imprints

1/
IAN TEAGUE
SET AND COSTUME DESIGN

ROUND THE TWIST - OR OLIVER NICKELFIELDS BLEAK LITTLE TALE OF TWO MUTUAL EXPECTATIONS. AND SON.
Brendan Murray (2011)

Eastern Angles
Sir John Mills Theatre Ipswich and tour
November 2011

IT: Round The Twist –or Oliver Nickelfields Bleak Little Tale of Two Mutual Expectations. And Son, was a Christmas show that was very much for adults. Take all the bits of Dickens you half remember from BBC Sunday afternoon adaptations and mix together with a fiendishly complicated plot that travelled between East Anglia and Victorian London and back again several times, add some Steam Punk inventions, a few songs and a mass of bad puns and old jokes and you have the Eastern Angles Christmas show 2011.

The Old Curiosity Shop became Lidl Nells cut price store and was inhabited by such characters as the Jammy Dodger, Miss Haversack, Fogerty and an Aged Parent who has been busy inventing edible shoes (The Beef Wellington) a steam powered spittoon and The Bah Humbug (a sweet that tasted like a roast Lamb dinner).

The script mixed references to actual Dickens stories with a completely invented narrative. In a similar way the design took references from both steam punk imagery and real Victorian patent drawings to create a world that was at one time familiar and surprising.

Director: Ivan Cutting
Set and Costume Designer: Ian Teague
Lighting Designer: Penny Griffin
Photographer: Ian Teague

2/
IAN TEAGUE
SET AND COSTUME DESIGN

GIANT TOURS
Devised (2012)

MakeBelieve Arts
Schools Tour
January 2012

IT: Giant Tours was an interactive participatory show for 5 - 9 year olds which provided first theatre experiences to children in London, Essex, Swindon and Bristol. Funded by The Welcome Trust and The Arts Council, the show used video, sound, puppetry and physical participation to engage children in learning about the body and how it works.

A giant girl has become sick and the children have to help find out what is wrong with her and how to help her. To do this they have to understand what is happening inside her body and train up one of the actors to "go in and clear the blockage".

We never see the giant but her doll gives us a clue about how big she might be. The set included a large map of the body and six movable abstract curved shapes. These shapes moved to create playing spaces that related to various parts of the body including the brain, the stomach and the rib cage. The audience participated at various times taking on roles such as bits of food, viruses and white blood cells.

Director: Trish Lee
Set and Costume Designer: Ian Teague
Sound Designer: David Baird
Photographer: Ian Teague

Images 1 & 2
Round The Twist

Image 3
Giant Tours

1/
YANNIS THAVORIS
SET AND COSTUME DESIGN

TOSCA
Giaccomo Puccini (1900)

Santa Fe Opera
Crosby Theater
June 2012

YT: Following an earlier very different production of the opera (updated to 1968) with the same director, the challenge here was to find a fresh way to set it in its proper period and locations for the wide and low stage of the Crosby Theater in Santa Fe.

We tilted the view-point, with the detailed chapel dome becoming a rich backdrop and the large framed painting becoming the main acting area. The transformations of the set were largely in full view of the audience. In the final seconds of the first act the front half of the painting tilted up to become the crumbling fresco of the second act. This, in turn, came down at the top of the third act to reveal the cupolas of the Roman skyline.

Director: Stephen Barlow
Set and Costume Designer: Yannis Thavoris
Lighting Designer: Duane Schuler
Photographer: Yannis Thavoris

2/
YANNIS THAVORIS
SET AND COSTUME DESIGN

THE LADY FROM THE SEA
Craig Armstrong (2012)

Scottish Opera
Kings Theatre Edinburgh
August 2012

YT: The mirrored side walls and flown back wall of the set allowed it to be fluidly transformed from domestic interior to limitless exterior, or to abstract psychological space. The heroine's complex symbolic relationship with water was explored through layers of rear and front video projection, selectively animating her world, be it wall panels or individual pieces of furniture. A dried red coral branch on the table (also echoed on her corset and dress details) was a subliminal reminder of her isolation from her natural state.

Director: Harry Fehr
Choreographer: Kally Lloyd Jones
Set and Costume Designer: Yannis Thavoris
Lighting Designer: Warren Letton
Video Designer: Finn Ross
Photographer: Yannis Thavoris

Image
Tosca

3/
YANNIS THAVORIS
SET AND COSTUME DESIGN

L'ENFANT PRODIGUE / FRANCESCA DI FOIX
Claude Debussy / Gaetano Donizetti (1884 / 1831)

Silk Street Theatre Theatre Company
Guildhall School of Music and Drama
November 2013

YT: The two works demanded a different aesthetic treatment, but using as many common design elements as possible.

L'Enfant Prodigue was set in a muted, nostalgic world, rooted in the time of the work's creation (1880s) rather than in the biblical past of the parable that it is based on.

The Renaissance court of Francesca di Foix was playfully transposed onto a contemporary Parisian fashion house, with the jousting tournament of the opera's conclusion becoming a tennis tournament. The costumes straddled the two periods eclectically.

Director: Stephen Barlow
Choreographer: Victoria Newlyn
Set and Costume Designer: Yannis Thavoris
Lighting Designer: David Howe
Photographer: Yannis Thavoris

Images
L'Enfant Prodigue / Francesca Di Foix

Image
The Lady From The Sea

Images
Grimes On The Beach

1/
LESLIE TRAVERS
SET AND COSTUME DESIGN

GRIMES ON THE BEACH
Benjamin Britten / Montagu Slater (1945)

Aldeburgh Beach, Norfolk
June 2013

LT: Peter Grimes had never been produced as a performance in Benjamin Britten's Aldeburgh, even though Britten spent much of his life in the seaside town, starting the Aldeburgh Festival and setting Grimes there. As part the Aldeburgh Festival's celebration of Brittens birth centenary it was decided to explore the feasibility of a Grimes premiere in Aldeburgh, although the Snape Maltings concert hall is too small to hold a full production.

One evening Tim Albery, the director, and

I sat on the beach staring out to sea. A view so familiar to Britten, it encapsulated, and was perhaps the catalyst for, the music of the piece. It became apparent that the hostile space between land and water could hold the key to doing something that could never be done in a conventional theatrical space. A high risk venture, the North Sea coast, prone to sudden storms and turbulent weather, could potentially play a part in the piece.

The shoreline became my starting point. I wanted to create something that felt as if it had always been there and was affected by its often brutal environment. With this in mind I designed a dilapidated structure reminiscent of an English promenade, battered by the elements and a constant reminder of the ferocity of this land-seascape. I wanted the structure, not only to make the performance visible to the 2000 plus audience, many of whom were sat on the shingle itself, but to have

a floating fragility below which the sea roared and the ever-changing sky would be embraced as vital components of the narrative.

It was decided to pre record the orchestra as fragile instruments do not take kindly to damp salt air but the majority of the singing was live. Performances were timed so that darkness fell during the performance.

Director: Tim Albery
Set and Costume Cesigner: Leslie Travers
Lighting Designer: Lucy Carter
Photographer: Robert Workman

Images
Jenůfa

2/
LESLIE TRAVERS
SET AND COSTUME DESIGN

JENŮFA
Leoš Janáček

Malmö Opera, Sweden
November 2011

LT: The aim of the design was to propel the characters through the piece. The set, from the beginning, was reconfigured in its deconstruction in one continuous action, which, by the end placed the characters in a radically new landscape. In this action the set brought each character into focus at the right point, concurrently reducing the emphasis on the characters not to the fore at each relevant point, and opening, gradually, what was to come by the conclusion of the piece. A sharp simplicity with no extraneous detail was the constant aim.

Using the vast stage at Malmö Opera we were able to create a sense of an isolated society with only glancing links to the outside world. Characters could not simply walk off stage into the wings. Somewhere they were present in an orbit around Jenůfa herself. I was able to utilise the space to give the fullest effect to my design and concept.

Director: Orpha Phelan
Set and Costume Designer: Leslie Travers
Lighting Designer: Thomas Hase
Choreographer: Lynne Hockney

1/
MAIRA VAZEOU
SET AND COSTUME DESIGN

THE THREE PRINCESSES WHO SUNG & DANCED
Stratis Panourios (2010)

THOC Theatre Organisation Of Cyprus
Touring
January 2012

2/
MAIRA VAZEOU
SET AND COSTUME DESIGN

MEDEA
Euripides (431 BC)

Theatre Lab Company
Riverside Studios
March 2014

MV: The Three Princesses is a musical piece for children that tells the story of three girls who, after the loss of their father, try to bring music and dance back to their household through dream sequences.

Performed both for entertainment and educational purposes, the set had to be adjustable and expandable to fit various theatre spaces and halls yet retain enough open space for dance and be easily transported.

The ideas were based on the multiple use of objects and their symbiotic relationships, the juxtaposition of their purpose within the dramatic action and artistic merit through performance narrative. Coverlets, for example, through music and choreography were changing from a functional object to colourful dresses and headboards when dream sequences were talking place.

Director: Stratis Panourios
Composer: Giorgos Hatzipieris
Set and Costume Designer: Maira Vazeou
Lighting Designer: Giorgos Koukoumas
Photographer: Maira Vazeou

MV: The woman who lives her life on the edge. The lover who poisons her rival. The mother who kills her own children.

I created two levels on a long and narrow theatre space; two different worlds. On the higher level Medea, who is isolated in her own grief and madness, observes from above her husband's moments of joy and happiness in his new found life which drives her to pursue justice and vengeance.

On the lower level a cheerful wedding scene is taking place upon a stage full of gravel until Medea's intervention. Gradually the wedding table changes to rocks, a killing pool and graves. The white balloons portray the hopes of the ceremony and at the same time the holding on to and letting go of something.

Director: Anastasia Revi
Composer: Daemonia Nymphe
Set Designer: Maira Vazeou
Costume Designer: Mayou Trikerioti
Lighting Designer: Yiannis Katsaris
Photographers: Maira Vazeou, Yiannis Katsaris

Images 1 & 2
Medea

Image 3
The Three Princesses Who
Sung and Danced

The Three Princesses Who Sung & Danced

Girls Nighties
The Doll
The Mother
The Boys
'The Holiday Song'
The Girls
'The Song Of The Melted Shoes'
First Dream
'Tarantella'
Second Dream
'The song Of The Curtains'
Waltz
Third Dream
'The Colour Song'

1/
MAYOU TRIKERIOTI
SET AND COSTUME DESIGN

ALL STONES, ALL SIDES
Samuel Beckett 1960's

Maria Theatre Company
Young Vic, London

MT: In this Young Vic Taking Part production, 80 students performed a collection of Samuel Beckett's short plays. Responding to the texts and their needs, I also had to consider the most important factor of how to facilitate 'non-performers' in the space and also allowing enough space for all of them to move freely, I chose to build them a 'make-believe Beckett house'. Through grounding them in a familiar yet abstract space, it restricted but also set them free to explore, understand and perform Beckett's pieces.

Director: Finn Beames
Set and Costume Designer: Mayou Trikerioti
Lighting Designer: Emma Chapman
Sound Designer: Cosmo Sheldrake / Amy Bramma
Photographers: Helen Murray / Mayou Trikerioti

2/
MAYOU TRIKERIOTI
SET AND COSTUME DESIGN

ALL WORK + NO PLAY (2011)
Pequod

Athens Festival / Pireos 260
June 2011

MT: A huge industrial space was the setting for this devised piece on work and routine in modern life and most importantly in Greece right at the dawn of the economic crisis.

I decided not to hide the elements of the space, but use them and accentuate reality. In the centre, I placed a big scaffolding, a modern apartment building of sorts. Big industrial lamps lit the space, and the scaffolding was mirrored in the surrounding windows of the space. The concrete floor (visible to all from the steep raked seating) was stencilled in all ways that the ground marks modern life under our feet: Parking space numbers, zebra crossings, yellow lines, and playfully, a large exit sign pointing to the actual fire exit of the building.

Director: Dimitris Xanthopoulos
Choreographer: Zoe Chatziantoniou
Set and Costume Designer: Mayou Trikerioti
Lighting Designer: Tasos Paleoroutas
Photographer: Mayou Trikerioti

Images 1 & 2   Images 3-5
All Stones, All Sides 1   All Work + No Play

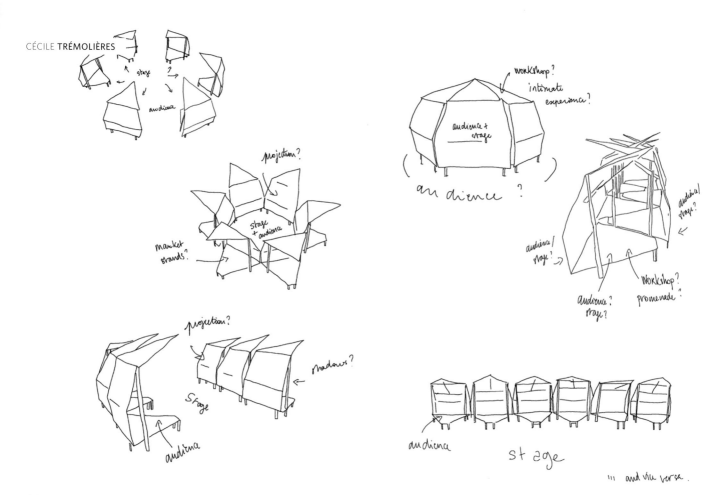

1/
CÉCILE TRÉMOLIÈRES
SET DESIGN

IMPERMANENT THEATRE
Impermanence Dance Theatre
(2014)

*Impermanence Dance Theatre
Touring music festivals: Taghore
Festival, Kelburn Garden Party,
Kendal Calling, Beacons,
Shambala, Bestival
June 2014*

CT: Impermanence Dance Theatre is a young dance company who create in the moment, without rehearsing their shows but accumulating material that will then be used, and transformed, according to their audience and the space they are in.

They were looking for "a structure or device, that has an innate quality and aesthetic depth to it, but is broad, open, and adaptable.... Something that is beautiful in itself, and will act as a way to frame the work." Touring in outdoor spaces, having no idea of the show they will have to do, I could not try to design for the show or the specific space, but to focus on the frame that they needed, thinking of space as being tangible and unexpected.

I decided to create a hexagon shaped structure, made out of six triangular pieces, adaptable to any terrain, that could be arranged in different configurations, giving the company the choice to respond to different spaces, assembling it as an open-air theatre, a promenade performance, an intimate auditorium, a corridor... In collaboration with the architect Patrick Morris, I created a simple wooden base that will grow in response to each performance, able to develop and evolve. The audience, as well as the company, is encouraged to engrave, stick, transform, draw and/or drape things to the structure.

Choreographer:
Impermanence Dance Theatre

Set Designer: Cécile Trémolières
In collaboration with architect
Patrick Morris

Costume Designer:
Impermanence Dance Theatre

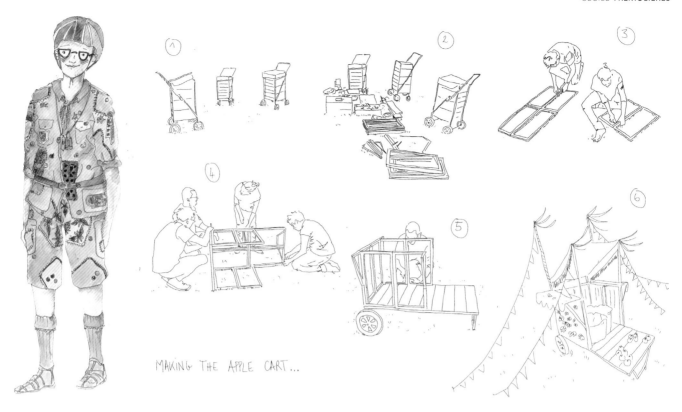

MAKING THE APPLE CART...

2/
CÉCILE TRÉMOLIÈRES
SET DESIGN

THE APPLE CART
FanSHEN (2014)

FanSHEN
Music festivals: Exceter, Latitude, Green Man, Tooting Foodival
May 2014

CT: The Apple Cart is touring around music festivals to tell the story of sisters Meryl, Beryl and Cheryl, on their way to Buckingham Palace with a carload of magic apples for the Queen, cleaning toilets in music festivals.

FanSHEN is a theatre company, committed to sustainable design. They wanted me to design a set that will be able to tour by train, carried by the company.

In collaboration with designer Chris Gylee, I created a set that could fit in three old lady's trolleys that the characters drag with them around the country. The cart is made out of ten metallic frames, easy to be bolted together by the company. As the cart needs to be seen, and heard, in the busy festival fields, we added to this frame flowery patterns oil cloth, big lacy pants, J-cloth buntings, pools and ribbons, games, a pop-up tent, a pedal-powered soundtrack and of course a lot of magic apples.

Director: Rachel Briscoe & Dan Barnard

Set Designer: Cécile Trémolières
in collaboration with Chris Gylee

Photographer: Nyisha Bill-Eteson

Images 1 & 2   Image 3 - 5
Impermanent Theatre   Apple Cart

Images 1 & 2
Vanessa and Virginia

Images 3 & 4
The Tempest

1/
KATE UNWIN
SET AND COSTUME DESIGN

VANESSA AND VIRGINIA
Elizabeth Wright (2010)

Moving Stories
Riverside Studios
March 2013

KU: This play explored the lives and relationships of sisters Vanessa Bell and Virginia Woolf. Their almost mythologised worlds, both actual and imaginary, and the rich visual and literary landscapes they created and left behind were my starting point.

I immersed myself in the work they produced and the way they lived. Visits to their house at Charleston in the South Downs were a major source of inspiration and I wanted to create a rich and detailed backdrop which was directly connected to them as artists and women. The floor needed to be kept clear for movement sequences so I created a canopy of fragments from their lives which they interacted with. Props and costumes were hung along with objects, letters, photos which were drawn from the months of research. A watery, fluid backdrop and a paint splattered floor defined the space.

The play covered their lives from children until their deaths and all changes happened onstage, so the costumes were layered and manipulated to convey the passing of time. I designed their costumes using photos, descriptions of their dress and paintings by Vanessa.

This production was nominated for Best Set Design in The Off West End Awards.

Director: Emma Gersch
Choreographer: Kitty Randle
Set and Costume Designer: Kate Unwin
Lighting and Sound Designer: George Seal
Photographer: Ben Caplan

2/
KATE UNWIN
SET AND COSTUME DESIGN

THE TEMPEST
William Shakespeare (1610)

Moving Stories
The Minack Theatre, Cornwall
July 2014

KU: We set the play in today's world. Prospero was a yoga guru whose new-age leanings had eventually got him thrown out of Milanese society.

Miranda, who had never seen another human being before had created an installation of the colourful bits of plastic washed up on the shore. Caliban created his gods out of the junk he had found on the island and Prospero had his spiritual healing books, wind chimes and buddhas.

Prospero, Miranda, Ariel and the spirits wore yoga outfits and the spirits wore dresses I hand stitched and dyed for the banquet and marriage scenes. I was inspired by oceanic organisms and spectacular pink sea fan forests and anemone reefs which live under the sea beneath the Minack itself.

Director: Emma Gersch
Choreographer: Kitty Randle
Set and Costume Designer: Kate Unwin
Lighting Designer: Matt Vale
Sound Designer: Matthew Reeve
Photographer: Lynn Batten

1/
JANET VAUGHAN
SET, COSTUME AND LIGHTING DESIGN

THE OAKMOBILE
Talking Birds for the National Trust (2013)

Talking Birds
Parks and open spaces in and around Birmingham.
June 2013

JV: The OakMobile was conceived in response to a commission from the National Trust in Birmingham and contains a mini theatre for an audience of about 6 at a time. It is home to the Story Collector who travels around collecting and telling stories for the people who visit the OakMobile.

I wanted the outside to reflect the OakMobile's surroundings; to give it a degree of camouflage, whilst also distorting familiar views to afford visitors an unexpected or fresh perspective on their environment. The architecture is a mash up of several Midlands National Trust properties together with key points of the Birmingham skyline (such as Selfridges and Spaghetti Junction). Inside, the OakMobile is totally different – a starlit woodland glade teeming with brightly coloured insects – just the place for a magical make believe theatre experience...

Director: Ola Animashawun

Set and Costumes Designer: Janet Vaughan

Lighting Designer: Janet Vaughan

Sound Designer: Derek Nisbet

Production/Media Designer: Janet Vaughan

Construction: Jonathan Ford

Photographer: Janet Vaughan

2/
JANET VAUGHAN
SET, COSTUME AND LIGHTING DESIGN

CAPSULE
Talking Birds (2010)

Talking Birds
Helen Martin Studio, Warwick Arts Centre
November 2011

JV: Capsule was a short immersive theatre piece created from materials available during a short residence in an empty warehouse space. It was devised around the re-use of a 3m x 2m pod that I'd originally designed for a conference. The audience sat inside the pod. The action happened in the large space outside of the capsule, so was mainly experienced through the rich soundscape (a mix of live and recorded sound) and live action glimpsed through the doorways at either end.

The show placed the audience within the journey that the capsule was taking, and it rapidly changed from boat to submarine to cable car to helicopter to spaceship throughout that journey. The final twist came as the audience docked, and realised the show they had just experienced had been performed by the previous audience – and it was now their turn to inhabit all those characters and perform for the next audience.

Director: Talking Birds

Set, Costume and Lighting Designer: Janet Vaughan

Sound Designer: Derek Nisbet

Construction: Andy Martin

Photographer: Edmund Collier

Images 1 & 2   Images 3 & 4
The Oakmobile   Capsule

Images
The Wonderful
Wizard Of Oz

ELIZABETH WRIGHT
SET AND COSTUME DESIGN

THE WONDERFUL WIZARD OF OZ
Based on the novel by L. Frank Baum (1900)
Adapted by Anna Clarkson, Julia Hogan,
Chris Hoyle, Terry Hughes, Mark Murphy, Eve Steele,
Jill Stephenson and Jennifer Tuckett (2011)

Octagon Theatre, Bolton
November 2011

EW: In this adaptation of the novel by L. Frank Baum,
created by writers at the Octagon Theatre, Bolton,
Dorothy believes that she has been transported by
a tornado from her home in Bolton to the Land of
Oz – a fantastical place filled with fairground and
circus imagery and characters. Staged in the round,
the transformation from Bolton to Oz took place in
front of the audience, with the distinctive black and
white awnings of Bolton Market becoming brightly
coloured fairground stalls. Sparkling patches of yellow
brick road were revealed around the auditorium and
a swirling monochrome floor was lit from below with
star shapes, glowing in different colours as Dorothy
made her journey from the Land of the Munchkins to
the Emerald City. Aspects of the Octagon's existing
architecture were transformed, with a balcony
becoming a hot air balloon and the well-worn
auditorium brickwork given a coat of sparkle.

Director: Elizabeth Newman

Set and Costume Designer: Elizabeth Wright

Lighting Designer: Ciaran Bagnall

Sound Designer: Andy Smith

Dramaturg: Elizabeth Newman

Composer and Musical Director: Barbara Hockaday

Associate Artist (Movement): Lesley Hutchison

Scenic Artists: Ged Mayo, Imogen Peer

Wardrobe Supervisor: Mary Horan

Costume Makers: Mary Rudkin, Carole Burke,
Alison Kirkpatrick

Costume and Prop Maker: Julie Ann Heskin

Photographer: Ian Tilton

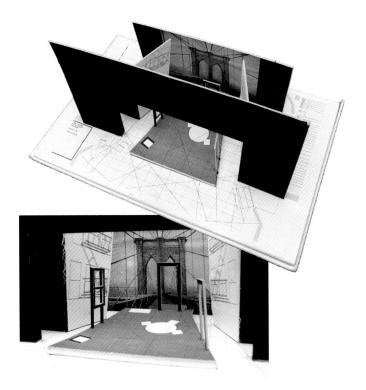

1/
JAMES WATSON
SET DESIGN

A VIEW FROM THE BRIDGE
Arthur Miller (1955)

Leicester Drama Society
The Little Theatre, Leicester
February 2011

JW: 1950's America - a New York tenement, sat in the shadow of the Brooklyn Bridge. The bold perspective encloses the space, illustrating the weight and intensity of society at the time, looking in at and threatening the private affairs of the individual. Suspicion was at the heart of American society, where neighbour turned on neighbour in fear of 'Un-American Activities'. However, among its illegal immigrant population, there was a strong sense of unity – their very existence depended on it. It is this unity that is put under scrutiny, the raised performance space acting as a pedestal, spotlighting the seemingly innocent affairs of family life, while society itself becomes the walls, the external restrictions that keep the characters caged. This unrelentingly drama is accentuated by the claustrophobic gloom of the set and lighting effects.

Director: Bryan Stanion
Set Designer: James Watson
Costume Designer: John Bale
Lighting Designer: Martin Scott and Jenny Harding
Sound Designer: Richard Payton
Photographer: James Watson

2/
JAMES WATSON
SET DESIGN

DICK WHITTINGTON
Nadine Beasley, Victoria Blasdale and Paul Beasley (2011)

Leicester Drama Society
The Little Theatre, Leicester
February 2011

JW: I believe the role of scenic design is to offer a portal into another world, a frame in which to hang the production. Pantomime is a world filled with magic and adventure. The opportunity to play freely with the art style, with perspective, and a vivid colour palette is very satisfying and acknowledges the audience's expectation of spectacle. I have a passion for the art of pantomime, but its importance within the theatre industry, the great sense of tradition, its need to be topical and on trend can make it a daunting prospect, especially for a relatively young designer. Pantomime is where theatre can become magical, and is rewarded with the captured imagination of young theatre goers, whom we desperately need to keep inspired if a love of theatre is to remain.

Director: Nadine Beasley
Choreographer: Radojka Radulovic and Louisa Gregory
Set Designer: James Watson
Costume Designer: John Bale
Lighting Designer: Jeremy Thompson and Jane Rowland
Sound Designer: David Atter
Photographer: James Watson
Musical Director: Leigh White

Images 1 & 2
A View From The Bridge

Image 3
Dick Whittington

SIMON WILKINSON
LIGHTING DESIGN

Images
Dragon

DRAGON
Oliver Emanuel

Vox Motus / National Theatre of Scotland / Tianjin People's Arts Theatre
Citizens Theatre, Glasgow (and touring)
October 2013

SW: Tommy can't sleep. He hasn't been able to since his mum died a year ago. Since then, life has gone from bad to worse. His dad is grief-stricken, his big sister ignores him and he's become the target for the school bully. Then one restless night, Tommy goes to the window, throws back the curtain and ... a dragon is looking at him. Straight in the eye.

Dragon is a play without words. Told using puppets, movement, music, illusion, design and light it chronicles Tommy's journey through grief. Taking inspiration from Eastern and Western dragon mythology, Dragon has been presented to acclaim in both the UK and China.

Director: Jamie Harrison & Candice Edmunds
Set Designer: Jamie Harrison
Lighting Designer: Simon Wilkinson
Composer: Tim Phillips
Sound Designer: Mark Melville
Puppet Designer: Jamie Harrison and Guy Bishop
Photographer: Drew Farrell

FIONA WATT
DESIGN AND CURATION

THE MARKETPLACE
Fiona Watt (2013)

World Stage Design 2013
Royal Welsh College of Music and Drama (RWCMD),
Bute Park and City Centre, Cardiff
September 2013

FW: The Marketplace is where things start. Our fleet of custom-made street carts occupied the polished new foyer at RWCMD, Cardiff City Centre and the route between them. They were designed to visibly demonstrate that there is a place for artists and companies who are just starting out among the eminent international community represented in the World Stage Design 2013 exhibition at RWCMD. Their portability was key to generating a physical link between the venue and Cardiff city centre; their animation key to engaging local people of all ages with the event.

Appearing as something-made-from-nothing, the reclaimed bits of timber, that no-one wants from the back of a scrapyard, were fashioned into these curious cabinets on wheels by a team of international student volunteers and small local companies. At the end of WSD community projects and small local businesses, that had a great idea about how to use them next, came to wheel them away. They live on in and around the city as catalysts for future dreams.

Designer and Curator: Fiona Watt

Associate Producers: Sophie jump, Louise Ryder,

Participating Artists and Companies: Almost Human, Yve Blake, Stagebitz, Headstrong, Anne Frank Experience, Bread and Goose, Kyle Legall (National Theatre of Wales), Ivo Kersmaekers (Theatre of the Obsolete), Sophie Jump, OISTAT, SBTD, Theatr Genedlaethol Cymru, RWCMD Puppetry and catering, Transplantable Garden Project

Construction: RWCMD workshops , Rorie Brophy, Headstrong, Anne Frank Experience, Kyle Legall and an international team of World Stage Design volunteers led by Flor Dias, Valeria Pacchiani and Hattie Ghent

Photographers: Mira Vinzents and Joel Enfield

Images
The Marketplace
at WSD2013

FIONA WATT

AN 'ARTICULATION' OF PROCESS IN RESPONSE TO THE MAKE/BELIEVE QUESTIONS....

WHAT WERE YOU EXPLORING IN YOUR APPROACH TO THE PIECES OF WORK / PROJECT ENTERED FOR MAKE/BELIEVE?

Within this planned international event structure (WSD2013) I was exploring the possibility of providing a platform for artists and companies to test new projects and ideas in a relatively spontaneous way. The idea behind the project was to explore the creative spirit of entrepreneurship that artists and designers have, and set it within the frame of reference of street carts and marketplaces that exist in cities all over the world. A pre-occupation of my own practice is to explore the possibilities of simple, portable structures and interventions in engaging new audiences in urban environments and events they would not usually consider participating in. I am very interested in transience and the impact of the momentary encounter between strangers. I wanted to explore the possibility of World Stage Design being a beginning rather than purely a culmination of months of pre-planned activity. I wanted to make a visible link between RWCMD and the city centre and I wanted the possibility of the arteries of

creative entrepreneurship opened up by the event to continue after the event had finished. Some companies customized their own carts from scratch while others booked cart space for a day or a few hours on carts made by our team of international student volunteers. After the event they were donated to the companies that made them or adopted by theatre companies and community projects around Cardiff. I was particularly thrilled that four were adopted by the community garden project that took part in Transplantable, and they are now used within the gardens, at farmers markets and food festivals, and to engage young people in learning to grow food.

WHAT INFLUENCES AND INSPIRATIONS HAVE CONTRIBUTED TO THIS / YOUR WORK?

I have been inspired by communities I have worked with in the past, particularly long term unemployed young adults who thrived on a means to tell and own stories they had created visually as well as verbally. Designing in these environments relies on simplicity and portability so that each person has a sense of their individual contribution whilst being held as part of a greater whole. These communities are often transient and temporary.

In the UK we seem to be losing the very direct nature of making a living that being a street vendor

or having a market stall provides, and with it a sense of community. Markets often consist of a blend of the regular stallholders who have been there for years and those who turn up on the day and take a chance. This project was inspired by an elderly street vendor that I first photographed in Prague in 2007 and who was still there in the same place on Charles Bridge when I returned in 2011. Having previously created a project with the communities referred to above inspired by Marcel Duchamp's Boites-en-valise, observing the street vendors of Prague led me back to the turn of the century photographer Eugene Atget's Petit Metiers series of images and accompanying essay. This in turn led me to link the urban regeneration that displaced these

I AM VERY INTERESTED IN TRANSIENCE AND THE IMPACT OF THE MOMENTARY ENCOUNTER BETWEEN STRANGERS.

hawkers and street traders to the outskirts of the city, with the way in which communities of artists are now seen as a way of attracting people to invest in previously run down parts of cities.

PLEASE TELL US A LITTLE ABOUT YOUR WORKING PROCESS(ES). DOES IT INCLUDE MODEL MAKING, DRAWING, WORK OTHER 3D METHODS, DIGITAL PROCESSES, OR OTHER? IN WHAT WAYS?

When I work with an existing text, drawing the words that resonate into my sketchbook is very important to me along with storyboarding. The time to make and document these first responses is a vital ritual for me. For projects such as The Marketplace, I am creating a social and political response to something I care about via the prism of a design process. It is a process of mapping and tracking in order to create a sense of reclamation, ownership and future possibility. The projects have a design life, followed by a performative life, followed by an idea or concept that might embrace a future possibility, which is often concluded by writing about the work.

ARE YOU AWARE OF A POLITICAL, SOCIAL OR INTERNATIONAL CONTEXT TO YOUR WORK? IF SO, HOW DOES THIS AFFECT OR CONTRIBUTE TO IT?

My work is driven by the theme of the relationship between people and land – our right to occupy and our right to cross boundaries and thresholds into environments that we may not feel we traditionally belong in or have access to. This started with my design work in Scottish new writing in the late 90s and early 2000s. Coinciding with the establishment of the Scottish parliament, writers emerging at this point, whose work I designed for, such as David Greig, Nicola McCartney, David Harrower and Zinnie Harris continually explored this theme of ownership and identity, building on the historic injustice of clearances and land ownership that are a part of the national Scottish psyche.

I located to my studio in North Kent at a time when this atypically very deprived part of the South East was beginning to become part of the major regeneration plans encompassed by the Thames Gateway Regeneration zone. It seemed as though none of these plans were being communicated out to the communities that lived there, that they did not have a voice. Twenty-five years on from Dockyard closure, arts consultants, brought in to take an overview, described it as a community still in a state of grief at the loss of identity and pride. European funding allowed me to develop projects with these communities that attempted to

restore the sense that this place had an international significance and that young unemployed people who lived here had the possibility of traveling and working beyond its boundaries. Creating miniature model worlds in suitcases allowed us to perform these stories in France and in organisations' and governments' buildings previously considered alienating and authoritative, such as town halls, council chambers, universities, museums and arts centres.

For SIX ACTS at PQ2011 our first site visit as lead artists, to the centre of Prague in November 2009, coincided almost to the day with the 20th anniversary of the Velvet Revolution. Developing an online research dialogue with students and emerging practitioners taking part in the project, was given additional resonance by these specific streets where, twenty years previously, we would not have been able to walk freely, let alone make the micro street interventions that ultimately became our Wayfinding project.

The Marketplace at WSD2013 questioned who was entitled

to be part of this prestigious international event in Cardiff; and, via these objects, created a visual provocation that invited international professionals to engage with locally based practitioners and the city of Cardiff itself. Their portability meant that a perceived barrier between the city and the award winning architecture of the campus was removed. WSD offered the city many legacies, but for all of the carts it was the intention that this was the beginning rather than the end of their life in Cardiff.

WHY IS TAKING PART IN THE SBTD EXHIBITION 2015 IMPORTANT / OF INTEREST TO YOU?

Being a part of the exhibition forces me to articulate my design process in a new way. I am much less interested now in exhibiting artefacts of something that has been, and more interested in finding ways to exhibit that communicate how I feel about the project now, rather than when it was first made.

LOUISE ANN WILSON
LANDSCAPE PERFORMANCE DESIGN

GHOST BIRD
Louise Ann Wilson (2012)

Louise Ann Wilson Company
Langden Valley, Trough of Bowland, Lancashire
Co-commissioned by Green Close, as part of
the Lancashire Witches 400 Programme,
and Live at LICA
September 2012

Images
Production photos from
Ghost Bird

Centre row left and right:
Julia Griffin

Bottom row middle:
Susan Hill

Bottom row right:
Jim Hendley

LAW: Ghost Bird was a silent walking-performance and live-art installation specific to the Langden Valley in the Trough of Bowland, an upland landscape internationally important for its heather moorland, blanket bog and rare birds. The show responded to the local environment and plight of the hen harrier in the North of England.

Referring to the ghostly grey feathers of the male hen harrier and the increasing absence, due to persecution, of nesting pairs in the Trough of Bowland, Ghost Bird celebrated the Hen Harrier's beauty whilst drawing attention to its fragile existence within the north of England. In doing so, the work became a means of reflecting on the journey taken 400 years earlier over the Bowland Fells to Lancaster Castle by the persecuted Pendle Witches.

In Ghost Bird participants walked up the valley, onto the moorland and into silence following signs which marked the place names in the local landscape and the history of the birds presence in the Trough of Bowland. En-route they entered Langden Castle shooting barn, the floor of which was covered in a deep layer of peat from which emerged a watery, womb-like sound-scape and in which an 8 ½ months pregnant woman danced. A peat fire burned in the hearth and in a shadowy corner white garments, lit by candles, hung on coat hooks. The floors of the two adjoining rooms were also covered, one with translucent-white eggs and the other with a snowy carpet of feathers. Onwards up the valley they circumnavigated a mound of spent gun cartridges before climbing a rough track at the top of which came into view a row of feather-like flags pointing upwards to the massive empty sky above. From here a figure, dressed in a ghostly white suit, beckoned then pointed them towards a narrowing valley down which they walked to discover heather-lined shooting butts inside which were nestled men and women naked and vulnerable to the elements.

Creator and Director: Louise Ann Wilson
Choreographer: Nigel Stewart
Production and Media Designer:
Louise Ann Wilson
Performers: Dancer Julia Griffin and a team of life models
Sound Designer: Lisa Whistlecroft
Film Editor: Janan Yakula
Photographer: Manuel Vason

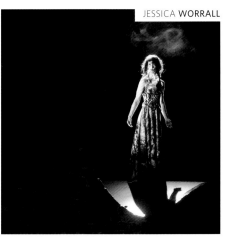

GRIT: GLEN LYON LAMENT

1/
SET AND COSTUME DESIGN

SHE STOOPS TO CONQUER
Oliver Goldsmith (1773)

Northern Broadsides
National Tour
August 2014

JW: I wanted to create something that emphasized the constraining nature of the rural society setting, so using the idea of 18th Century folding screens I expanded it to create two giant folding screens that function as walls whilst also enclosing the action to create a chamber piece atmosphere. The screens are covered with enlarged digital prints of Gainsborough landscapes and taxidermy bringing the exterior world inside. Designing for Broadsides is always a challenge as they play traverse, proscenium and in the round venues so the design has to be able to be reconfigured for each one without losing its essence. Perhaps because of this, costume is always a huge part of the story telling. Here we used strong colours and a heightened sense of realism, mixing 18th century fashion with modern fabrics to underscore the performance style.

Director: Conrad Nelson
Choreographer: Matthew Bugg
Set and Costume Designer: Jessica Worrall
Lighting Designer: Mark Howland
Photographer: Nobby Clark

2/
COSTUME DESIGN

GRIT – THE MARTYN BENNETT STORY
Kieran Hurley (2014)

Pachamama Productions with Tramway
and Comar
Tramway Glasgow
May 2014

JW: Grit is a Scots-Canadian site-specific production based on the life and music of one of Scotland's most pioneering and influential musicians: the late Martyn Bennett. The intensely biographical nature of the piece made me feel that the real life characters Martyn, his family and friends had to be as true to life as possible, so we referenced many personal photos taken during Martyn's life to get the detail exactly right. The other aspect of the costume design was that the dancers and trapeze artist, for me, functioned more as an embodiment of Martyn's music within the piece. To reflect this we created fabric designs using images of Scottish landscapes that were digitally printed which we then made into more contemporary clothes.

Director: Cora Bissett
Choreographer: Dana Gingras
Set and Lighting Designer: Kai Fischer
Costume Designer: Jessica Worrall
Sound Designer: Garry Boyle
Production Media Designer: Kim Beveridge
Photographers: Andrew Wilson, BJ Stewart
and John Wilkie

3/
SET AND COSTUME DESIGN

WE ARE THREE SISTERS
Blake Morrison (2011)

Northern Broadsides
National Tour
September 2011

JW: We Are Three Sisters is a reworking of Chekhov's Three Sisters to tell the famous story of the Bronte sisters; set exclusively in the Parsonage in Haworth where they lived and worked, a place I have visited many times. I felt in keeping with their writings, it was important to blend the external and internal worlds, so the key element in the set was the presence of the graveyard outside their door and the sense of death it symbolizes. I brought that inside by having the whole stage made up of the distinctive table top graves that are present in Haworth.

Director: Barrie Rutter
Set and Costume Designer: Jessica Worrall
Lighting Designer: Tim Skelly
Sound Designer: Kraig Winterbottom
and Conrad Nelson
Photographers: Nobby Clark and Jessica Worrall

Images 1 & 2
She Stoops To Conquer
(compilation)

Images 3 & 4
Grit

Image 5
We Are Three Sisters

1/
IAN WESTBROOK
SET DESIGN

CINDERELLA
Micheal Harrison

Qdos Pantomimes Ltd
Birmingham Hippodrome Theatre Main Stage
2011

IW: Pantomime is uniquely British, using all of the scenic elements. I always start with the portal as it frames the set. I must consider the edge décor as these portals have to reduce in height and width to fit different venues without looking unsightly. Qdos Pantomimes at Birmingham Hippodrome produce the largest pantos in the world. Cinderella's Finale Ballroom has etched ply portals with a glistening mother of pearl paint finish that changes with light, 4 metre high LED chandeliers that twinkle and a 10 metre wide staircase to finish.

Director: Micheal Harrison
Choreographer: Karen Bruce
Set Designer: Ian Westbrook
Costume Designer: Mike Coltman
Lighting Designer: Ben Cracknell
Sound Designer: Gareth Owen
Media Designer: Qdos Entertainment
Photographer: Ian Westbrook

2/
IAN WESTBROOK
SET DESIGN

ROBINSON CRUSOE
Micheal Harrison

Qdos Pantomimes Ltd
Birmingham Hippodrome Theatre Main Stage
2013

IW: Robinson Crusoe features a 9 metre long pirate ship sailing in to open the show. This ship was designed and built in four steel truck base sections with foam and fibre glass to you make the ship.

A quick release clamping method is hidden within the ships decks for the "Pirate crew " to separate each section as it travels into the wings.

The bow section splits first, then mid ships, then aft and so on. This happens seamlessly and very quickly as if by magic!

The portals are adjustable as in all my pantomimes to accommodate different venues.

Director: Micheal Harrison
Choreographer: Karen Bruce
Set Designer: Ian Westbrook
Costume Designer: Mike Coltman
Lighting Designer: Ben Cracknell
Sound Designer: Gareth Owen
Media Designer: Qdos Entertainment
Photographer: Ian Westbrook

3/
IAN WESTBROOK
SET DESIGN

SNOW WHITE AND THE SEVEN DWARFS
Micheal Harrison (2013)

Qdos Pantomimes Ltd
Birmingham Hippodrome Theatre Main Stage
December 2013

IW: The wicked Queens lair in Snow White gave me an opportunity to play with cut-out gothic style windows and magical potion tables, while for the finale layered cut cloths create more depth. This witches lair set is very simple, 1 full cut cloth and a back drop with a round Gothic window 2.5metres diameter, profiled in plywood.

The lighting designer could back light through the window to create great effects.

Director: Micheal Harrison
Choreographer: Karen Bruce
Set Designer: Ian Westbrook
Costume Designer: Mike Coltman
Lighting Designer: Ben Cracknell
Sound Designer: Gareth Owen
Media Designer: Qdos Entertainment
Photographer: Ian Westbrook

Image 1
Cinderella
Image 2
Robinson Crusoe
Images 3 & 4
Snow White

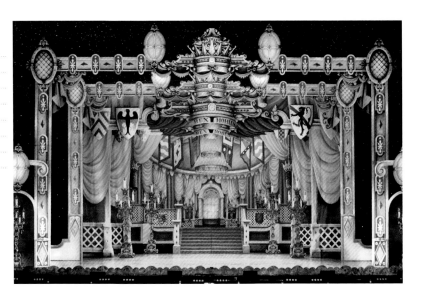

ASD
ASSOCIATION *of* SOUND DESIGNERS

ASSOCIATION OF SOUND DESIGNERS

'LISTENING AND RESPONDING TO SOUND IS SOMETHING WE DO, EVERY SECOND OF EVERY DAY FROM AROUND FOUR MONTHS BEFORE WE'RE BORN UNTIL THE DAY THAT WE DIE. WE CAN SHUT OUR EYES BUT WE CAN'T SHUT OUR EARS, WE CAN LOOK AWAY BUT WE CAN'T LISTEN AWAY. SOUND IS OMNIPRESENT AND TO IGNORE ITS EXISTENCE IS TO DISMISS ONE OF THE MOST IMPORTANT TOOLS WE USE TO UNDERSTAND OUR WORLD.'
STEVE BROWN, 2011

The Association of Sound Designers lost a great ambassador for sound design in 2013. Steve Brown was one of the founders of ASD and curator for many national and international sound design exhibitions, and I would like to dedicate this exhibition to him. Steve was an inspiration to many people in this field – he fought tirelessly for sound design to be recognised as an equal design element in theatre, and it was his passion for sound design that ultimately got me hooked on the creativity involved in the art-form.

Sound design is still regarded as the youngest of all the creative disciplines in theatre with the term 'sound designer' only being used for the past 50 years to credit the work carried out by those working in theatre sound. In reality, however, sound, music and effects have been used in theatre as far back as historical records go.

Sound designers in the UK work across a range of theatre productions and commercial projects – from fringe theatre to amateur, regional and West End productions, touring both nationally and internationally, with established award-winning production companies as well as new writers and directors.

Through the evolution of technology and educational courses in the UK, designed to train and inspire up and coming designers, the relationship between the theatre stage and sound has never been more exciting.

The role of a sound designer can be complex and extremely varied: from mixing orchestral instruments and voice, creating foley and sound effects, to designing surround sound playback systems, programming operating software and creating entire aural environments. Sound designers are therefore responsible not just for reinforcement (underlining the action on stage with specific sound queues), but for the overall shape and mood of a performance, much in the same way that stage designers or costume designers are responsible for creating the overall visual aesthetic.

There are of course crossovers between what constitutes theatre sound design and musical composition. It is becoming common practice, for example, to merge the role of a sound designer and composer together, especially on smaller-scale productions (often with tight budget constraints), sometimes referring to this hybrid role as 'creative sound designer' or 'composer/designer'.

Whatever the production is, there is quite often a need to create a form of overall aural ambiance, beyond mere spot effects. Sound designers will create palettes of sounds that can be manipulated and re-imaged by stretching, distorting, sampling, synthesizing and then reconstructing recorded source material and field recordings to create a series of textures that give a performance character, convey additional meaning and ultimately form an important part of the overall production. The emotional response produced by a soundscape or ambiance can be just as informative as any physical conversation or piece of music.

Sound design, like any design element, can have stage presence as it is performed and presented to an audience, much like its use in film and television. Sound design can manipulate the dynamic of a space and change an audience's perception – it can help to provide understanding and meaning and aid in conveying deeper layers of text-based narrative.

The discipline and art-form of sound design is moving forward at pace, and it certainly appears to be a revolutionary time with regards to the creation, appreciation and existence of sound design. Having a presence in exhibitions such as the Society of British Theatre Designer's MAKE: BELIEVE exhibition and its catalogue provides further opportunities for the discipline to be recognised, to be visible, and to grow with audiences and the theatre world at large.

The works presented in the exhibition and accompanying CD represent a small slice of current contemporary sound design and composition practice by UK-based designers – with contributions from Gareth Fry, John Leonard, Adrienne Quartly, Nick Sagar, Matthew Williams, Jon Nicholls, Nela Brown, Danny Bright, Karen Lauke, Mark Melville and Danny Krass. I am grateful to all contributors for sharing their designs, as they each help to demonstrate the variety and complexity of sound design works – from Sagar's work with National Theatre Scotland to Krass's innovative sound app and Leonard's long-standing global success.

KAREN LAUKE
ASD EXHIBITION COORDINATOR, 2014

As part of Make:Believe the Association of Sound Designers (ASD) has compiled a range of works by designers and composers that aims to showcase both the creativity of the discipline and the diversity of work ASD represents. This group exhibit presents work from some of the UK's top sound designers, as well as providing up and coming artists and designers with the opportunity to have their work recognised.

It is always difficult to exhibit sound design in an engaging and exciting way for people unaccustomed to the discipline, especially when the work is isolated and removed from its intended theatrical setting. However, the works on this disk are all capable of standing on their own merit, despite having originally been created for theatrical use.

I would like to thank all the designers for contributing to this exhibition and hope that you, the listener, will enjoy the sounds we have created.

Karen Lauke, 2014

DANNY BRIGHT:
- Dalloway (2014) 5'50"
- Subterranean Sound Tunnel (2013) 4'30"
- Woyzeck (2014) 6'30" *

NELA BROWN:
- Synaesthesia (2012) *1'36"*

GARETH FRY:
- Wildefire (2014) 1'23"
- The Master and Margarita (2012) 2'00"

DANNY KRASS:
- White (2014) *7'34"*

KAREN LAUKE:
- War Stories (2014) 7'12"
- Billy, the Monster & Me (2013) 1'18" *
- Not About Heroes (2014) 2'36" *

JOHN LEONARD:
- Ghosts (2013) 5'34"
- Moon Tiger (2014) 7'11"

MARK MELVILLE:
- Your Country (2014) *5'10"*

JON NICHOLLS:
- Idomeneus (2014) *3'43"*
- What I Heard About Iraq (2013) *4'54"*

ADRIENNE QUARTLY:
- Horse Piss (2012) *1'54"*

NICK SAGAR:
- Men Should Weep (2012) 2'41"
- Life and Death of Marina Abramovic (2012) 4'01"
- A Doll's House (2013) 3'09" *
- The James Plays (2014) 2'36" *

MATTHEW WILLIAMS:
- Ghosts (2014) 3'59"

* the starred tracks are in exhibition presentation only

BIOGRAPHIES

BECS ANDREWS /12

Becs trained as an artist at The Ruskin and as a stage designer at Wimbledon School of Art. She is the overall winner of the Linbury Prize 2003 and the DARE Fellow in Scenography 2011-14. Design credits: *Romeo and Juliet* (National Theatre), *Through His Teeth, The Crackle, Cassandra, Remote, La Serva Padrona* and *On The Rim of The World* (Royal Opera House), *Leaving Planet Earth* (Edinburgh International Festival), *Faster* (Birmingham Royal Ballet and National Ballet of Japan), *Momo* (Ballett:Bern), *The Art of Not Looking Back* (Hofesh Shechter Company), *All Alight* (Richard Alston/Phoenix) and *Jeff Koons* (ATC). As a lead artist, Becs has produced performance and installation work including: *Transmission* (Wellcome/York Festival of Ideas), *Phase Revivial: An Optical Harmonica*, (Royal Society of Chemistry/Opera North) *Conductor, Gold Dust: Of Memory and Light*, and *Phantasmagoria: Seduction and Psychosis* (University of Leeds). Becs is currently a Visiting Research Associate at the University of York.
http://becsandrews.com

ARTLINER / BKKR /14

The Wind Tunnel Project 2014, launched on June 9th in Farnborough, Hampshire, produced in collaboration between Artliner and BKKR. The inaugural intervention was housed in and around 1917 and 1935 Grade 1 and 2 Listed buildings which were open to the public for the first time in history. Salma Tuqan, the Contemporary Middle East Curator at the Victoria and Albert Museum invited artists to draw inspiration from Farnborough's heritage and the wind tunnels' dense archives. The artistic programme included a series of subtle site-specific interventions in the space using sound, light and performance, to create a sensory experience for visitors. Sound Designer Thor McIntyre-Burnie is one of the early artists to pioneer sound as a tool for site-specific public art. He has a depth of experience, transforming public sites and forgotten architectural spaces. McIntyre-Burnie creates immersive experiences, which invite the viewer to enter a peculiar space between the tangible and audible realms.
www.bkkr.co

CATHERINE BAINES /16

Since graduating in Theatre Design in 2009, Catherine has worked on a variety of theatre shows and events which include set and costume designs for: *Something for the Winter* (The Brit School, Southwark Playhouse), *Bernarda Alba* (Bernie Grants Arts Centre), *Hello Again* (Mountview). She has designed costumes for: *Days of Significance* and *There is a War* (2013), *American Clock* (2011) at Jacksons Lane Theatre.

Catherine has worked as Associate Designer on *From Here to There* (Tell Tale Hearts Ltd. UK Touring) and as Assistant Designer on: *The Secret Garden* (Chester Performs, Puppet Making Assistant), *The Exonerated and 6 Actors in search of a Director* (New Players Theatre), *Grumpy Old Women* (Novello +UK Touring).

Scenic Painting includes: *Oliver, The Woman in Black* and *Joseph* (Popular Productions, Dubai), *Alice in Wonderland* (Brewhouse Theatre, Taunton), *Room on the Broom* (Tall Stories, UK Touring).

As Model Making Assistant she has worked on: *Gianni Schicchi* (Opera Holland Park), *Mr Stink* (Kenny Wax Productions), *Lights Out Land Girls* (Bad Apple Theatre), *Shrek* (Wormland Opera, Sweden).
http://251561.heresmyprofile.com

MEGAN BAKER /15

Megan has designed and supervised costumes for many companies including The Theatre Royal Stratford East, The Globe Theatre and in the West End, before moving up to Scotland to run the highly acclaimed BA Hons MA and MFA Performance Costume courses at Edinburgh College of Art at the University of Edinburgh. She has continued to work as a freelance costume designer with her most recent productions including: *Village on the Roof* (Kickabout Films), *Ana* (Imago Theatre, Montreal, Canada, Traverse Theatre, Edinburgh and Scottish National tour), *Guid Sisters* a co-production between Royal Lyceum Theatre, Edinburgh, the National Theatre of Scotland and the Kings Theatre, Glasgow, also *Union* at the Royal Lyceum Theatre, Edinburgh.

SIMON BANHAM /18

Simon is a founder member of the theatre company Quarantine and is responsible for the scenography on all their productions over the past 16 years, most recently *Summer*, the first part in a quartet of works exploring the human condition.

He has a long working relationship with contemporary opera company Music Theatre Wales, most recently the World Premiere of Philip Glass' new opera *The Trial*. Before this he designed the British Premiere of *Luci Mie Traditrici* and *Greek* (Outstanding Achievement in Opera 2011).

Recently he has begun collaborating with Mike Pearson and Mike Brookes on a body of work with National Theatre Wales - *The Persians* (Best Design 2010 award by the TMA) and *Coriolan/us*, (chosen for exhibition at the *World Stage Design 2013*).

A freelance designer, he also teaches at Aberystwyth University, Wales; where he is a Senior Lecturer in Scenography and Theatre Design.

SARAH BEATON /24

Sarah graduated from the Royal Central School of Speech and Drama in 2011 with a First Class Honours. Later that year, she was awarded the Linbury Prize for Stage Design. She has since designed for theatre, opera and dance in a variety of venues including Sadler's Wells, The Oxford Playhouse, Theatre Rigiblick (Zurich) and Manchester Royal Exchange. In 2013, she was also selected to exhibit her work at World Stage Design in Cardiff.
www.sarahbeaton.com

SIGNE BECKMANN /25

Signe is a set and costume designer who works internationally in theatre, opera and dance. Theatre credits: *The Glass Supper* (Hampstead Theatre), *There has Possibly Been an Incident* (Royal Exchange / Berliner Festspiele), *Molly Sweeney* (Lyric Belfast / The Print Room), *Land of Our Fathers, A Handful of Stars* (Trafalgar Studios), *Larisa and the Merchants* (Arcola Theatre), *American Justice* (Arts Theatre, West End), *The Serpent's Tooth* (Almeida / Talawa), *Insufficiency* (Riverside Studios), *Benefactors* (Sheffield Crucible), *The Glee Club* (Hull Truck), *The Knowledge, Little Platoons* (Bush Theatre), *Ghosts* (Young Vic), *Dancing at Lughnasa* (Aubade Hall, Japan). Opera credits: *Don Giovanni* (The Royal Opera House, Copenhagen), *La Serva Padrona* (Sa de Miranda, Portugal), *Volume* (ENO Opera Works, Sadlers Wells), *Eugene Onegin, Giasone* (Iford Arts). Dance credits: *Gameshow* (Company Chameleon, The Lowry), *Meridian* and *Phantasy* (Rambert Company, Queen Elizabeth Hall). Screen credits: *The Club, Plan B - Killa Kela, Centrepoint* (Mike Figgis) and *The Headlong Theatre 2013 Season Trailer* (Rupert Goold).
www.signebeckmann.com

TANJA BEER /26

Tanja is a scenographer and performance maker exploring the intersection between performance and ecological design. Her projects seek to re-think traditional design practices and re-interpret materials to embrace the possibilities of 'ecoscenography' – a movement that integrates ecological principles into all stages of scenographic thinking and production. Tanja has more than 15 years professional experience, including 60 designs for projects in London, Cardiff, Melbourne, Sydney, Brisbane, Vienna and Tokyo. She has received numerous grants and awards, and was recently 'Activist-in-Residence' at Julie's Bicycle (London).
www.tanjabeer.com

GIUSEPPE BELLI /27

Giuseppe studied Theatre Design and Fine Art at the Slade School, and was the first theatre designer awarded the Worshipful Company of Painters Guild prize for fine art.
He became a Freeman of the Guild in 1999. As a fine artist he also produces many works for other artists and designers internationally; notable works including original models for *Miraculous Journey* for Damien Hirst. His set design for *A Soldier and a Maker* featured in 2014 as installation in Creating a Scene, at the National Centre for Craft and Design, and Oriel Davies Contemporary Gallery. Designs with co-designer Emma Belli include: *Sir John in Love, La Rondine, Lads in their Hundreds, Unknown Doors, A Soldier and a Maker* and *Journeying Boys* by Iain Burnside, *Falstaff, Carmen* and *West Side Story* (Grange park Opera/Pimlico Opera), *La Traviata* (Opera Holland Park), *Poetry or Bust*, written and directed by Tony Harrison.

DICK BIRD /8, 28

Dick Bird's designs for opera include: *La Donna Del Lago* (Royal Opera House), *The Pearl Fishers* (English National Opera), *House Of The Dead* (Opera North), *Beatrice ed Benedict* and *Der Freischutz* (L'opéra Comique), *Un Segreto D'importanza* (Teatro Communale Di Bologna), *Snegurochka* (Wexford Festival Opera), *The Gambler* and *Il Trittico* (Opera Zuid) and *Das Portrait* (Bregenz Festival).

Ballets include: David Bintley's *Aladdin* (Birmingham Royal Ballet), *La Bayadere* (K Ballet Tokyo), *The Nutcracker* and *Swan Lake* (Star Dancers Tokyo), *The Canterville Ghost* (English National Ballet) and *The Firebird* (National Ballet Of Japan).

In the theatre he has designed *Hamlet* and *La Grande Magie* (Comédie Francaise), *La Comedie Des Erreurs* (Theatre Vidy), *Twelfth Night* And *The Tempest* (Teatr Polski) *Lear* (The Crucible), *Light* (Complicite), *The Walls*, *Owen Meany* and *The Night Season* (National Theatre), *Harvest* (Royal Court Theatre), *The Enchanted Pig* and *Monkey* (Young Vic) And *Othello* and *As You Like It* (The Globe).

Most recent work Includes Kate Bush's *Before The Dawn* and *Nabucco* for the Opera National De Lorraine.
http://dickbird.co.uk

JOHN BISHOP /30

John is an immensely talented Lighting Designer and has designed the lighting for more than 190 original productions of opera, ballet, theatre and musicals in collaboration with many world class Directors and Designers. John's lighting is exciting, imaginative and beguiling. It is musically sensitive, beautifully atmospheric and utterly dramatic.

Highlights include: *Hänsel und Gretel* (Frankfurt), *Tannhäuser* & *Le Roi Arthus* (Strasbourg), *Der Fliegende Holländer* & *Der Ringen des Nibelungen* (Oslo), *Falstaff* (Maastricht), *The Marriage of Figaro* (Warsaw), *Tristan und Isolde* (Aarhus), *Peter Grimes* (Madrid), *Don Giovanni* (Sao Paulo), *A Chair in Love* (Montreal), *Demones* (Athens), *Ernani* (English National Opera), *Albert Herring* (Opera North & Tallinn), *Maiden in the Tower* & *Kashchey the Immortal* (Buxton Festival), *Dracula* (Northern Ballet), *Noddy and The Hidden Treasure* (Lisbon), *Woman in Black* (Dubai).

Future plans include: *The Great Gatsby* (Dresden), *Notorious* (Göteborg).
http://johnbishop.me.uk

SAMAL BLAK /36

Born in the Faroe Islands, Samal Blak graduated in Design for Performance from Central Saint Martins. In 2007 he was awarded the Thorvald Poulsen av Steinum award for a young Faroese artist and in 2009 he was one of the individual winners of the Linbury Prize for Stage Design. Subsequently he designed Verdi's *Otello* for Birmingham Opera Company, directed by Graham Vick, nominated for the 2010 RPS music award for Opera and Music Theatre. *Ghost Patrol*, which he recently designed for Scottish Opera & Music Theatre Wales, has just won the Southbank Sky Arts Award for Opera 2013.

Other productions include: *Khovanschina* and *Life is a Dream* (Birmingham Opera Company); *Les Mamelles de Tiresias* (La Monnaie-Brussels 2014); *Il Giasone, Agrippina, Simon Boccanegra, The Siege of Calais* & *Cosi Fan Tutti* (English Touring Opera); *Most of the Boys* (ROH2); *L'Incoronazione di Poppea* (RCM & English Touring Opera); *Les Mamelles de Tiresias* (Aldeburgh Music, Festival d'Aix-en-Provence); *Ghost Patrol* (Winner of South Bank Sky Arts Award for Opera 2013) & *In The Locked Room* (Scottish Opera & Music Theatre Wales); *Moon* (Sadari Theatre Company, Seoul, South Korea); *The Importance of Being Earnest* (Riverside Studios, London); *Cowardy Custard* (UK Tour); *The Kissing Dance* (Jermyn Street Theatre, London); *Macbeth* (Geurilla Theatre, Seoul, South Korea); *How To Be An Other Woman* (Gate Theatre, London); *Pins and Needles* (Cock Tavern Theatre, London); *Budam-Man* (Comedie de Caen, France); *The Madman's Garden* (Tallinn, Estonia); *Antoine and the Paper Aeroplane* (Edinburgh Festival; ACE! Festival Singapore, & Disk Theatre Prague); *Afenginn-Decenniale* (Husets Teater, Copenhagen, Denmark); *The Adventures of Pinocchio* (Faroe Islands) and the Jerwood Opera Writing Program at Aldeburgh Music.

Forthcoming work includes *Eugene Onegin* (Theater an der Wien) and *Tosca* (Opera Ostfold, Norway 2015).
www.samalblak.com

HAZEL BLUE /32

Hazel has worked as a set and costume designer and maker since graduating from RSAMD in 2007. She designs for drama, ballet, musical theatre and opera. Hazel graduated with a BA Fine Arts (Hons) degree in South Africa, specialising in printmaking. She will be part time Set Design lecturer at Royal Conservatoire of Scotland, 2014/15. Hazel's recent designs include: *Sea and Land and Sky* (Tron Theatre), *The Drawer Boy* (Tron Theatre), *Motherland* (RCS),

Dance School Scotland Shows 2012 and 13 (King's Theatre and Theatre Royal), *Il Ritorno d'Ulisse in Patria* (Agos Opera Studio), *RCS Modern Ballet Showcase 2012 and 2014* (RCS), *The Tempest 2014* (Tron Theatre).
www.hazel-blue.co.uk

MARIE BLUNCK /33

Marie's practice focuses on experimental performances, working across theatre, film and interactive installation. Her collaborations have won the Oxford Samuel Beckett Theatre Trust Award and the New Discovery Prize at the International Mime Festival in Périgueux, France. Her work has been shown at venues such as The Roundhouse and The Barbican in London. Her latest work will be part of a permanent exhibit at the V&A's new Europe 1600-1800 Galleries. She studied Theatre Design at Central St Martins and holds an MA in Fine Art from the Slade School of Art. Marie is a Senior Lecturer at Central St Martins and has taught Production Design at Wimbledon College of Art and Goldsmiths University.
www.blunck.org

LARA BOOTH /16

Lara trained at Bristol Old Vic Theatre School, graduating with a Distinction and winning the John Elvery Prize for Excellence. Lara aims to create environments that will serve the actors and the text as well as bringing an immersive experience to the audience. Lara is a Senior Lecturer in Costume Design at The University of Huddersfield, a regular guest designer for MMU Capitol Theatre and a founding member of Small Things Theatre Company. Lara's portfolio includes design for Bristol Old Vic, Edinburgh Royal Lyceum, Manchester Library Theatre, Lowry Quays, RNCM, Opera North, The Arcola, Southwark Playhouse, as well as site-specific venues. *Albert Herring* and *L'Elisir d'Amore* (RNCM) were both nominated for the MTA award for Best Opera.
www.larabooth.co.uk

REBECCA BRADBURY /17

Rebecca trained in Theatre Design at Nottingham Trent University. Since graduating in 2011, she became the resident theatre designer at Trent College, Nottingham, where she has designed over 20 shows ranging from musicals to Shakespeare, all done in a variety of spaces including traditional school hall, small studios and site specific. She also stage manages each production with the help of a team

of students who fulfil such roles as lighting operator, wardrobe mistress, design assistant and everything in between. Rebecca is committed to creating new, exciting and innovative performance design within education.

MARIE BRENNEIS /17

Marie uses 3D painting, installation, sculpture and performance as a locus for the exploration of social conventions and conformism. She explores rules society forces upon us. Working in a very interdisciplinary way, her work has been exhibited in the following platforms: Scenography, costume, design, theatre, architecture, photography, video, performance, dance, fine art, fashion catwalks and public sculpture. Her work has been performed, presented and exhibited on public buildings on the canals around Hackney Wick, Ravensbourne University, The National Gallery, Prague Quadrennial - Prague, The International Performance Pad, Mainz - Germany, Critical Costume Symposium, Edge Hill University, Liverpool, Space 65 Gallery, Aesthetica Art Prize Exhibition 2014 - York Museum, The Dark Room Gallery, Vermont, USA, The London Festival of Architecture 2014, Number 90 Hackney Wick, Stratford Circus Theatre, Bonnie Bird Theatre - Trinity Laban, Duckie, Ten Gales Art Gallery, Goldsmiths University, Deptford Town Hall, The Resistance Art Gallery, University of East London and the Hackney Wicked Festival.
www.mariebrenneis.com

DANNY BRIGHT /205

Danny Bright is a sound designer, composer, recordist, musician and sonic manipulator working across the fields of music, performance, installation, theatre and media. His work has appeared at the Brighton Digital Festival, New York City Electroacoustic Music Festival, MAGNA Science Adventure Centre, World Soundscape Conference, Victoria & Albert Museum, Prague Quadrennial, Museum of Science and Industry, British Science Festival, Manchester, Newcastle & Brighton Science Festivals, Edinburgh, Brighton, and Bedford Fringe Festivals, and toured the UK, Europe, Australia and the USA. Commissions and supporting organisations include: Arts Council England, Octopus Collective, MAGNA Trust, and the Arts and Humanities Research Council as funder of his on-going doctoral research in Music at the University of Sussex.
www.bogstandardaudio.co.uk

NELA BROWN /205

Nela Brown is a Croatian sound artist, composer and sound designer currently based in London. After graduating with a BA (Hons) in Sonic Arts, she got involved in designing sound for contemporary theatre, dance, interactive installations and documentaries as well as exhibiting her electroacoustic work.

In the past few years, her sound work has been heard by the audiences across Canada, Italy, Brazil, Spain, Checz Republic, England, Scotland and US where she was invited to present her work at USITT Conference and Yale School of Drama. Nela is currently undertaking PhD research supported by EPSRC at Queen Mary University of London, where she is also a leader of G.Hack, a collective of female researchers focusing on sharing knowledge and developing interactive media projects through collaboration with other universities and industry partners. G.Hack is an awardee of 2011 QMUL Small Grant for Development of Learning and Teaching and is currently involved in a number of high profile public engagement projects.

PAUL BROWN /40

Born in the Vale of Glamorgan, and trained under Percy Harris. Set and Costume design include: *Nabucco* (Tokyo), *Guilliaume Tell* (Pesaro), *Aida* (Bregenz), *Die Gezeichneten* (Palermo), *Hippolyte et Aricie*, *Fairy Queen*, *Pelléas et Melisande*, *Lulu*, *The Turn of the Screw*, (Glyndebourne), *Mitridate*, *Tosca*, *I masnadieri*, *Falstaff*, *Manon Lescaut* (Covent Garden), *Peter Grimes*, *Parsifal*, (Bastille Paris), *Lady Macbeth of Mtsensk*, *Moses und Aron* (Metropolitan New York), *Don Carlos* (Sydney), *Mittwoch aus Licht* (Birmingham), *Tristan und Isolde* (Berlin), *Rigoletto* (Madrid), *Thaïs* (Chicago), *Katya Kabanova*, *Lucio Silla*, *The Tempest*, (Santa Fe), *L'incoronazione di Poppea* (Bologna), *Traviata* and *Anna Bolena* (Verona), *Mefistofele* (Amsterdam), *Die Zauberflöte* (Bolshoi Moscow), *Die Frau ohne Schatten*, *Elektra*, *War and Peace* (Mariinsky St Petersburg), *Tannhäuser* (San Francisco), *Zémire et Azor*, *Tom Jones* (Drottningholm), *Vanessa* (Los Angeles).

MISTY BUCKLEY /34

Misty Buckley is a production designer from south London who specialises in live touring shows, TV and large-scale events. She works as creative director for many parts of Glastonbury Festival and won Set Designer of the Year at the TPi Awards in 2013 and again in 2014. Misty recently designed Coldplay's Ghost Stories Tour after collaborating with the band on the hugely successful Mylo Xyloto World Tour, and designed the Paralympics Closing Ceremony for London 2012. She has designed Biffy Clyro's touring and festival stage sets since 2010 and has worked on many other major stadium and arena tours and television performances for bands including Take That, Gary Barlow, Elton John and One Direction. Misty has designed large-scale televised music events for the BBC at Edinburgh castle and Children in Need. She won an award for her set design at Twickenham Stadium for the Help 4 Heroes concert in 2010.
www.mistybuckley.co.uk

PAUL BURGESS /46

Paul trained at Motley and has designed for venues including The Arcola, The Albany, Hampstead, The Bush, Shakespeare's Globe, Soho, Theatre 503, Hackney Empire and Southwark Playhouse (all London), Birmingham Rep, The Watermill (Newbury), The Royal Exchange (Manchester) Glasgow Citizens, Colchester Mercury, Teatro LATEA and Here (both New York), Pakistan National Council of Arts, The Black Box (Hanoi), Prithvi, Choice and Epicentre (all in India) and WUK (Vienna). As a director-designer he has led the creation of several projects in the UK and abroad, including for Daedalus Theatre Company, of which he is artistic director. Under the name Scale Project, he has led projects jointly with Simon Daw across the UK and in Siberia, where they worked in a disused nuclear bunker. He has taught design and general theatre skills for many youth arts projects and at various universities, including Goldsmiths (London) and the National College of Arts (Pakistan).
www.paul-burgess.yolasite.com

KATE BURNETT

Kate Burnett MA is Make/Believe Project Director and UK National Curator for the 2015 Prague Quadrennial. She is an award winning theatre designer and Reader in Theatre Design at Nottingham Trent University. She has designed extensively for regional, national and touring theatre companies; also large scale schools and community performance projects for orchestras, opera companies and art galleries. She has organised four national exhibitions for the SBTD; *Collaborators* in 2007 in Nottingham, Inverness, Newcastle-upon-Tyne, at PQ and at the V&A Museum, and three with Peter Ruthven Hall; 2D>3D (2002), which was awarded the Golden Triga at PQ'03), *Time+Space* (1999) and *MakeSpace!* (1994), awarded a Gold Medal at PQ'95.

Kate was Hon. Secretary to the SBTD from 2003 – 07 and Chair of the OISTAT History & Theory Commission from 2007 – 11. She is a co-founder of the new OISTAT Theatre Timeline Working Group. For World Stage Design 2013 in Cardiff, Kate was Editor of the WSD2013 exhibition catalogue.

ISABELLA BYWATER /42

Isabella has designed sets and costumes for many productions both in Britain and internationally. Recent productions include *La Boheme* and *The Elixir of Love* (both at ENO), *Don Pasquale* (Royal Opera House Covent Garden and La Scala Milan) and *Rutherford and Sons*, (Northern Broadsides).

Her debut as director designer was *Gounod's Faust* (2013 at the Mariinsky Theatre in St Petersburg, conducted by Valery Gergiev) and she has also directed and designed *Lucia di Lammermoor* (2014 for Den Jyske Opera which toured Denmark, conducted by Martin Andre) Future productions include designs for *La Traviata* (at the Mariinsky June 2015) and revival director for *La Boheme* (at San Diego Opera January 2015)
www.isabellabywater.com

KITTY CALLISTER /44

Kitty graduated from Fashion Textile Design at The University of Brighton in 2001 and went on to work in the tailoring department at Glyndebourne Opera House, as well as at the National Theatre, London and Robert Allsopp and Associates. During this time she independently took on a number of small design projects and eventually decided to concentrate on developing her passion for design by studying an MA in Theatre Design at the Royal Welsh College of Music and Drama, Cardiff in 2010.

Recent work includes: Set and Costume Design for *The White Feather* (Theatr na nÓg), *In The Penal Colony* (Shadwell Opera), *The Prodigal Son / The Burning Fiery Furnace* (Mahogany Opera), *The Yellow Sofa* (Glyndebourne), *Towards an Unknown Port* (English Touring Opera), and Costume Design on *Wakening Shadows* (Glyndebourne), *A Time There Was* (Jubilee Opera).
http://kittycallister.carbonmade.com/about

NERISSA CARGILL THOMPSON /47

Nerissa studied Theatre Design at Nottingham Trent University. Since graduating in 1995, she has been based in Manchester working as a freelance set and costume designer for both theatre and film and as a community artist facilitating projects and workshops in a variety of visual arts. Nerissa specialises in working alongside drama, music or dance professionals to bring a visual element to a performance based project or workshop. She is joint Creative Director and Head of Design of Aqueous Humour, a physical theatre company who create devised work using bouffon, clown and mask.
www.ncargillthompson.co.uk
www.aqueoushumour.com

FIONA CHIVERS /49

Fiona is a designer, maker and occasional performer. Originally a dancer, her background has led to a passion for high-energy physical performance. She trained at Rose Bruford and on the MA Scenography at Central Saint Martins and was a 1997 Linbury prizewinner for *Sabina* (The Bush).

Fiona works in the U.K. and internationally; creating designs for dance, opera, drama and site specific installation. Collaborations include: Panta Rei Danse Teatre, Moko Dance, C-scape, Kneehigh, Dance Republic2, Hannah Silva, BEA and Theatre Royal Plymouth.

Fiona is an Associate Lecturer at Plymouth College of Art. She is a strong believer in the value of the arts as an educational tool. Her teaching experience includes workshops with professional artists from a variety of artistic disciplines, children, and community groups.
www.mischivers.com

DAVID COCKAYNE /48

David trained in Theatre Design at Birmingham Art School in the 1960s, on a course including theatre design and fine art. He has worked at numerous British regional theatres including Birmingham Repertory Theatre, Mac - Birmingham,

Manchester Library Theatre, Liverpool Playhouse, The Traverse Theatre -Edinburgh, Sheffield Crucible and Leeds Playhouse. He designed the premieres of *Tomorrowland*, a musical in English, in Moscow in 1999 and also *Boris Goudenow*, an opera written in 1711 by Johann Mattheson, for Boston Early Music Festival in 2005. He worked as Resident Designer at Birmingham Rep and Head of Design at Manchester Library Theatre, from 1973 to 1979, and then at Liverpool Playhouse before teaching Theatre Design at Nottingham Trent. For the Royal Northern College of Music productions include: *Into The Woods*, *The Queen of Spades*, *Don Giovanni*, *The Rake's Progress*, *Paradise Moscow*, *Orpheo et Euridice* and *Company*. He also works as a fine artist.

SUE CONDIE /52

Sue trained at Middlesex Poly and The Nottingham Trent University BA Hons Theatre Design. She has been designing nationally for a wide variety of both main house theatres and touring companies for over twenty years. These include Salisbury Playhouse, Cheltenham Everyman, Harrogate Theatre, Oldham Coliseum, Coventry Belgrade, Northern Broadsides/Dukes, Stroud Theatre Co, Spitz & Co, Oxford Touring Theatre, Kazzum, Reach Inclusive Arts, and Action Transport. She regularly designs for the Stephen Joseph Theatre, Scarborough where recent productions include: *The Schoolmistress* and *Beauty & the Beast* and for Sixth Sense Theatre: most recently *Splosh!* and *Lady Johanna's Miracle Garden*, an outdoor site-specific production. Sue spent two years as Associate Resident Designer at The New Vic, Staffordshire where her designs included *Ghosts*, *Overture*, *The Hound of the Baskervilles*, *Private Lives* and returned as a freelancer to design *Sweeney Todd*, *Don Giovanni* and most recently *Ugly Duck*. Sue also works regularly as a Tutor at University of the Arts London (CSM), Bristol Old Vic Theatre School and Staffordshire University.
www.suecondie.co.uk

LUCÍA CONEJERO RODILLA /50

Lucía Conejero Rodilla is a multidisciplinary artist trained in Fine Arts at the Polytechnic University of Valencia and in Scenography at Royal Central School of Speech and Drama in London (MA with Distinction). She was the artistic director and

designer of music videos for the band 'La Pulqueria' (Sony-BMG), for dance companies and short films. She also worked in the Costume Department of the 'Palau de les Arts Reina Sofía' (Valencia Opera House).

In 2008 she moved to NY and in 2009, to London, where she joined the Costume Department of the National Youth Theatre. Afterwards, Lucía has worked as a freelance designer and maker (mainly in costume) for *Woman Bomb* (Tristan Bates), the opera *The Moonflower* at Tête à Tête Festival and *Peer Gynt Recharged* (both at Riverside Studios), and as accessories designer in the private opera event *Sumptuous Supper* by Edible Opera at the English National Opera, among others.
www.behance.net/sulia

PATRICK CONNELLAN /53

Theatre credits include: *One Night in November*, *The Rink*, *A Midsummer Night's Dream*, *The Dice House*, *This Lime Tree Bower* (as director and designer, also Edinburgh Festival), *Silas Marner*, *She Stoops To Conquer*, *Leader of the Pack*, *Neville's Island*, *The Wedding* and *Big Nose* (set - Belgrade Theatre), *The Taming of the Shrew*, *The Merchant of Venice* and *Into The Woods* (nominated for TMA Best Musical Award - Derby Theatre/Playhouse), *20th Century Boy* (New Wolsey), *Who's Afraid of Virginia Woolf*, *The Price*, *Ghosts*, *All My Sons*, *The Seafarer*, *Meet the Mukherjees*, *Popcorn* (also director), *Broken Glass*, *Twelfth Night*, *Little Malcolm*, *The Weir* and *The Hypochondriac* (Octagon, Bolton), *Edward III* (RSC/West End), *A Passionate Woman*, *Misery* (West End), *The Slight Witch* (National Theatre/ Birmingham Rep), *Where Have I Been All My Life*, *Abigail's Party* (also director) *Copenhagen* and *Alphabetical Order* (New Vic, Stoke) and for Hampstead Theatre: *Amongst Friends*, *Life After Scandal* (also Plymouth), *Taking Care of Baby* (also Birmingham Rep), *The Maths Tutor*, *Osama the Hero/A Single Act*, *My Best Friend* (also Birmingham Rep), *Nathan the Wise* and *When the Night Begins*. Patrick has previously won the Linbury Prize for Theatre Design and was a Prague Quadrennial Gold Medal finalist. He is the Course Leader in Theatre Design at Nottingham Trent University.

FRANK CONWAY /54

Frank is from Ireland and trained at the Motley Theatre Design Course at English National Opera. On completion, he assisted Tanya Moiseiwitsch at

the Metropolitan Opera House, New York and designed *Touched* by Stephen Lowe at the Royal Court Theatre, directed by Bill Gaskill. He has designed extensively for Irish theatre and film, including the Oscar nominated film *The Field*, and the Bafta Award winning documentary *Beautiful Mistake*. Frank is a former Head of Design at the Abbey Theatre, Dublin and a former Associate Designer at Druid Theatre, Galway. He has designed productions for the Royal Court, Donmar Warehouse, The Old Vic and Greenwich Theatre in London, the Shakespeare in the Park Festival - New York and The Shakespeare Festival - Stratford Ontario. He designed the premiere of Sam Shepard's new play *A Particle of Dread* (Oedipus Variations) for Field Day Theatre Company, as part of Derry's European City of Culture 2013, and designed the US premiere for Signature Theatre in New York.
www.frankconway.net

RUSSELL CRAIG /55

Russell initially trained and worked in New Zealand. British theatre companies he has designed musicals and plays for include: The Royal Shakespeare Company, Manchester Royal Exchange, The Royal Lyceum Edinburgh, Chichester festival theatre, The Unicorn Theatre and many touring and regional companies throughout the UK. He has designed numerous Opera productions for Scottish Opera, Opera North, Welsh National Opera, English National Opera, Glyndebourne, Wexford Festival and companies throughout Europe and the USA. He represented Britain at the Prague Quadrennial in 1983 and currently designs the sets for the Chipping Norton pantomimes.
http://www.russellcraig.co.uk

CHARLIE CRIDLAN /56

Charlie studied at The University of Kent at Canterbury and Bristol Old Vic Theatre School. She is a set and costume designer working predominantly in Theatre (Bristol Old Vic, Regional & National Touring, West End), Opera (Wedmore Opera, Barbican, BYO), and TV (Ch4, BBC). She has found the creativity and imagination of design for production directly transferable to the design of events and exhibitions and in recent years has enjoyed sharing her skills and aptitudes collaborating on their production. Thinking in precise detail about the way people look, feel and move around in space and how it

affects them has led her to create dynamic, unusual environments for companies in the Corporate and Heritage sectors (Charles Dickens Museum, London ?What if!, Innovation & Wavelength Ltd). Charlie is always thrilled to engage and collaborate and has a passion for transforming space, the endless possibilities there are to engage, enhance and form space, be it transient, theatrical or permanent.
www.charliecridlan.com

DAVID CRISP /57

David Crisp is currently the resident set and costume designer for the Department of Drama and Theatre Arts at the University of Birmingham. He was formerly the scenic designer for the Birmingham School of Acting, designing over 150 productions, working with professional directors in various venues throughout Birmingham. David's freelance career has enabled him to work on operas, dance, new writing, devised pieces as well as traditional and contemporary theatre such as *Anna Karenina* (The Arcola, London) and *Mill on the Floss* (The Patrick Centre, Birmingham) and the anniversary of *Kindertransport* (University of Birmingham).

JUDITH CROFT /60

Judith Croft is a set and costume designer. She has worked as Head of Design at the Library Theatre Company in Manchester and has designed for many of their award winning productions including *Waiting for Godot*, *Translations* and *Hard Times*. She has also worked in the West End- *Laughter on the 23rd Floor*, Opera- *Falstaff*, and has designed extensively for Theatre Clwyd, most recently for a new play, *Somewhere in England*. Other work includes many site specific productions, including the 2013 cycle of the Chester Mystery Plays. She has represented designers within Equity as Chair of the Designer's committee.

BOB CROWLEY /58

Recent productions: *Skylight* (Wyndhams Theatre, London), *Aladdin* (Disney – Toronto & Broadway), *The Glass Menagerie* (American Rep Theatre, USA & Broadway), *The Audience* (Gielgud Theatre), *Once* (London, Broadway & US Tour), *People* (National Theatre), *The Dark Earth & Light Sky* (Almeida), *Disney's The Little Mermaid* (Netherlands, Russia), *Once* (Broadway – Tony Award).

He has designed numerous productions for the National Theatre, including most recently: *Travelling Light, Collaborators, King James Bible, Juno & the Paycock* (Abbey Theatre, Dublin), *The Habit of Art, The Power of Yes, Phèdre, Every Good Boy Deserves Favour, Gethsemane,* and *Fram* (which he also co-directed with Tony Harrison), *The History Boys* (Broadway - Tony Award), *His Girl Friday* and *Mourning Becomes Electra,* plus more than twenty-five productions for the RSC, including: *Les Liaisons Dangereuses* and *The Plantagenets* (Olivier Award). For the Donmar Warehouse: *Into the Woods* and *Orpheus Descending.* Other credits include: *Mary Poppins* (Prince Edward Theatre, UK Tour & Broadway - Tony Award) *Disney's Aida* (Broadway - Tony Award), *Disney's Tarzan* which he also directed (Broadway, Germany & The Netherlands), and *The Year of Magical Thinking* (Broadway & NT), *The Coast of Utopia* (New York - Tony Award), *Carousel* (New York - Tony Award), *The Seagull* (Public Theatre New York), Paul Simon's *The Capeman, The Sweet Smell Of Success.* Opera & Dance include: *The Winter's Tale, Alice in Wonderland* (ROH & Canadian Ballet) *Don Carlos* (MET, NY) *Pavane and Anastasia* (Royal Ballet), *La Traviata* (ROH), *The Cunning Little Vixen* (Châtelet). Film include: *Othello, Tales of Hollywood* starring Jeremy Irons and Alec Guinness, *Suddenly Last Summer* directed by Richard Eyre and starring Maggie Smith for the BBC, plus Costume Design for the film of *The Crucible* starring Daniel Day-Lewis and Winona Ryder.Future projects: *An American in Paris* (Châtelet & Broadway). He is the recipient of the Royal Designer for Industry Award and Robert L. B. Tobin Award for Lifetime Achievement in Theatrical Design at the TDF/Irene Sharaff Awards in New York.

ANNE CURRY /59
Anne has a first class degree in Theatre Design. After receiving the Sir Barry Jackson Memorial Scholarship and a Royal Society of Arts Travel Bursary, she completed postgraduate studies in Theatre Design at the Slade. Anne was awarded an Arts Council Theatre Design Bursary, and began her career as a freelance Theatre Designer. She designed set and costumes for *Dreams of San Francisco* (The Bush Theatre), winner of the Thames Television Best Production. Costume design work includes: *The Vivien Ellis Musical Theatre Showcase* (Her Majesty's), *The Boys in the Band* (Aldwych) plus extensive U.K. touring design and work with Druid Theatre, Galway. Anne has an MA in Education and

Professional Development and extensive experience of designing Shakespeare in Education. Anne is Senior Lecturer in Costume Design and Interpretation at Nottingham Trent University. She regularly exhibits with The SBTD, and at V&A 2000 and 2008; National Theatre Tokyo 2001, Prague Quadrennial 1999 and 2007, and World Stage Design 2013.

ANGELA DAVIES /61
Angela trained at Cardiff College of Art and Nottingham. She is a winner of the Linbury Prize for Stage Design. Theatre designs include *The Mouse and his Child, Victoria, Night of the Soul* (RSC), *The Malcontent, Henry Viii* and *The Maid's Tragedy* (Shakespeare's Globe), *The Syndicate, The Father* and *Stairs to the Roof* (Chichester), *The Prince of Homburg* and *Life is a Dream* (Donmar Warehouse), *The Dark Philosophers* (National Theatre Wales / Told by an Idiot), *A Good Night Out in the Valleys* (National Theatre Wales), *Bronte* (Lyric Hammersmith), *After Mrs Rochester* (Duke of York's), *The Dolls House, Mother Courage, The House of Bernarda Alba, The Clearing, The Odyssey, The Magic Carpet* (Lyric Hammersmith), *Twelfth Night* (Bristol Old Vic), *The Nativity* (Young Vic) and the *Portugese Boat Plays* (Gate) with Director David Farr. Opera: *Rigoletto* and *Falstaff* (Grange Park Opera), *La Cenerentola* and *La Gazza Ladre* (Garsington Opera), *The Magic Flute* (Graz Opera House Opera). Film Production Design; *Simon Magus.* Angela is currently Head of Design at Bristol Old Vic Theatre School.

BECKY DAVIES /64
Becky Davies graduated from The Royal Welsh College of Music & Drama in 2007 with first class honours in Theatre Design. In the same year she won The Lord Williams Memorial Prize for Design and was shortlisted in The Linbury Biennial Prize for Stage Design. Based in Cardiff, she has been designing site-specific, outdoor, small-scale and touring theatre, for companies such as Theatr Genedlaethol Cymru, Welsh National Opera Max, Sherman Youth Theatre, Mr and Mrs Clark Ltd, Acting Out, Fluellen Theatre, Theatr Iolo, Mess Up The Mess and Spectacle Theatre, in addition to assistant work for Welsh National Youth Opera and BBC Wales. Becky is also an Associate Artist for Taking Flight Theatre Company, a National Diversity Award winning

company who produce inclusive and accessible theatrical experiences. In addition to her work in Theatre Design, Becky works as a Visual Artist and Senior Lecturer at the University of South Wales.
http://beckydavies85.tumblr.com

SIMON DAW /62
Simon studied Fine Art at Glasgow School of Art and a Postgrad at Motley Theatre Design Course.

Design credits include: *Owen Wingrave* (Set, Aldeburgh Music/ Edinburgh International Festival), *Wonderful Tennessee* (Lyceum, Sheffield), *The Secret Agent* (Traverse Theatre/Young Vic), *Eventual Progress* (Ekaterinburg State Ballet), *The Winters Tale, Democracy* and *The Daughter-in-law* (Crucible, Sheffield), *The Metamorphosis* (Linbury, ROH), *Dead Heavy Fantastic* and *Lost Monsters* (Liverpool Everyman), *As One* (Set, Royal Ballet), *Romeo and Juliet* (Shakespeare's Globe), *DNA, Baby Girl, The Miracle, The Enchantment* (National), *Elling* (Bush/Trafalgar Studios), *French without Tears* (ETT), *Rutherford and Son* (Royal Exchange, Manchester), *Romeo and Juliet* (RSC, Stratford/Albery), *Adam and Eve* (TPT, Tokyo), *Kebab* (Royal Court Theatre Upstairs), *Bloom* (Rambert) and *The Stepfather* (Candoco). Installation/ performance commissions include: *The Competition* (Shoreditch Town Hall), *3rd Ring Out* (UK tour), *Wave Structures, Hopefully it Means Nothing, Sea House* (Aldeburgh Festival), and *New Town* (site specific/Arches).
www.simondaw.com

MATT DEELY /65
Matt studied at Motley. He assisted Carl Tomms, associate to Stefanos Lazaridis on 20 operas including: *Lohengrin* (Bayreuth), *Faust* (Munich), *Macbeth* (Zurich), *Midsummer Night's Dream* (Venice), *Greek Passion, Wozzeck, Ring Cycle* (ROH) and *The Italian Season 2000* (ENO). Set Designer for: *iTMOi* (Akram Khan Company), *Kwubuka20* (Rwanda), *Celtic Woman, ELITE models look* (Shenzhen), *Beethoven's Symphony no.9* and *Romeo & Juliet* (K-Ballet, Tokyo), *Southwark Splash* (Royal Festival Hall), *Sun & Heir* and *Voices* (ROH), *2 Graves* (Arts theatre), *Pas, Pas moi, Va et vient, Beckett,* (TNP Lyon), *Petra von Kant* (Southwark Playhouse), *Ali to Karim* (USA tour). Video artist: *La nuit du train* (CDNT), *Satrouville* and *The Little Prince* (Le Grandes Ballets, Montreal). Art director: *Tor Hill* (Olympics opening ceremony).

Associate designer: *The Master and Margarita,*(Complicite), *Le Troyens* (ROH). Currently working with Chloe Obolensky and Debra Warner, *Fidelio* (La Scala Milan).
www.mattdeely.net/HOME.html

ES DEVLIN /66
Es designs for opera, theatre, live music, events and dance. She designed the Closing Ceremony of the London 2012 Olympics and is currently working on *Carmen* on the lake at Bregenz. Since 2005 she has collaborated with Kanye West designing for *Touch the Sky, Glow in the Dark, Watch The Throne* and *Yeezus* tours.

Other recent adventures include: arena, stadium and theatre tours for Muse, Miley Cyrus, Lady Gaga, Pet Shop Boys, Imogen Heap, Goldfrapp. Es has designed operas for The Royal Opera House Covent Garden, English National Opera, Glyndebourne, La Scala, Vienna; plays for National Theatre, Royal Shakespeare Company, Complicite, Almeida, Broadway; dance for The Royal Ballet, Sadlers Wells, Cullberg Ballett, Rambert, Russell Maliphant.

Es's designs have been awarded Olivier, Critics Circle, TMA, TPI and Linbury awards.
http://esdevlin.com

ROBIN DON /72
Robin studied Art and Engineering in Scotland and theatre design with Ralph Koltai. Bush Theatre premieres include *When I was a Girl I used to Scream and Shout,* Jonathan Harvey's *Beautiful Thing.* For the National Theatre *The Ticket of Leave Man* and *The Emperor Jones.* For RSC *Les Enfants du Paradis* and *Twelfth Night.* The Almeida Theatre production of *The Winter Guest* won him the Critics Circle and TMA Award Designer of the Year. Also production designer on the film with Alan Rickman directing Emma Thompson and Phyllida Law. Opera Premieres - Thea Musgrave's *Mary Queen of Scots* Scottish Opera - Deirdre Gribbin's *Hey Persephone!* Almeida Opera and Aldeburgh - American premiere Tippet's *The Midsummer Marriage* San Francisco Opera.

Robin is pleased to be working with Ralph on a new unified production -*The Figaro Trilogy* for WNO - *Barber of Seville* - *The Marriage of Figaro* - *Figaro's Divorce* (new) composer Elena Langer- Libretto David Pountney. Robin was part of the team winning Golden Troika, Prague Quadrennial.
www.robindon.com

MAX DOREY /74

Max trained in Theatre Design at Bristol Old Vic Theatre School, following a degree in English Literature and Theatre Studies at Leeds University. While at University, Max developed an interest in puppetry, writing and creating his own puppetry theatre shows, and building puppets for a variety of companies including Bristol Old Vic, Birmingham Rep and The Tobacco Factory. In 2013, he took the role of one of two assistant/trainee designers at The Royal Shakespeare Company. That year he was also a finalist for the Linbury Prize for Stage Design, held biannually by the National Theatre, during which time he worked with the National Theatre of Scotland. He also illustrates. He works across the country, and has been twice nominated for the Off West End awards in the "Best Set Design" category.
www.maxdorey.com

SUZI DOREY /75

Suzi designs predominantly within devised physical theatre and dance, on diverse projects ranging from large scale and site specific performances, to intimate studio shows. She trained at Aberystwyth University and followed the postgraduate course in Theatre Design at RWCMD in Cardiff. She has designed for *Hinterland* UK & International, *Serenade*, *Revolution*, *Paper Skies*, *In the New Moon* (The National Dance Company of Wales), *The Boy Who Went To The West Wind*, UK and US tour (Welsh National Opera), *Threshold* (Volcano Theatre, choreographer Marc Rees), *Beauty* (Aberystwyth Arts Centre) and has collaborated for the last ten years with choreographer Sean Tuan John on film and theatre work *Happiness Repeats Itself*, *Phantasma*, *The Deadhead Show*, *Kill the Klowns*, *Wonderfully Grimm*, *Tear Us Apart*, and also for his children's dance theatre company Bombastic Dance. She has taught Theatre Design for the last 8 years at University of Wales Trinity Saint David.
http://suzidoreydesign.moonfruit.com/profile/4551973912

OLIVIA DU MONCEAU /76

Olivia du Monceau lives and works as a set and costume designer in the UK. Her career has developed through a number of theatrical disciplines; including theatre, exhibitions and art installations. Recent prominent collaborations have been with LGBT organisation Homotopia, exhibiting the life of transgender icon April Ashley and designing with the site-specific company dreamthinkspeak. Other unusual site-specific designs have taken place in cathedrals, warehouses and fire stations. In 2012 she was nominated for an Off the West End Award for *A Russian Play*. In 2013 she was selected to represent the UK as part of the World Stage Design exhibiting *Gale Force Council House Movie Star*, an installation exploring ageing Drag Culture. Her recent commission by the Liverpool Art Biennial, reconstructing the infamous Peacock Room for the Whistler Exhibition, is on view at The Bluecoat Gallery. The *April Ashley Portrait of a Lady* exhibition runs at the Museum of Liverpool until December 2014.
http://oliviadumonceau.com

ALEX EALES /78

Design for Opera: *Marriage Of Figaro* (Salzburg Festival), *Don Giovanni* (Danish Royal Opera), *The House Taken Over* (Festival d'Aix-en-Provence), *Cosi fan Tutte* (Opera Holland Park), *Clemency* (ROH2 Linbury Studio and Scottish Opera), *Idomeneo* (English National Opera), *Tarantula in Petrol Blue* (Aldeburgh Music), *The Crocodile* (Arcola Theatre). Design for Theatre: *Regeneration* (Royal Northampton and Tour), *Into The Woods* (Châtelet Theatre, Paris), *Not I*, *Footfalls*, *Rockaby* (Royal Court and tour), *Alles weitere kennen Sie aus dem Kino* (Deutsches Schauspielhaus, Hamburg), *Fraulein Julie* (Schaubühne, Berlin and Barbican), *Reise durch die Nacht* (Schauspielhaus, Cologne, Berlin and Avignon festival), *Brimstone and Treacle*, *Ghosts* (Arcola Theatre), *Design For Living* (Salisbury Playhouse), *Say It With Flowers*, *Small Hours* (Hampstead Theatre studio), *The Breath Of Life* (Lyceum Theatre, Sheffield), *Dyled Eileeen*, *Spring Awakening - the musical* (Theatr Genedlaethol and Tour), *The Devil Inside Him* (National Theatre Wales), *Wunschkonzert* (Schauspielhaus, Cologne and Berlin), *Jungfruleken* (Kungsliga Dramatiska Teatern, Stockholm).
www.alexeales.co.uk

MATT EDWARDS /80

Matt trained at the Motley Theatre Design School in London. He has designed for Vanessa Redgrave and was awarded Best Design for the London New Play Festival. He has over fifteen years' experience in Theatre Set and Costume design, Installation Art, Design for Choreography and Film and Television set design, and also designs, produces and installs for galleries and exhibitions. He collaborates closely within teams and has extensive experience as a scenic artist, prop maker and sculptor / craftsperson. He is currently a Visiting Tutor for University of the Arts London and Rose Bruford College and has recently assisted Tim Goodchild on Elf. He is also on an internship at Brighton and Hove Museums Design Department and training in AutoCAD at Brighton College. His design for *The Old Woman, The Buffalo and The Lion of Manding* is currently on a second tour. Matt completed his MA in Museum and Exhibition Design in November 2012, from Lincoln University. In addition to this, he is a fully qualified teacher (P.G.C.E. in Art and Design from Brighton University 2004) with experience of working with students at post-graduate and graduate tutor/lecturing in Set and Costume design at Arts University Bournemouth (BA and MA students, April 2013- April 2014), Laban (BA and MA students) and Rose Bruford College. He has worked with undergraduate, Sixth Form, Secondary and Primary level students (2005-2009), including teaching Art and Design in Ghana with Global Link. He has run design-based workshops for the Royal National Theatre and has delivered his own Art, Design (2D and 3D) and Computer Aided Animation based Workshops.
www.behance.net/Matt_Edwards

PAUL EDWARDS /81

Paul Edwards studied Stage Design graduating with honours from the Royal Academy of Dramatic Art where he is now an associate member. He has designed internationally for theatre, ballet, rock shows and opera in 22 countries. He was a member of the winning British design team of the *Golden Triga* at the Prague Quadrennial 2003.

RICHARD EVANS /82

Richard is a set, costume and production designer for theatre, film and installation, working throughout the UK and Internationally. Richard trained at the Royal Scottish Academy of Music and Drama in Glasgow, and when graduating he was presented the Julia Stewart Award for the Best Undergraduate Student in the School of Drama. Alongside his freelance theatre work, Richard is Associate Designer for Sell A Door Theatre Company, whom he has worked with since 2011. He has also worked extensively in TV and Film, as a buyer, art director and set dresser. Richard's recent design credits include: *Seusssical* (2012 West End Premiere, 2013 revival, 2014 Hong Kong National Premiere), *Avenue Q* (2013 Edinburgh, 2014 UK National Tour, 2014 Hong Kong), *Kidnapped* (UK National Tour), *The History Boys* (Greenwich Theatre, London Revival) and set design for *Merchant of Venice* (Lazarus Theatre) for which he was nominated for an Off West End Award.
www.rdevans.com

JONATHAN FENSOM /83

Jonathan trained at Nottingham Polytechnic. Theatre productions include: *Julius Caesar, The Duchess of Malfi, A Midsummer Nights Dream, Henry V, Henry IV part 1 and 2, Loves Labours Lost, Hamlet, King Lear ,Gabrial, The Mysteries* (Shakespeare's Globe Theatre), *Becky Shaw, The Homecoming, Big White Fog* (Almeida), *The Accrington Pals* (Royal Exchange Theatre), *Happy Now?* (National Theatre), *The Goat* (Traverse), *Pygmalion* (Broadway), *Rapture, Blister, Burn* (Hampstead), *Journey's End* (West End and Broadway), *The Faith Healer* (The Gate, Dublin and Broadway), *The American Plan* (New York), *Smaller* (West End and UK tour), *Burn / Citizenship / Chatroom* (National Theatre), *God of Hell* (Donmar), *What the Butler Saw* (Hampstead and Westend), *Some Girls* (Westend), *Duck, Talking to Terrorists* (Out of Joint, Royal Court and UK tour), *Six degrees of Separation, National Anthems* (Old Vic), *Twelfth Night* (West End), *Cloud Nine; Copenhagen* (Sheffield Crucible), *The Sugar Syndrome* (Royal Court), *M.A.D., Little Baby Nothing, Backroom* (Bush), *Small Family Business* and *Little Shop of Horrors* (West Yorkshire Playhouse), *Born Bad, In Arabia We'd All Be Kings, Abigail's Party* (Hampstead), *My Night With Reg* and *Dealer's Choice* (Birmingham Rep), *Be My Baby* (Soho and UK tour), *After the Dance, Hay Fever* (OSC), *The Mentalists* (National Theatre). Opera: *Wozzeck* (Birmingham Opera and European tour), *The Jacobin* (Buxton Opera). Ballet: *Swan Lake* (San Fransico Ballet). Designs for television and film include: *tvSSFBM EHKL a Surreal Film* (Arena for BBC), *Tomorrow La Scala* (BBC). Jonathan was Associate Designer on *Disney's The Lion King*, which premiered at the New Amsterdam Theatre on Broadway and has subsequently opened worldwide. Jonathan was nominated for a Tony Award for his set design for *Journey's End*, the production won the Tony Award for Best Revival. Jonathan won the UK Theatre Award for best design in 2013 for *The Accrington Pals*.

RICHARD FOXTON /84

Design credits include: *Blonde Bombshells of 1943*, *Chicago* (Coliseum Theatre, Oldham), *Takeaway* (Theatre Royal Stratford East), *The Winter's Tale* (Mercury Theatre, Colchester), *And then the dark...*(New Wolsey Theatre, Ipswich), *Ladies' day*, *Noises Off* (Royal Court Theatre, Liverpool), *The Picture of Doreen Gray* (Lipservice), *On the Piste* (John Godber Co.) in addition to designs for: Watford Palace Theatre, Salisbury Playhouse, West Yorkshire Playhouse, York Theatre Royal, Octagon Theatre – Bolton, Bath Theatre Royal, Sheffield Theatres, Harrogate Theatre, Hull Truck, Wakefield Theatre Royal, TAG Glasgow, North Country Theatre and Contact Theatre -Manchester. He has twice been nominated for the TMA design award & has won five Manchester Evening News Design Awards most recently in 2008 for *Oh, What a Lovely War!* (Octagon Theatre, Bolton). He was a designer judge of the Linbury Prize and his design for *Murderer Hope of Womankind* (Whitworth Art Gallery) was exhibited at Prague Quadrennial.

LIZZIE FRENCH /85

Lizzie French and Cadi Lane studied Theatre Design at Royal Welsh College of Music and Drama, graduating with first-class honours in 2014. Both are interested in the creative nature of devised theatre and the exciting design process that accompanies this. Together their work is surreal, playful and imaginative.
www.lizziefrench.co.uk

GARETH FRY /205

Gareth Fry is an award winning sound designer best known for creating work for leading UK theatre directors such as Katie Mitchell and Complicite's Simon McBurney. In 2011 he was voted chair of the newly formed Association of Sound Designers (ASD). In 2012 he was asked by Danny Boyle to design the sound effects for the Opening Ceremony of the 2012 Olympic Games. He won the 2007 Olivier Award for his work on *Waves* at the National Theatre with Katie Mitchell, for which he was described by The Guardian newspaper as "visionary". He won the 2009 Olivier

Award for his work on National Theatre of Scotland's *Black Watch* directed by John Tiffany, and the 2009 Helpmann Award for the shows performance in Australia.

His work includes 20 productions at the Royal National Theatre, 12 at the Royal Court, and countless more at venues such as the Donmar Warehouse, Old Vic, Young Vic and in the West End. He has worked extensively internationally, including New York, Berlin, Cologne and Dublin.

PATRICIA GRASHAM

Patricia graduated with a first class degree in Spatial Design in 2010 and has since worked as a freelance designer and project manager. As well as teaching at The Royal Welsh College of Music & Drama, Bristol Old Vic Theatre School and Bucks New University she has her own practice designing, visualising and producing artwork for landscape, exhibition and event. Patricia recently collaborated on an exhibit at the Brighton Festival. She was heavily involved in the production of *World Stage Design 2013* and the UK tour of *Transformation & Revelation: UK Design for Performance* in collaboration with the V&A, Summerhall in Edinburgh and Bonnington Gallery at Nottingham Trent University.

CHRIS GYLEE /86

Chris's process places the story and its needs at the centre of his designs, whether from text or in the devising room, for a theatre or in less traditional surroundings. He has designed for The Tricycle, Bristol Old Vic, Tobacco Factory, Oval House, Theatre 503, Southwark Playhouse, The Egg, and also in a burnt-out violin workshop, a Victorian ball-court, a vast 1960s school hall, an Oxford Street office, and a cemetery. Chris trained at the Bristol Old Vic Theatre School and with Cheek by Jowl, and was nominated in 2012 for an Arts Foundation Fellowship. He is also an illustrator.
www.chrisgylee.co.uk

PAUL HALGARTH /87

Since gaining a first-class honours degree in Performance Design and Production at Bretton Hall, University of Leeds, Paul has worked as a freelance lighting designer, re-lighter, programmer and production electrician on tour and in producing and receiving theatres. Having also worked in the electrics department at the West

Yorkshire Playhouse, he has now moved into a career in education. He is currently a lecturer in Theatre and Performance Design and Technology at The Liverpool Institute for Performing Arts, with academic interests in the use of light as a communicate element, scenography and the role of technology in performance.

ABIGAIL HAMMOND /88

Abigail's dance background includes experimental dance at Dartington College of Art in the 1970's, followed by studying Dance Theatre at the Laban Centre, graduating in 1985. She has created costumes for over 100 choreographic works. She is the resident designer for the National Youth Dance Company for 13 years and Tavaziva Dance for 6 years. Theatre work includes *The Hobbit* (VFP Ltd), which had two West End runs. Currently working with Jasmin Vardimon on *The Maze Project*, this is their fifth collaboration following *7734*, *Freedom*, *Inbetween* and *Park*. Teaching: The Royal Academy of Dance, London College of Fashion, Laban, and Croydon College. Community projects: National Theatre Education Unit, English Heritage, English National Ballet, the Barbican Centre, the V&A and most recently with Sadler's Well's Creative Learning department. Abigail is Pathway Leader in Costume Design at Wimbledon College of Art. Her research focuses on the uniqueness of costume design in contemporary dance.
www.meledesign.co.uk/Mele_Design/Home.html

AMELIA JANE HANKIN /90

Amelia is currently Trainee Designer at the Royal Shakespeare Company. She trained in Postgraduate Theatre and Costume Design at RADA after a previous degree in Architecture from The University of Nottingham. Recent design credits include: *64 Squares* (Rhum and Clay, The New Diorama Theatre), *The Way You Make Me Feel* with Bryony Kimmings and Tim Grayburn at (The Soho Theatre), and *Forest Fringe*, *Mother Courage and Her Children*, directed by Annie Tyson (Drama Centre, London), *The Itinerant Music Hall* for the Lyric Hammersmith, Latitude 2014, Watford Palace Theatre and Greenwich and Docklands and *The Box* at Theatre Delicatessen and Latitude 2014. Previous design credits for Look Left Look Right include: *The Many Whoops of Whoops Town* (The Lyric, Hammersmith), *You Once Said Yes at Perth* (International Festival and UK Tour at The Roundhouse, Camden,

The Lowry, Salford and The Nuffield Southampton). Previous other design credits in 2013 include: *Six Pictures of Lee Miller*, (RADA Vanbrugh, Directed by Edward Kemp), *Love for Love*, (RADA Vanbrugh, Directed by Annie Tyson) and *The Red Helicopter* (Arcola Theatre, Directed by Alex Brown).

SHIZUKA HARIU /91

Shizuka is a multidisciplinary designer and co-director of SHSH Architecture+Scenography. After graduating with a masters' degree in Architecture from Tokyo University of Science, she worked for Shoichi Haryu Architects & Associates, for the architecture firm Adjaye Associates and for the scenographer Jan Vereswyveld. She also studied MA Scenography at Central Saint Martins and transferred her PhD at Leeds Metropolitan University. Her major works are *Sacred Monsters* for Akram Khan and Sylvie Guillem, *Cloud Crowd* (Japan Dance Project), *Penombre* (Les Ballet C de la B), *Compil D'Avril* (Charleroi Danses), *Benjamin Britten's Opera* for Frederic Wake-Walker and *Trout Stanley* for Matt Steinberg. Recently, she completed the exhibition and lighting design for *Sensing Spaces* (Royal Academy of Arts, London). She received many awards, such as Japanese Government Agency for Cultural Affairs, POLA Arts Foundation and many others.
www.shizukahariu.com/previous/cv/

KEN HARRISON /92

Ken trained at Motley Theatre Design Course. Recent works include: *Outlying Islands* (Firebrand Theatre), *Whisky Kisses*, *The Admirable Crichton*, *Single Spies* (Pitlochry), *Cinderella*, *The Snow Queen*, *The Lion, the Witch and the Wardrobe*, *Trumpets and Raspberries* (Royal Lyceum Theatre), *Death of a Salesman*, *Jane Eyre* (Perth Theatre) and *Our Man in Havana* (Nottingham Playhouse). Designs for National tours include *The 39 Steps*, *The Ladykillers*, *Time and the Conways*, *Mindgame* and *Stepping Out*. Past works include: *The Tempest*, *The Hound of the Baskervilles*, *Travesties* (Nottingham Playhouse), *Piaf*, *Intimate exchanges* (Dundee Rep), *Vanity Fair* (Northcott, Exeter), *The Fifteen Streets* (Mercury, Colchester), *The American Clock* (York Theatre Royal), *Famine* (Druid Theatre, Galway), *Castles in the Air* (Lyric Theatre, Belfast), and *Artists and Admirers* (Riverside Studios).
www.designersformation.com/project/ken-harrison/

KATHARINE HEATH /93

Katharine Heath trained in Theatre Design at Wimbledon School of Art and Central Saint Martins. With a love of unravelling stories in the walls of old buildings, Katharine enjoys working on immersive and site-responsive productions. Katharine is an associate creative of Theatre Delicatessen, and has worked in various roles with Punchdrunk, dreamthinkspeak and Geraldine Pilgrim. Recent designs include: *The Importance of Being Earnest*, *The Two Worlds of Charlie F* (Theatre Royal Haymarket), *Bee Detective* (Southbank Centre), *Savitri*, *The Wandering Scholar* (The Arcola), *Bush Bazaar* (The Bush), *My Heart is Hitchhiking Down Peachtree Street* (Contact), *Dorian Gray* (Riverside Studios), *The Canterbury Tales*, *A Study in Scarlet* (Southwark Playhouse), *SPACED*, *Henry V*, *Shelf-Life*, *A Christmas Carol*, *Chaika Casino* (Theatre Delicatessen), *L'Orfeo* (Silent Opera), *La Boheme*, *Flocking/ Crowd Joy*, *Dido and Aeneas*, *Edward Sharpe* (Old Vic Tunnels), *TOYNBEE* (Arts Admin, Toynbee Hall).
www.designersformation.com/project/katharine-heath/

SUSANNAH HENRY WOOD /94

Susannah trained at Wimbledon School of Art and Central Saint Martins. Her designs include *The Royal Duchess Superstore* (Broadway Theatre - Barking), *War Game* (Bristol Old Vic), *Scan Artists* (Roundhouse), *Nothing Is The End of the World (Except the End of the World)* (Finborough Theatre), *Being Tommy Cooper* (Franklin Productions - UK Tour), *179 Hackney Road* (Brighton Fringe and Bussey Building), *Gianni Schicchi / Zanetto* (Opera Holland Park), *The Wright Brothers* (Oxford Playhouse), Daniel Kitson's *It's Always Right Now Until It's Later* (NT and Traverse Theatre) and *C90* (Traverse Theatre and Sydney Opera House), *Little Voice* (Hull Truck), *Alice in Wonderland* (Brewhouse Theatre), *Pushing Up Poppies* (Theatre 503), *The Tempest* (Guildford Shakespeare Co), *Trilogy Part 2* by Nic Green (Arches Glasgow, BAC and Barbican), *Grumpy Old Women Live 2* and *Fifty Shades of Beige* (National Tour and West End), *The Christ of Coldharbour Lane* (costume design, Soho Theatre) and *Sweet Yam Kisses* for Kush Ensemble (Lyric Hammersmith).
www.susannahhenry.co.uk

INGRID HU /95

Ingrid is a scenographer who practises on an urban scale. She has designed for theatre, dance and sound performances, as well as public art projects. She received her MA in Scenography from Central St Martins in London in 2002, and subsequently joined Heatherwick Studio for 7 years, where she worked on a wide range of projects including the Lubetkin winning UK Pavilion for the 2010 World Expo. Her design for the exhibition of the instruments used in the 1000-year composition, *Longplayer*, is shorted listed for the 2014 Aesthetica Art Prize (3D design/sculpture), and a recreation of the work is part of the exhibition of eight contemporary artists at York St Mary's. Originally from Taipei, Taiwan, Ingrid is currently based in London. She is a member of the Society of British Theatre Designers and an associate lecturer at University of the Arts London.
www.jiachiann.net/about/

RICHARD HUDSON /96

Richard Hudson was born in Zimbabwe. He won an Olivier Award in 1988, and a Tony Award for *The Lion King* in 1998. He is a Royal Designer for Industry and received the Gold Medal for set design at the 2003 Prague Quadrennial. In 2005 he was given an Honorary Doctorate by the University of Surrey, and is a Companion of the Liverpool Institute for Performing Arts, and a Fellow of the RWCMD.

JACOB HUGHES /97

Jacob is a graduate of the Royal Welsh College of Music and Drama and is now based in London. He was a Linbury Prize for Stage Design finalist in 2011 and an Off West End Award and Theatre Critics of Wales Award nominee for best Set Designer last year. His design credits include: *The Aeneid* (Oxford Playhouse), *Napoleon Blown Apart* (Arcola Theatre) and *Titus Andronicus* (Bedlam Theatre and York Theatre Royal).
www.jacobhughesdesign.com

REBECCA HURST /97

Becky trained at Motley and has an MA in Communication Design (Illustration) from Central St Martins. For twelve years she was resident designer and latterly co-company director of Cartoon de Salvo, designs include: *The Ratcatcher of Hamlin*, *Meat & Two Veg* and *The Sunflower Plot*. Other designs include: *Kes* (Manchester Royal Exchange Main House), *Pinocchio* (York Theatre Royal), *Knives in Hens*, *Electra*, *Pomegranate*, (Manchester Royal Exchange Studio), *Treasured* (Birmingham Mac), *The Real Thing* (Northampton Theatre Royal), *The Tempest* and *Romeo and Juliet* (New Wolsey Ipswich), *Master Harold and the Boys* (Bristol New Vic Studio), and *Measure for Measure* (Cambridge Arts Theatre). She's worked with companies such as Punchdrunk, The House of Illustration, The V&A and The RSC as a visual artist on participatory projects. She also works as an Illustrator and animator. She in an associate lecturer on the BA Costume Design Course at Wimbledon College of Arts.
www.rebeccahurst.co.uk

ANA INÉS JABARES PITA /98

Ana Inés is a graduate from MA Scenography at The Royal Central School of Speech & Drama 2012. She has been trained as a Fine Artist in Sevilla and in the Accademia di Belle Arti di Palermo where she first came into contact with scenography. In parallel she has an extensive grounding in music, which made her become interested in sound as a fundamental part of the scenography. Her work includes an award-winning play *Sappho... in 9 fragments* (Best Design award –Ottawa Fringe Festival 2013) among others. Recently she has been announced as Overall Winner 2013 of the prestigious Linbury Prize and as one of the Gate's Jerwood Young Designers for 2014.
http://anainesjabarespita.blogspot.co.uk

KELLY JAGO /99

Kelly is a theatre designer and maker based in Bristol. As a designer she creates worlds that hold many secrets and surprises, revealed slowly to the audience as the stories unfold. Kelly particularly enjoys designing for site-specific performance, working in unusual spaces and has a great interested in designing more collaboratively on devised pieces of theatre. Working extensively as a prop maker and scenic painter, Kelly has undertaken a diverse range of projects including: Making a monster costume and god cloak for the *Book of Mormon* in both 2013 and again in 2014, fried breakfast costume details and sunflower headpieces for *X-factor the Musical*, jewel encrusted treasure chests for *La Corsaire* (The English Nation Ballet) and making giant broccoli for *Hippolyte* (Glyndebourne).
http://kellyjago.blogspot.co.uk

SOPHIE JUMP /100

Sophie was chosen to receive the Gold Award for exceptional achievement across all categories at *World Stage Design 2013* and has been selected to represent the UK at every Prague Quadrennial between 1999-2011. She is Associate Director of Seven Sisters Group who are well known for their site specific performances. Former Joint Honorary Secretary of the Society of British Theatre Designers, she is co-editor of the SBTD journal and of their Transformation & Revelation catalogue. Sophie is on the Linbury Prize Committee and is a visiting lecturer at CSSD, CSM and Wimbledon College of Art. She is currently working on a PhD about theatre designers Motley and Jocelyn Herbert.
http://sophiejump.co.uk

MONA KASTELL /101

Trained at Croydon College, Mona works as a theatre and costume designer in theatre, dance, film, experimental work, devised, street and physical theatre. She creates exciting visual concepts through a collaborative approach and with a constant interest in an eco friendly theatre industry. Mona pushes the boundaries of costume, bringing it to the centre of the performance instead of its typically established simple decorative role. In 2012, Mona was awarded the quality production funding by Creative Scotland to develop her sculptural creations in the costume-led performance *L'Eveil*, which was then devised and directed as part of Glasgow Arches Live. Recent works include: Cathy Marston's *Walking Shadows* (David Hughes Dance) as well as *Ghosts in the Garden* and *Escaping War* (Edinburgh International Festival).
www.monakastell.com

MERCEDES KEMP /130

Mercedes Kemp is Associate Director of Community and Research for WildWorks and Senior Lecturer in Fine Art at Falmouth University. Mercedes was born and grew up in Southern Spain. For the past thirty years she has lived in West Cornwall. Her freelance work includes commissions from The Eden Project, The Guardian and BBC Radio 3. She worked as a writer for Kneehigh Theatre Company in *Strange Cargo*, *Manel's Mango*, *Shop of Stories*, *Doubtful Island*, *Island of Dreams* and *A Very Old Man with Enormous Wings*. Since 2001 she has worked in close collaboration with Bill Mitchell, developing storylines and text for site-specific pieces in Malta, Cyprus, France, Belgium, the Occupied Territories of Palestine and all over the UK.

As well as the production of text and story line, her role within WILDWORKS involves creating and maintaining relationships with host communities, exploring their relationships with place and memory and creating text to fit each new location.

Her method involves a kind of eclectic ethnographic research into a variety of sources: archives, libraries, cemeteries, village halls, bus stops, local historians, town gossips, snapshots, old photographs, conversations, and, above all, a close observation of the process of memory and its effect on the value that people place on their environments.

SIMON KENNY /102

Simon trained in set and costume design at the Central School of Speech & Drama.

Recent designs include: *Ghosts* (Clwyd Theatr Cymru), *Saturday Night Fever* (UK tour), *Venus in Fur*, *The Collector* (English Theatre Frankfurt), *The Merchant of Venice* (Shakespeare's Globe), *Sweeney Todd, The Demon Barber of Fleet Street* staged in a pie and mash shop (Tooting Arts Club), *In the Next Room or the vibrator play* (St James/Ustinov Studio, Bath), *Island* (National Theatre and tour), *Vivienne* (Royal Opera House, Linbury Studio), two American Seasons at the Ustinov Studio, Bath, including *4000 Miles, Fifty Words* and *Red Light Winter; The Cunning Little Vixen* (Ryedale Festival), *Sleuth* (Watermill), *The Machine Gunners* (Polka), *Gross Indecency* (Duckie), *Someone Who'll Watch Over Me, The Belle's Stratagem, Antigone* (Southwark Playhouse), *Tales From the Bar of Lost Souls* (imitating the dog/National Theatre of Greece) and *Pedestrian*, a new play for one man and a goldfish (Bristol Old Vic and tour).
www.simonkenny.co.uk

DANNY KRASS /205

Danny has been living and working as a composer and sound designer in the UK since 2007. Theatrical credits include: *Spoiling, The Artist Man and the Mother Woman, Quiz Show, The Devil Masters* (Traverse Theatre); *Up To Speed* (Imaginate/ Ros Sydney); *The Adventures of Robin Hood* (Visible Fictions/Kennedy Centre); *The Voice Thief, Stuck, The Ballad of Pondlife McGurk, White, Kes*

(Catherine Wheels); *My House, A Small Story* (Starcatchers); *Peter Pan* (Sherman Cymru); *Skewered Snails, He-La* (Iron Oxide); *Mikey and Addie, Littlest Christmas Tree, Rudolf & Mr Snow, The Little Boy that Santa Claus Forgot* (Macrobert); *The Infamous Brothers Davenport* (Vox Motus/Royal Lyceum Theatre, Edinburgh); *One Thousand Paper Cranes* (Lu Kemp); *The Curious Scrapbook of Josephine Bean, Huff* (Shona Reppe Puppets) and *The Day I Swapped My Dad for Two Goldfish* (NTS Learn); *Couldn't Care Less* (Plutôt la Vie/ Strange Theatre), *The Tin Forest Govan & South West* (NTS), *Sanitise* (Melanie Jordan), and *Smokies* (Solar Bear). Danny will create and direct his own show, *Kind of Silence* in 2015.
www.dannykrass.com

EMMYLOU LAIRD /104

Emmylou recently completed an MA in Costume for Performance at London College of Fashion, graduating with a distinction in February 2014. Emmylou is interested in narrative and how it can be explored in design, the relationships between the performer and the audience, the costumes, setting, props and the body and how to make these different facets work in new, interesting and challenging ways in concert with and in support of performance and direction. "I work with material and process, idea and narrative. As an artist and designer I construct narratives for consumption and consideration by an audience".

CADI LANE /85

Lizzie French and Cadi Lane studied Theatre Design at Royal Welsh College of Music and Drama, graduating with first-class honours in 2014. Both are interested in the creative nature of devised theatre and the exciting design process that accompanies this. Together their work is surreal, playful and imaginative.

KATE LANE /104

Kate is a designer for performance specialising in live performance specifically costume design and is a founding member of performance collective Brave New Worlds. As a designer she is interested in creating moments where the design is the central feature of the performance. Her work has been shown both nationally and internationally, including at the Lilian Baylis Studio- Sadler's Wells, Southbank Centre, V&A and at the

Ravenna Festival- Italy and Musique Cordiale- France. As a Performance Artist with Brave New Worlds they have held residencies at Barbican Pit Lab and the Point, Eastleigh. Performances include Soho Theatre Downstairs and MK Gallery, Milton Keynes. She graduated in 2008 from the MA Costume Design for Performance (Distinction) where she won the MA Centenary Award for Costume. She has a BA in Visual Arts: Sculpture from Camberwell College of Arts and is an Associate Lecturer at Central Saint Martins.
www.katelane.co.uk

KAREN LAUKE /205

Karen Lauke is a sound designer, composer and sound artist with experience of creating and producing sound and music for theatre, live performance, installation, exhibition and most recently, film. In addition to traditional theatre sound design, Karen also works with field recordings, video and text, creating works that respond to local situations, environments and place. Her site-specific public artworks experiment with sound as the main focal point and incorporate many different forms of digital technology. Recent sound designs include: *House of Memories* (Collective Encounters/ Museum of Liverpool); *Out of Order* (Collective Encounters/Imperial War Museum North); *Not About Heroes* (Feelgood Theatre); *Wings* (PYFOP); *War Stories* (24:7 Theatre Productions); *Street in the Sky* (Encounter Productions); *Billy, the Monster and Me* (Colour the Clouds).
www.karenlauke.com

MARIE JEANNE LECCA /106

Marie-Jeanne was born in Bucharest and is now based in London. She has designed costumes for companies throughout the UK and Europe, including Vienna State Opera, Zurich Opera, Bavarian State Opera, The Bolshoi, Opera Bastille, Deutsche Opera Berlin, Bregenz Festival, Opéra de Lyon, English National Opera, Royal Opera House, WNO and Salzburg Festival. Operas for which she has designed cosumes include : *Wilhelm Tell, Mosè in Egitto, Lulu, Prince Igor, Les Troyens, Un Ballo in Maschera, Agrippina, Wozzeck, Der Ring des Nibelungen, Maskarade, The Greek Passion, Die Zauberflöte, Carmen, Moses and Aron, Khovanshchina, Il Trittico, Turandot, Jenůfa, Katya Kabanova, Die Frau ohne Schatten, Krol Roger* and late-20th-

century works include Weinburg's *The Passenger* and Zimmermann's *Die Soldaten*. She has designed sets and costumes for productions including: *Falstaff* and *Pellćas* and *Mélisande* (ENO), *Carmen* (Houston, Seattle, Minnesota) and *Thérèse Raquin* (Dallas). She is also known for her innovative and inventive puppet design which features widely in her work for opera including: *Faust, Un Ballo in Maschera* and *Die Zauberflöte*. The Martinů Foundation awarded her a medal for her costume designs for Martinů's operas *Julietta* and *The Greek Passion*. She was nominated for a BAFTA for *Amahi and the Night Visitors* and was a member of the British team that won The Golden Triga at the 2003 Prague Quadrennial.

MIKE LEES /105

Mike trained in Production Design at Rose Bruford School. Mike has designed sets and costumes for more than 200 productions throughout the UK, Europe, Middle East and America. The range of his work incorporates designs for large scale operas and musicals through to small single performer plays and pantomimes, including *Gone* (New Ambassadors Theatre), *Mathilde* (Vaudeville Theatre), *Fred Astaire: His Daughter's Tribute* (London Palladium), *What I Heard About Iraq* (Arts Theatre), *The Little Mermaid* (National Theatre of Dubai), *Sommer:14* (Finborough Theatre), *Count Oederland* (Arcola Theatre), *Calendar Girls* (Leicester and Tour), *Holding Hands At Paschendale* (Lyric Theatre Belfast and Tour), *The Stanhope Sisters* (Theatre Royal Bath), *Pete & Dud: Come Again* (Leicester Square Theatre) and *Whistle Down The Wind* (Churchill Theatre Bromley). As a Costume Designer and maker, he has created costumes and outfits for the National Theatre, the BBC, V&A, The Theatre Museum, the World Trade Fair, numerous recording artists including Lady Gaga's *Art Pop* and most recently for the *X Factor*.
www.mikeleesdesigns.com

VERENA LEO /108

Verena Leo is an interdisciplinary artist and a designer with a strong interest in the study of movement, the experience of time and the perception of spatial relations. Photography and drawing are important tools during the creative process and an integral part of her work. Like layers of paint she uses motion and stillness when composing

sceneries or using site-specific settings. Her objective is to evoke emotions and to spur the imagination of the spectator, who then develops his or her own stories. In 2011 she won a bursary for further studies in her field. It allowed her to work more intensively with dancers and to deepen her understanding of choreography and design in a contemporary context. Over the years she designed costumes and sets for various dance and short film productions.
http://verenaleo.com

JOHN LEONARD /205
John Leonard has been producing soundtracks for theatre for over forty years. Freelance since 1989, he was head of sound and associate artist for The Royal Shakespeare Company and has worked for theatre companies all over the U.K., in New York, Los Angeles, Ireland, Germany, Norway and Japan. He is a Fellow Of The Guildhall School and an Honorary Fellow of The Hong Kong Academy of Performing Arts.
www.johnleonard.co.uk

SARAH LEWIS /109
Sarah graduated with a first class degree in Theatre Design from Nottingham Trent in 2010. Within the month, she began working for the Education Department at Nottingham Playhouse, designing *The Red Shoes* for their youth theatre. This initial employment flowered into a solid working relationship and four years on, Sarah has designed eighteen productions for the Playhouse, from rural tour, *The Second Minute*, the 50th anniversary celebratory piece, *The Lost Plays* (both directed by Giles Croft), to main house youth theatre piece, *Enron* and many various Young Company pieces, including *4:48 Psychosis* and *A Clockwork Orange*. Sarah also works in Art Direction for Film and Events. She led the design for Toploader's music video *This is the Night* and has worked with Dave UKTV, styling the central venue at the Leicester Comedy Festival. Sarah is also a prop and puppet maker and runs her own business, Sarah Makes Puppets.
www.sarahlewisdesignportfolio.tumblr.com

ADRIAN LINFORD /110
Adrian studied at Wimbledon School of Art, and works mainly in Theatre and opera.
    Recent work includes: *Falstaff* (LA Opera), *The Grand Duchess of* Gerolstein (Santa Fe Opera), *Il Turco in Italia* (Nantes Opera & Grand Théâtre, Luxembourg), *The Castle*, *The Witch of Edmonton* and *The Tyrant* (RADA), *Eugene Onegin* (Royal Academy of Music), and the costume for *Sunday in the Park with George* (Théâtre du Châtelet Paris).
    Past designs include; *Poppy*, *Stars in the Morning Sky*, *Camino Real*, *The Glass Menagerie*, *Sondheim's Assassins*, *Orfeo ed Euridice* , *Betrayal*, *Kátya Kabanová*, *Die Fledermaus*, *King Priam*, *The Turn of the Screw*, *Così fan tutte*, *The Promise* and the co-design for *Il Trovatore* (Bastille Opera Paris), *The Shoemakers Wonderful Wife*, *Yerma* and *When Five Years Pass*, also *The Bald Soprano* and *The Maids* (Off-Broadway, New York).
    New productions in 2015 include *The Rake's Progress* for RAM and *Rigoletto* for Santa Fe Opera.
www.adrianlinford.com

SOPHIA LOVELL SMITH /112
Sophia trained at Bretton Hall. Recent productions include: *Duck!* (Z-Arts), *Shooting the Moon* (Strangeface), *The Mountain Shakers* (Spitalfields Music), *Kabaddi Kabaddi Kabaddi* (PBAB) and *Flathampton* (Royal & Derngate Theatres, Northampton). This won the 2013 Brighton Festival Children's Award. Sophia is now designing *Wave* for Nottingham Playhouse, *Inside Out* for Tell Tale Hearts and a second Spitalfields Music show; *Catch a Sea Star* for 0 - 2 year olds. Past productions: The Unicorn Theatre's *The Snow Queen* (BC India tour with Trestle Theatre), *Handa's Surprise* (LAT), 7 shows for Theatre by the Lake, Keswick, including *The Caretaker*, *The Flower Girls* (Graeae/Hampstead Theatre), *Spacehoppers* (Tell Tale Hearts), Trestle Theatre's *Tonight We Fly* (Arts Theatre & tour), *Jemima Puddle Duck & Her Friends* (The Unicorn Theatre), *Blackberry Trout Face* (20 Stories High), *Common Heaven* and *The Tales of Molly Moonshine* (Theatre Centre) and *Through the Wardrobe* (Royal & Derngate Theatres). Sophia's primary schools projects include outdoor play structures. She works with the National Theatre running design workshops and designs for Mountview Theatre School and Bennison Fabrics.
www.sophialovellsmith.co.uk

RACHEL MACALLAN /113
Rachel is a set and costume designer and a recent graduate from The Royal Conservatoire of Scotland. Over the last few years, as an emerging designer, Rachel has designed set and costume for many productions including: *The Birthday of the Infanta* (Solar Bear), *Miseryguts* (The Royal Conservatoire of Scotland) and *Bubble Wrap* (Aberdeen Performing Arts Youth Theatre Company) as part of NTS' Tin Forest Festival. Rachel also works regularly as an assistant designer and costume maker and has previously worked with Bard in the Botanics, Sell a Door Theatre Company and BBC Comedy.
www.rachelmacallan.com

NADIA MALIK /116
Nadia is a costume designer, lecturer and researcher. Her work has encompassed new writing, original and adapted period classics, opera, traditional folk and contemporary dance, musicals, site-specific/experimental devised work and live art since 2002. Recent show credits include design for the Greenwich and Docklands Festival, the V&A and the award-winning Elastic Theatre. With a collaborative approach to performance devising, Nadia's design concepts explore the human body and movement, and develop character and narrative through visual experimentation, using design practice to engage an audience and communicate meaning within performance. Nadia has taught at various universities including University of the Arts London, the Royal Academy of Dance and is currently a Lecturer in Costume at the University of Huddersfield. She has worked nationally and internationally as a performance practitioner and has a BA in Textile Design (Nottingham Trent) and an MA in Costume Design for Performance (London College of Fashion, UAL).
www.nadiamalik.com

GARANCE MARNEUR /114
Garance is an award-winning international stage and costume designer. Her work crosses a range of genres: theatre, dance, opera, and museums. She is also an Associate Lecturer and Visiting Practitioner for Central Saint Martins School of Art. She studied fine art in Paris, and went on to graduate with First Class Honours in Design for Performance from Central Saint Martins in London. Garance has worked with many leading theatre companies in the UK and Internationally, and has exhibited her work in major Institutions such as the V&A and the National Theatre in London, the National Exhibition for the Prague Quadrennial'11 in Czech Republic, and London Architecture Week. Overall winner of the Linbury Biennial Prize for Stage Design 2007, she has also been nominated Most Successful Freelancer in the Creative Enterprise Awards 2009 & 2010.
www.garancemarneur.com

THOMASIN MARSHALL /117
Originally a graduate from Rose Bruford College, Thomasin went on to train at Motley. Alongside her designs she is also a freelance scenic painter. Theatre work has included: *Chants Des Catacombs* (Present Tense Ensemble, Castlemaine Theatre Festival, Melbourne), *The Last Polar Bears* (National Theatre of Scotland), *Roma and the Flanelettes*, *A Dolls House*, *Colder Than Here*, *Knives in Hens* (Theatre by the Lake, Keswick), *The Snow Queen* (Assosciate Designer, The Rose Theatre Kingston), *Bunnies* (Bike Shed Theatre, Exeter), *Serendip* (Bike Shed Theatre, Exeter), *Henry IV Part One* (Drum Theatre, Plymouth), *The Misanthrope* (Drum Theatre Plymouth), *The Hidden City Festival* (Part Exchange Co). For the Rose theatre, Kingston; *Hamlet* (IYAF festival),*The Beggars Opera*, *Two*, *The Musicians* and *The Girl Who Never Forgot* (Youth Theatre Productions). As Assistant designer: *The Knowledge* (Bush Theatre), *Little Platoons* (Bush Theatre), *One Small Step...One Giant Leap* (Barbican Theatre, Plymouth).
www.thomasindesign.co.uk

TUPAC MARTIR /119
Tupac is a visual designer and creative director who has created a varied portfolio of projects in the arts and entertainment scene. He is also the founder of Satore Studio, which creates light and visual design for live entertainment productions. Born in Reading, Berkshire, Tupac obtained his BFA, from Creighton University under the guidance of John Thein and National Geographic Photographer Fr. Don Doll. He has provided production design, visuals and lighting direction for Elton John, Sting, Beyoncé, Alexander McQueen, Vivienne Westwood, Thomas Tait, Coachella, Nederland Dans Theater, the V&A Museum and the Serpentine Gallery. His work has been published in major publications, such as Wallpaper* Magazine, Live Design and LSI, and he has developed a reputation for creating unique productions for several art forms including fashion, music, theatre, opera and ballet.

LOIS MASKELL /118

Lois is a set and costume designer. Her approach considers the manifold interpretations of the performance space, responding with imagination, intelligence and relevance. Lois has enjoyed consistent work as a freelance designer, scenic artist and lecturer since 2005, in all genres of performance. Recent collaborations include Action Transport Theatre Company, Northern Spirit, 20 Stories High, dreamthinkspeak, Monkeywood Theatre, COAL Theatre, Royal Exchange Manchester, The Lowry and Liverpool Everyman and Playhouse Theatres. Lois is a lecturer in Theatre and Performance Design and Technology at The Liverpool Institute For Performing Arts (LIPA).
www.loismaskell-design.moonfruit.com

GARY MCCANN /120

Gary trained at Nottingham Trent University. Recent productions include: *Die Fledermaus* (Norwegian National Opera), *La Traviata* (National Opera Bucharest), *The Pitmen Painters* (National Theatre, UK, Friedman Theatre Broadway, Volkstheater Vienna), *La Voix Humaine*, *L'heure Espagnole*, *The Barber Of Seville* (Nationale Reisopera Of Holland), *Fidelio* (Garsington Opera), *The Flying Dutchman* (Yekaterinburg State Opera Russia), *The Girl In The Yellow Dress* (Market Theatre, Johannesburg, and Baxter Theatre, Capetown), *33 Variations* (Volkstheater Vienna), *Owen Wingrave* and *La Pietra Del Paragone* (Opera Trionfo, Amsterdam), *Cosi Fan Tutte* (Schoenbrunn Palace Vienna), *Three Days In May* and *Dangerous Corner* (Kenwrights, National Tour), *Faramondo* (Goettingen Festival Germany And Hobart Festival Tazmania). Forthcoming Productions include: *Macbeth* (Vienna State Opera), *The Golden Cockerel* (Santa Fe Opera), *L'assedio Di Calais* (Nationale Reisopera), *Becoming Santa Claus* (Dallas Opera), and *The Sound Of Music* (National Tour).
www.garymccann.com

HOLLY MCCARTHY /122

Holly graduated from the Royal Welsh College of Music and Drama in 2005, with a BA Hons in Theatre Design and has since worked both as a maker and designer of set and costume.

Her theatre credits include work for companies such as Music Theatre Wales and the Hamburger Kammerspiele, National Theatre Wales, Volcano and Theatr Pena. Along side her theatre and teaching work she has branched out into television, working for the BBC (*Doctor Who*) and most recently Starz/BBC Worldwide (*Da Vinci's Demons*). She is also honoured to have co-designed the last SBTD exhibition - Transformation and Revelation - and to have been a key part of the team, which took the exhibit into the V&A. Holly is extremely proud to be a founding member of Theatr Pena – a company that has a passion for classic drama and features older women at the heart of all their work.
http://hollymccarthydesign.
carbonmade.com

IONA MCLEISH /123

Iona McLeish has enjoyed an extensive career as a designer for theatre and performance. Productions include: *Heldenplatz* by Thomas Berhard (Arcola Theatre), *Abundantly Yours from Zimbabwe* by Gillian Plowman (Oval House Theatre), *Women of Troy* (Olivier National Theatre), *For the Love of a Nightingale* by Timberlake Wertenbaker (RSC), *India Song* by Duras (Theatr Clwyd), *Miss Julie* by Stridberg (Oldham Coliseum), *House of Mirth* adapted from Edith Wharton's novel (Cambridge Theatre Company), *Configurations* by Shobana Jeyasingh Dance Company, *The Resistible Rise of Arturo Ui* by Brecht (Half Moon Theatre), *Pal Joey* by Rodgers and Hart (New Half Moon Theatre and Transfer), *Merchant of Venice* (Young Vic), *Savannah Bay* by Duras (BAC and Tour). She received the London Theatre Prize for Best Design for *Heresies* by Deborah Levy (RSC at the Barbican). She is currently Programme Director of BA (Hons) Theatre Design at Rose Bruford College of Theatre and Performance. She is a committee member of the SBTD.
http://ionamcleish.com

MARK MELVILLE /205

Mark is a composer and sound designer for theatre, dance and film and trained at Leeds College of Music. His composition and sound design work has been presented through the UK and internationally and exhibited as part of the Prague Quadrennial theatre design festival in 2011 and at the Victoria & Albert Museum in 2012.

Recent theatre projects include: *God Bless the Child* (Royal Court Theatre); *Tomorrow* (Vanishing Point/ Cena Contemporânea festival (Brasilia)/ Brighton Festival), *Tramway* (Glasgow), *National Theatre Studio* (London); *Dragon* (Vox Motus/National Theatre of Scotland/ Tianjin People's Art Theatre, China) winner of the 2014 CATS award for Best Technical Presentation; *The Beautiful Cosmos of Ivor Cutler* (Vanishing Point/National Theatre of Scotland) winner of the 2014 CATS award for Best Music and Sound; *Swallows & Amazons* (Theatre by the Lake); *Saturday Night* (Vanishing Point/National Theatre of Portugal); *My Shrinking Life*, *Knives In Hens*, *Miracle Man*, *Empty* (National Theatre of Scotland).

Mark is also an Associate Artist of The Dukes Playhouse and has worked as composer and sound designer on a number of their productions including: *Hamlet*, *Your Country Needs You (but I don't need my country)*, *No Fat Juliets*, *Robin Hood*, *Pierrepoint*, *The Unsociables*, *The BFG*, *Two*, *Merlin*, *Quicksand*, *The Snow Queen*, *Peter Pan*, *Children of Killers*, *Of Mice and Men*, *Jason & The Argonauts*.

ANNE MINORS /124

AMPC design any type of performance space; anywhere that people gather or observe. Since 1996 the practice has been creating the best conditions for presenting and enjoying performance, delivering award winning, high quality, value for money performance spaces with well integrated technical facilities. Working with architects, engineers and acousticians, we provide a link between the worlds of building and live performance, representing the needs of the end user; directors, designers, performers, technicians and audience who will use the building in a variety of different ways. We are a creative, dynamic team from a number of different backgrounds with experience in architecture, lighting design, production management, engineering, set and costume design, prop making and as clients, teachers and performers. Past projects include: The Royal Opera House redevelopment and Linbury Studio – London, Koerner Hall- Toronto, The Egg Children's Theatre- Bath, Hull Truck Theatre and the recently completed Zorlu Center- Istanbul.
www.ampcstudio.com

BECKY MINTO /126

Becky works as a set and costume designer covering a wide range of productions for main-house theatre, site-specific and large outdoor spectacles, dance and aerial performances. Theatre companies she has designed for include: National Theatre of Scotland, The Royal Lyceum, Citizen's Theatre, Vanishing Point, Grid Iron, Dundee Rep, Visible Fictions, Perth Rep and Lung Ha's. Outside of theatre she has designed for Scottish Dance, outdoor spectacle specialists Walk The Plank and Aerial Performance companies All or Nothing and Upswing. Becky designed the opening ceremony for the European capital of Culture in Turku 2011 and more recently was Design Associate for the Opening Ceremony and designed the Closing Ceremony for Glasgow 2014 Commonwealth Games. She teaches on the Performance Costume course at the University of Edinburgh and mentors design students for the Royal Conservatoire of Scotland.
www.stellarquines.com/2013/05/01/
becky-minto/

BILL MITCHELL /128

Bill is WildWorks Artistic Director. He has worked as director /designer with Perspectives, Theatre Centre in London, Roundabout Young Peoples Theatre, Walk the Plank and the Young Vic Theatre in London.

As a freelance designer he has worked with many theatre companies including Avon Touring, Theatre Foundry, Birmingham Rep, Soho Poly, the Royal National Theatre, The Donmar Theatre, Lyric Theatre Hammersmith and with The Shaman Company in Budapest.

Bill became a member of the Kneehigh team in 1988 when he moved to Cornwall and then their Artistic Director from 1995 until 2005.

For Kneehigh he devised and directed many productions including *Ship of Fools*, *Carmen* and *Arabian Nights* and designed most shows from *Tregeagle* in 1989.

Recent design projects include, *The Red Shoes*, *The Bacchae*, *Tristan & Yseult*, *Nights at the Circus* and *A Matter Of Life And Death* all directed by Emma Rice.

His work has been seen in Europe, USA, China, Syria, Australia and New Zealand.

Over the years he has created many large site-specific and landscape theatre projects including *Ghost Nets*, *Hells Mouth* and *A Very Old Man with Enormous Wings*. This last production was inspired by a Gabriel Garcia Marquez short story and performed to great acclaim in Malta (2003), Cyprus (2004) and in 2005 performed to sell out audiences in Hayle, Cornwall. In 2005 Bill created his own company WildWorks to explore a theatre involving place and the people who belong to it as a vital part of the production. Over the past 9 years

Bill's vision and ideas have grown into several large scale, acclaimed shows such as *The Beautiful Journey*, *Souterrain*, and most notably *The Passion*, for which Bill was awarded Best Director by the TMA in 2011.
http://wildworks.biz/about/the-team/bill-mitchell/

CATHERINE MORGAN /134

Catherine graduated from Nottingham Trent University in 2009. Since then she has gained experience in film and television including working regularly for the BBC but has predominately worked in theatre. Her theatre design credits include: *Twelfth Night* (the New Wimbledon Theatre Studio), *Othello* (the Bussey Building, London), *Ring of Envy* and *Verona Road* (Intermission Theatre), *Eisteddfod* (High Tide at the Latitude Festival), *Baba Shakespeare* (RSC Courtyard Theatre and for Arcola Theatre), *London Let's Get Visceral* (the Old Vic Tunnels), *Gerbils in a Glass Cage* (The Space, London), *Fit for Purpose* (the Pleasance Theatre, Edinburgh), *Story Project 2* (the Southwark Playhouse), *Macbeth* and *Hobson's Choice* (the Broadway Theatre, London). She has acted as assistant to leading designers including Giles Cadle, Leslie Travers, Tom Cairns, Soutra Gilmour, Tim Goodchild, Ben Stones and Helen Goddard.
www.catherinemorgandesigns.co.uk

RUARI MURCHISON /135

Designs include: *Mappa Mundi*, *Frozen*, *The Waiting Room*, *The Red Balloon* (National), *Titus Andronicus* (RSC), *Othello* (Trafalgar Studios), *The Solid Gold Cadillac* (Garrick), *A Busy Day* (Lyric), *Peggy Sue Got Married* (Shaftsbury), *The Snowman* (Peacock), *Toyer, Betty and Jane* (Arts), *The Three Sisters on Hope Street*, *The Glass Room*, *Gone to L.A.* (Hampstead), *Henry IV- I and II* (Washington Shakespeare Company, USA), *West Side Story*, *The Sound of Music* (Stratford Festival, Canada), *Hamlet* (Elsinore), *Oleanna*, *Educating Rita*, *Pravda*, *The Critic*, *The Real Inspector Hound* (Chichester). Ruari has designed for many regional theatres in the United Kingdom including: Birmingham Rep (Associate Artist), West Yorkshire Playhouse, Northern Stage, Watford Palace, Bristol Old Vic, Nottingham Playhouse, Plymouth Theatre Royal, Liverpool Everyman and Playhouse, Salisbury Playhouse, Theatr Clwyd. Operas include: *Der Freischutz* (Finnish National Opera), *Peter Grimes*, *Cosi fan Tutte*

(Luzerner Opera), *La Cenerentola*, *Il Barbiere di Siviglia* (Garsington), *L'Italiana in Algeri* (Buxton), *Les Pelerins de la Mecque*, *ZaZa* (Wexford). Ballets include: *Bruise Blood* (Shobana Jeyasingh Dance Company), *Landschaft und Erinnerung* (Stuttgart), *The Protecting Veil* (BRB), *The Snowman* (Seoul, London, National Tour).
www.ruarimurchison.com

CONOR MURPHY /136

Conor studied Theatre Design at Wimbledon School of Art in London and later gained an MA in Scenography in Holland. He has designed sets and costumes for opera, theatre and dance productions in the UK and internationally for companies including the Royal Opera House, Opera North, the Royal Swedish Opera, the Nationale Reisopera, the Korean National Opera, Rambert Dance Company, Birmingham Royal Ballet, the Abbey Theatre and the Bristol Old Vic. He was recently awarded the bronze medal for exceptional achievement at the *World Stage Design 2013* exhibition in Cardiff.
www.conormurphy.com

NEIL MURRAY /138

Neil Murray was resident director/designer at Dundee Rep between 1980 and 1991. As director/designer at Northern Stage between 1991 and 2012 his work included designs for: *A Clockwork Orange*, *Wings of Desire*, *Animal Farm* and *1984*. Other work includes *Pandora's Box*, *Brief Encounter* and *Steptoe and Son* (Kneehigh Theatre), *Mrs Warren's Profession*, *Vanity Fair*, *Copenhagen*, *Romeo and Juliet* (Royal Lyceum, Edinburgh) *Tutti Frutti* (National Theatre, Scotland) and *A Tender Thing* (The Royal Shakespeare Company). Awards include The Evening Standard, Critic's Circle, an Obie and Outer Critic's Circle award for Brief Encounter in London and on Broadway. Designs for 2014 include: *The Threepenny Opera* (Nottingham and West Yorkshire Playhouses/Birminham Rep/New Wolsey, Ipswich and Graeae co- production), *An Audience with Meow Meow* (Berkeley Rep, California), *The Lion the Witch and the Wardrobe* (Rose Theatre, Kingston) and *The Venetian Twins* (Royal Lyceum, Edinburgh).
www.neilmurray.org.uk

KIMIE NAKANO /140

Kimie Nakano studied Literature at University in Tokyo, Theatre Costume at ENSATT in Paris and holds a Theatre Design MA at Wimbledon College of Art in London. She strives to create intercultural projects for stage and film, internationally. Set and costume designs include: *Carmen* (Lithuanian National Opera and Ballet Theatre), *The Little Prince* (Les Grands Ballets Canadiens de Montréal, choreographer Didy Veldman). For Akram Khan Company, *Vertical Road*, and costume design for *TOROBAKA*, *iTMOi*, *Gnosis*, *Rashomon*, *Kaash* (Akram Khan Company), *DUST – Lest We Forget* (English National Ballet), *Kwibuka20 ceremony* (Rwanda), *Now Is*, *Timeless*, and *Within* (Aditi Mangaldas Dance Company). Other design collaborations include: Ballet Rambert, Megumi Nakamura, Miguel Altunaga, Carlos Acosta, Hirata Oriza, Mansai Nomura and Carmen Jacobi. For film: assistant costume designer for *8 ½ Women* by Peter Greenaway and designer for *Basho*, starring Yoshi Oida. Currently designing: *Tristan and Isolde*, (Loughborough Festival Opera and for Ballet Rambert).
www.kimienakano.com/home.html

ALISON NEIGHBOUR /144

Alison is a designer for theatre, events and film. She trained at RADA. Her work most often responds to the site in which it is performed, and she is interested in creating performance in unusual spaces, bringing the unexpected into everyday environments. Alison is also founder and co-artistic director of Bread & Goose, a company formed with the aim of creating engaging journeys for audiences, through collaborative working practices and a design-led approach. Recent work includes: *Lost in the Neuron Forest* (touring), *Crazy Gary's Mobile Disco* (touring), *Phenomenal People* (Camden People's Theatre & ARC, Stockton), *I Told You This Would Happen* (ARC Stockton & touring), *Spine* (Underbelly & Soho Theatre, Fringe First & Herald Angel winner), *Square Bubble* (National Theatre Watch This Space), *The Eyes Have It* (Imagine Watford), *Wedding* (Shoreditch Town Hall), *The Literary Ball* (L'institut Francais), *Spectra* (mac, Birmingham), *Romeo & Juliet: Unzipped* (Salisbury Playhouse), *Followers* (Southwark Playhouse).
www.alisonneighbourdesign.com/Welcome.html

JON NICHOLLS /205

Jon Nicholls' eclectic work ranges from operas and electroacoustic compositions, to numerous collaborations with theatre and film-makers. He has also done extensive music and sound design for BBC radio drama (Prix Italia Jury Special Mention), new music for Javanese gamelan and over 200 music/sound-scores for theatre companies including the National Theatre, Shared Experience, Sheffield Crucible, the Gate, Birmingham Rep, Northern Stage, Theatr Clwyd and many others. He has composed several operas and music-theatre pieces integrating electronics and live musicians, most recently Flicker, developed in collaboration with the Royal Hospital for Neuro-Disability with support from the Wellcome Trust, which was premiered at Sadlers Wells in 2013. Some of his long-standing compositional interests include: the extended possibilities of the human voice, opera/music-theatre, the combining of instrumental forces with electro-acoustic textures/soundscapes, the integration of music and sound with a strong visual/theatrical language, and an interdisciplinary collaborative approach to the creation of new work.

FRANCIS O'CONNOR /142

Francis trained at Wimbledon School of Art. He has designed musicals, plays and operas throughout the UK. He is most closely associated with Garry Hynes and Druid Theatre, Galway for whom he has designed numerous productions. His work on Jonathon Doves new opera *Pinocchio* was nominated for the Faust Prize. He is twice winner of the Irish Times Award and recipient of Boston Globe and the Critics Circle Awards. His work was a part of the UK Prague Quadrennial Golden Triga winning entry in 2003.

BEK PALMER /145

Bek trained at LIPA and studied Post Graduate Theatre Design at Royal Welsh College of Music and Drama. Previous set and costume designs include: *Shaun The Sheep* (Dan Coleman), *Betrayal* (London Classic Theatre), *What The Ladybird Heard* (Kenny Wax Ltd.), *The Grumpiest Boy in the World* (Paper Balloons), *Luna* (Theatr Iolo & Theatre Hullabaloo), *Lemony Snicket's The Latke Who Couldn't Stop Screaming* (TYaD Arts & Tall Stories), *The Elves and the Shoemakers*, *Angel* and *The Night Pirates* (Theatre

Hullabaloo), *My Mother Told Me Not To Stare* (Theatre Hullabaloo & Action Transport Theatre). Bek specialises in designing/making puppets. Other work includes Wardrobe Mistress for Qdos Pantomimes.
www.bekpalmer.com

ROMA PATEL /146

Roma Patel is a scenographer and digital artist based in Nottingham. She trained in Stage and Screen Design at Wimbledon College of Arts and her work and research focus on the points of intersection between performance, site-specific scenography and interactive technologies. Her recent work includes the research and development of *Riot1831* an augmented reality mobile app and exhibition at Nottingham Castle. Her stage designs for site-specific production of *The Tempest* can be found in the V&A Theatre and Performance collections. Since 1998 she has designed performances, projections and installations for several companies in the UK and abroad, including London International Festival of Theatre, Corcardorca Theatre Company, Theatre Centre, Manchester Library Theatre and SCENOFEST, Prague Quadrennial. Roma has also worked as a part-time lecturer on several theatre design courses and is currently a PhD student at the University of Nottingham investigating the integration of wearable technology and smart material in performance.
www.digitalsetdesign.com

MICHAEL PAVELKA /147

Michael trained at Wimbledon College of Arts, and is now leading the MA Theatre Design course.

Over 180 designs include: *The Fishing Trip* and *Holiday for Lindsay Anderson* (Old Vic Theatre). Founder member Propeller Theatre, designing their world-touring Shakespeare productions along with Rose Rage at Chicago Shakespeare Theater (also New York, nominated Best Costume Design, Chicago's Jeff Awards). Michael won the Theatre UK's Best Set Design 2009 for Propeller's *The Merchant of Venice*. Dance work: *Revelations* (QEH) and *Off the Wall* that re-opened the RFH and represented the UK at Prague Quadrennial 11. West End: *Absurd Person Singular*, *The Constant Wife*, *How the Other Half Loves*, *Leonardo*, *Other People's Money*, *Blues in the Night* (Dublin, New York & Tokyo). Rose

Rage: *A Midsummer Night's Dream*, *Macbeth*, *A Few Good Men* and *Twelve Angry Men*. RSC: *The Odyssey*, *The Two Gentlemen of Verona*, *Henry V* and *Julius Caesar*. NT (Olivier); Edmond with Kenneth Branagh. Recent work: World Premiere of Frank McGuinness' *The Hanging Gardens* (Abbey, Dublin).
www.michaelpavelka.com

XRISTINA PENNA /148

Xristina is a designer, performance maker and a researcher at the PCI department of the University of Leeds. Penna's work is cross-disciplinary and has as principal focus to create a collective, archetypal language that communicates visually. In her current performance practice, the *aswespeakproject*, she uses multimedia and the stage space as temporal and spatial representations of the human brain. Scenography is used as the backbone of the project's methodology in devising work exploring new hybrid spaces in which the private and the public are intertwined. Her research aim, through her performance practice, is to experiment and develop processing mechanisms that can be applied to the "stage". These mechanisms/systems draw inspiration from cognitive science(s) and the theories of systems thinking and complexity. Her work has been presented internationally in various festivals and venues such as *Currents 2013*, *The Santa Fe International New Media Festival*, New Mexico, USA, *The Bluecoat*, Liverpool (2013), *The Round House*, London (2011), *The Benaki Museum*, Athens, Greece (2010). She has contributed to scholarly debates and international academic conferences in the field of scenography.
www.pci.leeds.ac.uk/people/christina-penna/

ANTONELLA PETRACCARO /149

Antonella holds an MA in Costume Design for Performance from London College of Fashion. Her final work was based on Hoffmann's *The Sandman* and was exhibited at *World Stage Design, Cardiff 2013*. She designed costumes for *Collider*, an exhibition at The Science Museum, London, and the costumes for *The Beautiful*, a solo piece by Petar Miloshevski which premiered at Camden Fringe Festival 2013. Antonella designed and made the costumes for *We Are Free* by Fabian Reimair (the English National Ballet's Choreographics 2014). Antonella also

works as a freelance costumier for the English National Ballet and the Royal Opera House.
www.antonella-petraccaro.com

ANNA PILCHER DUNN /150

Anna graduated from the Liverpool Institute for Performing Arts in Theatre and Performance Design in 2013. Prior to her studies at LIPA she created artworks and murals with patients attending a palliative day care centre. Anna originally trained as a textile designer and designed bespoke carpet, deciding to retrain as a set and costume designer to fulfil a lifelong ambition to work in theatre. While at university she designed and worked on many productions including *A Christmas Carol* and *The Summer of '42*. Also working as an Art Department runner on the Channel 4 series *Utopia* and the film *The Quiet Ones*. In 2013, Anna designed the costumes for a new musical, which was nominated for a sustainability award at the Edinburgh festival Fringe. Anna completed her ten months internship with Theatre by the Lake in August 2014 where she designed the Summer Season plays for the Studio Theatre.

TOM PIPER /150

Tom studied theatre design at the Slade and has worked extensively in the UK and abroad. His role as Associate Designer at the RSC has allowed him to get involved in large-scale building projects such as the redevelopment of the RST, the Courtyard theatre and also residencies at the Roundhouse and in New York. Recent explorations outside the normal theatre world have included exhibition design at The British Museum and Birmingham Rep, working with the Tricycle Theatre on their new spaces and creating the poppies installation at the Tower of London.
www.tompiperdesign.co.uk/about-tom/background/

ADRIENNE QUARTLY /205

Adrienne Quartly studied Cello and Piano, and following a BSc. in Music at City University, became a radio producer. Later, after gaining an MA (distinction) at RCSSD, she began work as a sound designer for theatre. Her work has appeared all over the world. She is a regular designer for Told by an Idiot with Paul Hunter whose shows include *Ghost Train*, *Get Happy*, *Too Clever By Half*, *You Can't Take it With You*, *And the Horse you rode in on* and *Every*

Last Trick with Spymonkey. Other work includes *Inside Wagner's Head* (Royal Opera House), *Fräulein Julie*, (Barbican/Schaubühne, Berlin), *Rings of Saturn* (Cologne), *Stockholm* (Frantic Assembly), *The Container*, *The Shawl* (Young Vic), *Tale of Two Cities*, *Body of an American* (Royal & Derngate, Northampton), *Grand Guignol* (Southwark), *Horse Piss for Blood* (Drum Plymouth), *Importance of Being Earnest* (Hong Kong Arts Festival), *Woyzeck* (St. Ann's Warehouse, New York), *Thomas Hobbes/Mary Spindler* (RSC), *365* (National Theatre of Scotland), *Lungs* (Paines Plough), *93.2* (Royal Court), *The Fastest Clock* (Hampstead), *Faustus, The School for Scandal*, *Volpone* and *The Duchess of Malfi* (Stage on Screen).

KATHERINA RADEVA /154

Katherina designs costume and set for theatre, contemporary dance, performance and everything in between. A Wimbledon School of Art graduate, Katherina was a Linbury Prize for Stage Design finalist in 2005. Since then she has worked on numerous small, big, touring and non-touring exciting and spectacular projects. Credits include: *Falling in Love with Frida* by Caroline Bowditch (2014), *Near Gone* (Two Destination Language, 2013), *The Sphinx* and *The Books* (Lorena Rivero de Beer, Bluecoat Liverpool, 2012), *Epic* (Foster&Dechery, national tour, 2011), *Lay Me Down Safe* (Scottish Dance Theatre, 2011). International Tour: *Elephant 21* (Royal Court Theatre Local for the Mayhem Company, 2010), *Ill Met by Moonlight* (2010). National Tour: *Moon Fool The Glass Mountain* (Trestle Theatre, 2009), *Hungry Ghosts* (Lost Dog Dance Theatre, 2007-2008), *Veil* (Horse and Bamboo Theatre, 2008).
www.katherinaradeva.co.uk

COLIN RICHMOND /155

Originally from Northern Ireland, Colin trained at the Royal Welsh College of Music and Drama gaining a first class Hons Degree.

A selection of work includes: *Wendy and Peter Pan* (RSC), *Antony and Cleopatra* (Shakespeare's Globe), *Pressure* (Chichester/Edinburgh Royal Lyceum), *Titus Andronicus* (RSC), *The Taming of the Shrew* (RSC), *Sweeney Todd* (Welsh National Opera/ WYP/ Manchester Exchange), *Crime and Punishment* (Citizen's Theatre/ Liverpool Playhouse/ Edinburgh Royal

Lyceum), *Spring Awakening* (Headlong), *Beautiful Thing* (West End), *My Fair Lady* (Aarhus Theatre, Denmark), *Men Should Weep* (National Theatre Scotland), *La Boheme* (Opera, Holland Park), *Betrayal* (Sheffield Crucible).
www.colinrichmond.viewbook.com

FRANCISCO RODRIGUEZ-WEIL /156

Though born in England, it was Francisco's South American upbringing that shaped his style: a sense for vibrant colours and energetic sets he is now well known for. Francisco worked in a theatre since early age, moving on to study architecture and set and costume design, graduating with distinction from the Bristol Old Vic Theatre School. His formal training gave him the artistic and technical tools to deliver his designs. He has immersed himself in different art forms, ranging from operas and musicals to TV, film, experimental, ballet, and dance, each one of them contributing to shape and enhance the other. Most recently, he created the imposing stage and costumes for *The Coronation Festival Gala* (Buckingham Palace) and costumes for the feature film *Set Fire To The Stars*, shot in Black and white.
www.fr-w.co.uk.

PETER RUMNEY /162

Peter Rumney is a poet, award winning playwright and director. His career as a performer ranged from the RSC, Scottish Opera and Glasgow Citizens to Theatre in Education and work with adults with learning disabilities. Peter is joint Artistic Director of Dragon's Breath Theatre which was shortlisted for the Times Higher Education Supplement / Arts Council England Excellence and Innovation Award, and won the 2014 Nottinghamshire Heritage Award for Inspiration in a Special Project for the company's immersive performance work at Papplewick Pumping Station Museum. This heritage work develops three years collaboration with the Centre for Advanced Studies at the University of Nottingham developing a Water Literacy curriculum for schools. Peter is Senior Lecturer in Theatre Design in the School of Art and Design at Nottingham Trent University, where his research intersts include children's literacy, the exploration of multimodal learning, and the potency of theatre to communicate complex scientific ideas.
www.dragonbreaththeatre.com

ALEXANDER RUTH /158

Alexander Ruth works as a visual artist and designer in various media across the Performing Arts. He has worked as a fashion designer in Paris and London before starting his research and practice in performance. Initially trained at Central Saint Martins and London College of Fashion, Ruth's practice focuses on the performative nature of costumes and spaces.

He lectures Research in Performance across the Undergraduate Performance Courses at LCF and works as an Associate Lecturer with the MA Fashion Futures Course. His research interest is in Future Studies in design for the Performing Arts, examining the process of performance design and creation, key relationships within creative teams, and new models of cross disciplinary collaboration as well as the subject of speculative design within narrative based performance. Recent exhibitions and Awards: Linbury Prize for Stage Design, London, 2013; World Stage Design Exhibition, Cardiff, 2013; Production Design for Scottish Dance Theatre, 2014.
http://alexanderruth.com/about/

NICK SAGAR /205

Notable Theatre Sound Design credits include: the *James Plays* (National Theatre of Scotland/National Theatre), the highly acclaimed *Life & Death of Marina Abramovic* (directed by Robert Wilson) which recently performed in New York (as well as International Festivals in Manchester, Madrid, Basel, Amsterdam, Antwerp, Toronto), *A Doll's House* for National Theatre of Scotland (for which I also composed the music), *End Of The Road* for the Young@Heart Chorus/No Theatre in Europe, New York and Singapore, *Men Should Weep* (Tour), *Caledonia* (Edinburgh International Festival) and *Appointment with the Wicker Man* (Tour & Edinburgh Festival) for the National Theatre of Scotland.

Nick is also Sound Designer for the highly acclaimed (and longest running children's' show in London's West End) *Horrible Histories 'Barmy Britain'* which has performed in London, across the UK, Edinburgh (Fringe Festival), Abu Dhabi, Bahrain, Dubai, Hong Kong, Singapore, Sydney & Melbourne, as well as touring productions of *Horrible Histories (Romans, Eygptians, Tudors & Victorians)*, *Tom's Midnight Garden* and *Jungle Book* for Birmingham Stage Company.

Nick also recently provided the Sound Design for the CBeebies Christmas show with an expected initial TV audience of over 7 million.
www.nicksagar.com/

MILA SANDERS /160

Mila trained at the University of Wales, Aberystwyth and Wimbledon School of Art. Her designs include: *Queen of the Nile* (Hull Truck), *Parallax, The Door Never Closes, All the Little Things We Crushed* (Almeida), *The Only Way is Chelsea's* (Root Theatre/ York Theatre Royal), *The Rite of Spring / Romeo and Juliet* (Concert Theatre), *Pub Quiz* (New Writing North) *Jelly Bean Jack* (Little Angel), *A Midsummer Night's Dream* (NT Education). As Costume Designer: *Macbeth, Twelfth Night* (NT Discover), *Tombstone Tales and Boothill Ballads* (Arcola), *Jason and the Argonauts* (BAC and tour), *Unfolding Andersen* (Theatre-rites).
www.milasanders.co.uk

HANSJORG SCHMIDT /159

Hansjörg is a lighting designer, working regularly with a group of UK based artists and theatre companies. He is also the Programme Director Lighting Design at Rose Bruford College, and his research interests lie in the area of lighting, site-specificity and narrative. Recent lighting designs: *Dusk* (Fevered Sleep), *Krapp's Last Tape* (Sheffield Crucible), *Zero* (Clod Ensemble / Sadlers Wells), *Above Me The Wide Blue Sky* (Fevered Sleep / Young Vic Theatre), *Silver Swan* (Clod Ensemble/ Tate Modern), *An Anatomy in Four Quarters* (Clod Ensemble/Sadlers Wells Theatre), *On Ageing* (Fevered Sleep/ Young Vic Theatre), *Kursk* (Sound & Fury/Young Vic), *The Forest* (Fevered Sleep), *Under Glass* and *Red Ladies* (Clod Ensemble). Also with David Harradine: *Stilled*, and *Camera Obscura*. Other recent projects: *Kew Kitchens*, an architectural installation at Kew Palace, *The Beautiful Octopus Club*, for Heart 'n Soul and the South Bank Centre and shows for Jessica Ogden and Mika Fukkai at London Fashion Week.
www.hansjorgschmidt.com

JO SCOTCHER /166

Joanna Scotcher received the Whatsonstage Best Set Designer Award for her site-specific design of *The Railway Children*, Waterloo, which went on to win the Olivier award for Best Entertainment in 2011.

Joanna trained at the Royal Shakespeare Company. From this classical initiation in stage design, her design projects have taken her from performances on lakes, through journeys under forgotten London, to games in Royal Palaces. As well as her theatrical stage design, her work

specialises in the world of immersive performance and site responsive design, inhabiting spaces from the intimate to the epic.

Recent work includes: *Pests* (Clean Break & The Royal Court), *Antigone* (Pilot Theatre & Stratford East), *A Harlem Dream* (Young Vic) and *Anna Karenina* (Royal Exchange). She is Creative Art Director for Torch Ceremonies, at the inauguration of The European Games, Baku 2015.
www.joannascotcher.com

NETTIE SCRIVEN /161

Nettie Scriven is Joint Artistic Director of Dragon Breath Theatre, whose current site-specific project at Papplewick Pumping Station *A Crack in Time* won the Nottinghamshire Heritage Award for Inspiration in Best Special Project 2014. Animating a range of performance spaces, from traditional theatres to art galleries and heritage sites, Nettie specialises in developing performance text through collaborative process, with emphasis on working with young people through research and development. Current work includes: *Inside Out of Mind* (Lakeside Arts Centre/Meeting Ground), *Grandpa in My Pocket* (Nottingham Playhouse), and *Shiny* (Turned on its Head), and her arts consultancy in schools.
www.dragonbreaththeatre.com

ASHLEY SHAIRP /167

Ashley trained in theatre design at Trent Polytechnic, Nottingham. His first professional design job after graduating in 1986 was with Michael Boyd at The Tron, Glasgow. He had a happy time as the Associate Designer at The Dukes, Lancaster, designing many shows for Ian Forrest including pantomimes, two promenades in Williamson Park and, best of the bunch, *Tis Pity She's A Whore* (The Dukes, Lancaster). His country wide freelance work includes sustained relationships with the Everyman Liverpool, Bolton Octagon, Cheltenham Everyman and Ludus Dance Company. He designed *Angels in America* (Unity, Liverpool) and at the same venue devised, designed and performed a puppet performance, *Front Window*, with partner Sam Heath. An installation based on the show was exhibited at the design exhibition *Collaborators* in Nottingham and at the V&A. He is the Course Leader for Theatre and Performance Design at the Liverpool Institute for Performing Arts (LIPA).

RAJHA SHAKIRY /168

Rajha Shakiry was born in Iraq and educated in England. After an honours degree in Mathematics, she re-trained in Theatre Design, graduating from Wimbledon School of Art in 2003. Rajha has since worked as a freelance theatre designer and scenographer and has also obtained a distinction in MA Scenography from Royal Central School of Speech and Drama. Rajha has extensive experience in small-scale, middle-scale, national and international touring productions, in the United Kingdom, Southern Africa and the Middle East. She has designed and collaborated on numerous devised and text based projects, physical theatre, musical theatre and opera. Most recent designs have included: *How Nigeria Became* (The Unicorn Theatre), *I Stand Corrected* (Cape Town, London and Singapore), *Richard II* (Jericho, Palestine and Shakespeare's Globe) and *Still Life Dreaming* (Spare Tyre and Wellcome Trust at the Pleasance, Edinburgh Fringe). Rajha has recently been awarded an Arts Council Grant to develop work in progress.
www.rajhashakiry.co.uk

NICKY SHAW /169

Nicky is an international set and costume designer, working for all scales of company; from small to major opera houses in the UK, Belgium, Denmark, Germany, Ireland, Italy, Russia, Netherlands, Norway, Poland & South Korea. Most recently designing: *Don Quichotte* and *Katya Kabanova* (Danish National Opera), *Norma* (Teatro Lirico, Sardinia), *Carmen & Acis & Galatea* (Mid Wales Opera), *Faust, Mariinsky* (costumes) and *Marathon 33*, (GSMD). Many of her productions have been nominated for awards, these are: *La Traviata*, (Scottish Opera, joint winner 2013 The Renee Stepham Award for Best Presentation of Touring Theatre), *Mignon* (Buxton Opera, nominated - Best Opera Production, South Bank Sky Awards 2012), *The Magic Flute, The Diary of Anne Frank* and *The Coronation of Poppea* (Opera Theatre Company, all nominated - Best Opera, Irish Times 2012, 2011, 2007), and *Dancing Shadows*, (Opera Theatre, Seoul, winner 5 Korean Musical Awards 2007, including Best Musical).
www.nickyshaw.co.uk

DAVID SHEARING /170

David works in collaboration with artists, composers and writers; he creates highly reflective, immersive environments that explore the relationship between high and low technologies - including video, light and sound. He is interested in how audiences engage both physically and conceptually with performance. He explores audience engagement by creating intimate, and at times spectacular, art and performance installations. David has an MA in Performance Design and Practice, from Central Saint Martin's (2008-2009) and is conducting PhD research into *Audience Immersion and the Experience of Scenography* at the University of Leeds. In 2014 David was awarded a Sky Academy Arts Scholarship. In 2014 – 2015 he will be creating *The Weather Machine*, a new immersive installation performance in partnership with the West Yorkshire Playhouse and stage@leeds.
www.davidshearing.com

JULIET SHILLINGFORD /171

Juliet trained at Ravensbourne and Croydon, obtaining a Sculpture degree and Theatre Design diploma. She was awarded an Arts Council Bursary and since then has designed over 100 productions. During the last four years she has designed for the Mercury Theatre, Colchester, Nuffield Theatre, Southampton, Curve, Leicester (both spaces) and New Perspectives, Nottingham where one of the productions *The Love song of Alfred J Hitchcock* also formed part of the 2014 Brits off Broadway Festival in New York. She also designed National tours of *The Butterfly Lion* and *Kindertransport*. One of Juliet's designs formed part of the British entry for Prague Quadrennial 2007.
www.julietshillingford.co.uk

ANDREAS SKOURTIS /173

Andreas is a practicing scenographer and architect, and lecturer in scenography at Royal Central School of Speech and Drama. His designs of the *Nea Skin* (Athens National Theatre's space), completed in 2009, were awarded a Gold Medal for Best Work in Theatre Architecture and Performance Space in Prague Quadrennial 2011. He trained in Architecture at AUTH, Design at Ecole d' Architecture de Lille, Drama at Theatre Lab in Thessaloniki and studied for an MA Theatre Design – Scenography at Wimbledon College of Art exploring *Visualising The Invisible: The Creation of a Theatrical Topos*. Both his practice and academic research focus on exploring *Architecture as a Scenography Tool*. He is based in London, UK.
http://skourtisandreas.gr/site/

GABRIELLA SLADE /178

Gabriella first specialised in theatre whilst studying at the Wimbledon College of Art (2008-9). She then trained at the Royal Welsh College of Music and Drama and graduated with a first class degree in Theatre Design (2012). For over two years Gabriella has worked extensively as a set and costume designer, and assistant designer on over 20 professional theatre productions including physical theatre, site-specific, musicals, community, touring and devised theatre. Most notably Gabriella has worked and designed for National Youth Theatre Wales, Frantic Assembly and National Theatre Wales. Gabriella was one of the final 20 candidates in The Linbury Prize (2013) and reached the final of the JMK prize in association with the Young Vic (2014) with her design for *Mr Kolpert*.
www.gabriellaslade.co.uk

RAE SMITH /176

The Olivier, Tony and OBIE award-winning British designer Rae Smith works in a wide variety of styles and genres. Her work is seen in Britain in the West End, Europe and Broadway. Rae has recently illustrated *War Horse: An Illustrated Special Edition* by Michael Morpurgo and has designed set, costume and drawings for *War Horse*. She is currently working on *Cavilleria Rusticana* and *Pagliacci* at the Met Opera House New York, *The Tempest* for Birmingham Royal Ballet and *Wonderland* for the National Theatre. Recent work includes *Benvenuto Cellini* (ENO), *The Prince of the Pagodas* (Birmingham Royal Ballet), *Light Princess* (National Theatre), *Sweet Bird of Youth* (Old Vic), *This House* (National Theatre).
www.raesmith.co.uk

JASON SOUTHGATE /177

Jason has worked for a number of prestigious companies in the UK including Theatre Royal Haymarket (West End), Royal Opera House Covent Garden, English National Ballet, Welsh National Opera, Young Vic, Gate London, Citizens Theatre, The Globe, Buxton Festival and Nottingham Playhouse.

Internationally he has worked for Bregenz Opera Festival, Savonlinna Opera Festival, Hong Kong Arts Festival, Landestheater Salzburg, Frankfurt Opera, Opera Zuid , OMMA Athens, Wexford Opera, Teatro Comunale Bolzano, Komische Oper Berlin, Stanislavski Music Theatre Moscow and Mariinsky Opera St Petersburg.

Jason is also an acclaimed puppet designer/maker.
http://jasonrsouthgate.blogspot.co.uk

ZOE SQUIRE /180

Zoe Squire trained at the Bristol Old Vic Theatre School and designs shows both throughout the UK and overseas. She also runs her own theatre company, Pins and Needles Productions, which she co-founded in 2009 with director Emma Earle. Zoe recently won the Young Angels Theatre-Makers award with Company of Angels and York Theatre Royal. Productions from Pins and Needles include: *Father Christmas* (Lyric Hammersmith and West Yorkshire Playhouse), *Ernest and the Pale Moon* (with Les Enfant Terribles), *Holly and Ivan's Christmas Adventure* and *Scoop* (Lyric Hammersmith) *Flies* and *Elves and the Shoemakers* (Tobacco Factory Theatre). Other recent works include: *Helver's Night* (York Theatre Royal), *Happy Prince* (Chantry Dance), *Captain Flinn and the Pirate Dinosaurs* (UK and International tour), *The Queen's Knickers* (Theatre Royal Bath and Southbank Centre), *Glenngarry Glen Ross* (Ustinov Theatre) *Riot, Beast and Beauties, The Witches* and *James and the Giant Peach* (egg theatre, Theatre Royal Bath).
www.pinsandneedlesproductions.co.uk

LAURA JANE STANFIELD /182

After studying Theatre Design at Wimbledon School of Art, Laura has worked predominantly in theatrical costume. Design Credits include: *Linenopolis: the Opera*, set and costumes (NI Opera/Belfast Buildings Trust), *La Boheme* - co-designer costumes (Nevill Holt Opera), *King – A Cathedral Opera* by Stephen Barlow - costumes, *The Flying Dutchman* - co-designer costumes (NI Opera), *Britains Got Bhangra* - co-designer costumes (Rifco Arts), *Noye's Fludde* - co-designer costumes (NI Opera), *118 118 Summer tour* - costumes, *Three Wishes, Second Movement* - costumes, *Parallel Lives* by Jon Oram - set and costumes, *Matters of Chance* by Jon Oram - set and costumes, *Macbeth* - associate costume designer (NI Opera/WNO), *Magic Flute*- associate costume designer (Nevill Holt Opera/ NI Opera). Alongside her design work Laura has also worked as a costume supervisor, working on many large-scale productions. She was Head of Costume at Laine Theatre Arts for three years, designing all in-house shows and showcase productions.

CHIARA STEPHENSON /66

Chiara trained in Theatre and Performance Design at the Liverpool Institute for Performing Arts. Since graduating in 2008 with First Class Honours she has been working in London on productions for both the West End and Broadway as well as international opera and arena and stadium tours. As Design Associate work includes: *American Psycho The Musical* (Almeida), *Chimerica* (Almeida), *Miley Cyrus Bangerz* World Tour, *London 2012 Olympic Closing Ceremony, Kanye West and Jay Z Watch the Throne Tour, Beatrice and Benedict* (Theatre an der Wien), *Cunning Little Vixen* (Royal Danish Opera), *Les Troyens* (ROH), *Master and Margarita* (Complicite), *Batman Live* (World Tour), *Don Giovanni* (Met, New York), *Madame Butterfly* (Houston Grand Opera), *Street Car Named Desire, Hamlet, Madame De Sade* (Donmar Warehouse), *Sister Act The Musical* (Palladium), *Hairspray* (European Tour). As Designer work includes: *The Making of Don Giovanni* Exhibition Design (ROH), *Miley Cyrus and Madonna MTV unplugged 2014, All's Well That Ends Well* (Abigail Anderson, PMA Theatre, Liverpool), *Arcadia* (Unity Theatre, Liverpool), *The Massacre* (Theatre Royal, Bury St Edmunds). Chiara is currently working as Associate Designer on the Rio Opening Ceremony for the Olympics.

AMANDA STOODLEY /172

Amanda trained in Theatre and Performance Design at Liverpool Institute for Performing Arts, having previously studied and worked in illustration, graphic and interior design. Designs for theatre and exhibition include: *Hamlet, Black Roses* (Best Studio Production, Manchester Theatre Awards 2013 and UK Tour), *Winterlong* (Soho Theatre), *Two, Truth About Youth* (Festival), *Making an Exhibition of Ourselves (at home)* (Royal Exchange Theatre), *Untold Stories* (West Yorkshire Playhouse), *Duet for One* and *Separation, Robin Hood, Can't Pay? Won't Pay!* (Bolton Octagon Theatre), *Anon* (Welsh National Opera), *The Maw Broon Monologues* (Tron Theatre, Glasgow), *The Masque of Anarchy* (Manchester International Festival), *Fireface* (JMK Award, Young Vic Theatre), *Manchester Sound: The Massacre, Manchester lines* - Best Design, Theatre Awards UK 2012 (Library Theatre), *Epstein* (Epstein Theatre, Liverpool & Leicester Square Theatre), *I Know Where the*

Dead are Buried (24:7 Theatre Festival, Manchester), *Dark Side of the Building* (Unity Theatre, Liverpool), *The Innovasion* - Liverpool Biennial (Hope Street Ltd.), *Four Corners* (Bluecoat Arts Centre, Liverpool), *Wish you Were Here* (Liverpool Everyman).
www.amandastoodley.com

TAKIS /181

Takis is a London based performance designer. Working both nationally at many of the UK's leading theatres, and internationally, he has designed a wide range of productions in diverse genres. His nominations include four Off West End Awards for Set Design for the productions of *In The Heights* (Southwark playhouse), *Fear* (Bush Theatre), *His Teeth* (Only Connect) and *Stovepipe* (National Theatre/HighTide). Takis studied at the Romanian National University of Arts in Bucharest, the Royal Academy of Dramatic Art in London and Aalto University in Helsinki. As artistic director of ARTLUXE, he has designed and produced interdisciplinary installations and performances across Europe, collaborating with organizations such as the Design Museums of both London & Helsinki, Hampton Court Palace and Greek International Festival of Ancient Drama.
www.takis.info

SHEREE TAMS /182

Sheree, an artist and theatre designer, was born in South Wales and studied Theatre Design at Motley in London. In addition to theatre she has exhibited art installations, video and photography in several solo and group shows. She has worked on a wide range of design projects differing in scale, budget and content. Most recently; devised theatre, site specific events, a season of theatre for the elderly, theatre for young audiences, theatre in education, theatre of the oppressed, music theatre, experimental theatre, exhibition design, dance and opera. For the past eight years she has collaborated with renowned Canadian playwright Sky Gilbert on shows at Buddies in Bad Times Theatre - a leading centre for the creation and presentation of alternative theatre in Canada. Sheree has been nominated for a Dora Mavor Moore Award in Design and was recently shortlisted for Best Hat Design in the Queens Plate Hats and Horses Competition. A passion for travel and art has taken her all over the world, which contributes to her global

design perspective. She has designed productions in the United States, Canada, the UK and Europe.
www.shereetams.com

IAN TEAGUE /183

Ian trained in Theatre Design at what was then called Trent Polytechnic (now Nottingham Trent University) graduating in 1982. He has designed over 150 productions for a wide range of companies including: Cardboard Citizens, MakeBelieve Arts, Eastern Angles, The London Bubble, Barking Broadway, Spare Tyre, Polka, Rose Bruford, Oxfordshire Touring, GYPT, Everyman- Cheltenham, Action Transport, Everyman- Liverpool, 7:84, Dukes Theatre- Lancaster, Torch Theatre Milford Haven, Durham Theatre Company, Forest Forge, Theatre Venture, Theatre Royal Stratford East and Nuffield Theatre Southampton. He is also a lecturer and workshop facilitator. His designs for small cast productions of Shakespeare formed part of the British Golden Triga winning entry at the Prague Quadrennial 2003. Ian is represented by The Designers Formation.
www.designersformation.com

YANNIS THAVORIS /184

Yannis studied Architecture in Greece, and Scenography at Central Saint Martins College of Art and Design in London. He was the overall winner of the 1997 Linbury Prize for Stage Design. Recent designs for opera include: *La Donna del Lago* - costumes (Royal Opera House), *Rigoletto* (National Opera Bucharest), *Tosca* (Santa Fe Opera), *La Finta Giardiniera* (Buxton Festival). Also: *The Lady from the Sea, Orlando, Madama Butterfly* (Scottish Opera), *Pelléas et Mélisande* (Teatro Colón, Buenos Aires), *Aida* - set (Welsh National Opera), *Così fan Tutte* - set (Opéra National du Rhin), *La Clemenza di Tito* (Royal Danish Opera and ENO), *Oprichnik* (Teatro Lirico di Cagliari), *The Marriage of Figaro, The Rake's Progress, The Rape of Lucretia* (ENO), *La Fanciulla del West, Cavalleria Rusticana & Pagliacci, Pelléus et Mélisande, Don Giovanni, Katya Kabanova, Tosca, Nabucco, Jenufa* (Opera Holland Park), *Les Contes d'Hoffmann, Opera Seria* - set (Nationale Reisopera). Theatre: *Gigi* (Regent's Park Open Air Theatre), *Annie Get Your Gun* (UK Tour), *The Great Extension* and *The Battle of Green Lanes* (Theatre Royal, Stratford East). Dance: *Petrushka* (Scottish Ballet).
www.yannisthavoris.com

LESLIE TRAVERS /186

Leslie trained at the Wimbledon School of Art. He has designed extensively for theatre, opera and dance in the uK and internationally. Opera designs include: *La Bohème* Malmö Opera; *Grimes on the Beach* (Aldeburgh Music) which was won Best Anniversary Production – International Opera Awards 2014 and What's On Stage – Opera Event of The Year; *Albert Herring* (Opera North); *Alice's Adventures in Wonderland* (Opera Holland Park); *L'elisir d'amore* (Opera Holland Park), *Tannhäuser* (Estonian National Opera), *Otello* (Scottish Opera/ Opera North) winner of the Manchester Theatre Awards 2014 – Best Opera. Also *Don Giovanni* (Garsington Opera), *Giulio Cesare* (Opera North), *Jenufa* (Malmö Opera, Sweden), *The Merry Widow* (Opera Australia/Opera North), *Les Contes d'Hoffmann* (Malmö Opera, Sweden), *Roméo et Juliette* (Opera Ireland), *L'Arbore di Diana* (Palau de les Arts Reina Sophia, Valencia), *The Children's Crusade* (Luminato Festival, Toronto) which was winner of the Dora Mavor Moore Award Best Opera Production 2010, nominated for best overall design in all categories.

Theatre designs include: *Twelfth Night* (Chichester Festival Theatre), *The Duchess of Malfi, Streets of Rage* and *Silent Cry* for West Yorkshire Playhouse; *The Persian Revolution* (Lyric Hammersmith) *The Man with Two Gaffers* (York Theatre Royal), *Shirley Valentine* (Derby Playhouse), *Majnoun* (Lyric Hammersmith, *Riverside* Studios and Tour), *Death by Heroin(e)* (Riverside Studios), *Taj* (UK Tour), *Veriete* (Lindsay Kemp Company, World Tour) and *Vurt* (Contact Theatre, Manchester) winner of the Arthur Peter Design Award and nominated for the Manchester Evening News Design Award

Leslie's dance and ballet designs include: *Cinderella, Le Corsaire, The Nutcracker* and *Swan Lake* for K-ballet Japan, winning the Asahi Award in 2005 and 2006); also *Cinderella* (National Ballet of Portugal) and *The Lark Ascending* (English National Ballet).

Current projects include: *The Marriage of Figaro* for Opera North; *Salome*, Santa Fe Opera; *The Turn of The Screw*, Opera Holland Park; *Alice's Adventures in Wonderland* – Opera Holland Park.

And future projects: *Billy Budd* for the National Reisopera, Holland, September 2015; *Otello*, Gran Teatre del Liceu, Barcelona, March 2016; also new commission – Den Norske Opera, Oslo in September 2016 and *Otello*, Scottish Opera in September 2018.
www.leslietravers.com

CÉCILE TRÉMOLIÈRES /190

Born in Paris, Cécile initially spent three years at the Sorbonne University studying modern literature, before deciding to combine her passions for text, performance and fine art by studying Stage Design at Wimbledon College of Art, graduating with a first class degree in June 2013. Since graduating, she has been shortlisted as one of the twelve finalist of the Linbury Prize for Stage Design 2013, awarded the Royal Opera House Linbury bursary (2015) and is one winner of the IdeasTap Graduate Design Award. She now develops work with freelance directors Tom Hughes and Ilinca Radulian and companies like Impermanence Dance Theatre, fanSHEN, Invertigo Theatre, Opera South and Complicité Young Company. She has been assisting Naomi Dawson, Tom Piper, Michael Pavelka and Antoine Fontaine. Upcoming projects are: *This is not a slog* (Oval House), *La Traviata* (Haslemere Hall), *The Tower* (Sherman Cymru), *Europe as a Theme Park* (The Yard).
www.ceciletremolieres.com

MAYOU TRIKERIOTI /189

Mayou trained at the Bristol Old Vic Theatre School after finishing her BA Hons in Drama and Theatre Studies at the University of Kent. Since then she has been designing for the stage mostly in Greece and more recently in the UK. She has designed for all of Greece's major theatres and festivals including the National Theatre in Athens. She now lives in London where she has recently designed at the Young Vic and Riverside Studios. She works on all scales grand and small, and her portfolio ranges from plays that enjoyed successful runs of two-three years to one-off, site-specific performances. Since 2007, Mayou has also designed feature and short films that have travelled across the globe and screened at international film festivals, including Venice Film Festival, Berlin and Toronto IFF.
www.mayoutrikerioti.com

KATE UNWIN /192

Kate has worked as a freelance set and costume designer for thirteen years. Highlights include: *The West End Men* (Milton Morrissey Ltd, Vaudeville Theatre), *Macbeth* (Shakespeare 4 Kidz), *Inside Out* (Curve, Leicester), *Vanessa & Virginia* - nominated for Best Set Design, Off West End Awards (Moving Stories, Riverside Studios), *Melody Loses Her Mojo* (20 Stories High Liverpool Everyman), *Refugees of the Septic Heart* (Tom Dale Company), *FIB & Trackdown* (Metro-Boulot-Dodo, National Theatre), *Girls Night No. 1 tour* (Goodnights Entertainment), *A Christmas Carol* (Only Connect) *Wormwood Scrubs, Zhe & The African Company Presents Richard III* (Collective Artistes), *Godspell No. 1 tour* (Oftrot Productions), *Animal Farm* (Derby Playhouse), *Hot Stuff, To Kill a Mockingbird, An Ideal Husband, Macbeth, The Cripple of Inishmaan,* (Leicester Haymarket Theatre).Numerous site-specific installation work and art direction for music video. Set and costume design for many commercial clients including Lynx, Pepsi, and an award winning Samsung.
www.kateunwin.co.uk

JANET VAUGHAN /193

Janet trained in Theatre Design at Nottingham Trent Polytechnic, and was the Resident Designer at the Belgrade TIE Company before embarking on a freelance career encompassing a wide range of performance, installation and digital projects. For the last 20 years, Janet has been leading and collaborating on projects with Coventry based company of artists Talking Birds, exploring and making work in spaces as diverse as an Irish livestock mart, a 14th century monastery, a 1960's underground car park and a geodesic dome on the English-Welsh border. Her *portable-aluminium-whale-that's-really-a-theatre* is regularly seen at festivals around the UK and motorways in between.
www.vornster.co.uk

MAIRA VAZEOU /188

Maira trained at the Central School Of Speech and Drama. Her work has been seen in various indoor and outdoor spaces around England and abroad. Some of her credits are: *Medea* (Riverside Studios), *Salvadores Dei* (Megaron Athens Hall), *Two-Headed* (Rose Theatre), *I'm a Minger* (Belgrade Theatre & National Tour), *Antigone* (Riverside Studios & International Festival Of Ancient Greek Drama, Cyprus), *Chutney* (National & Australian Tour), *The Three Princesses Who Sung and Danced* (Theatre Organisation Of Cyprus), *Fresh Meat* (Courtyard Theatre), *Velvet Scratch* (Edinburgh, Prague, Athens and New York Festivals), *Guernica* (National Theatre Of Greece) and collaborated with Mountview Academy of Theatre Arts, designing various end of year shows for the post graduate directors course. Maira has worked as a set dresser in various films in studios around London such as *Les Miserables, Snow White & The Huntsman, Robin Hood, The Duchess, Sweeny Todd* and worked as a prop coordinator at the Opening & Closing Ceremonies of the Olympic Games Athens 2004.

MYRIDDIN WANNELL /132

WildWorks Associate Designer. Myriddin Wannell is a set and costume designer specialising in site and people specific work. Mydd studied a BA Hons in Theatre Design at Wimbledon School of Art and a second degree in Fine Art at Falmouth College of Art. As a freelance designer Mydd has worked, amongst others, with Kneehigh Theatre (*The Wild Bride*), Cut to the Chase Productions (*Tony Teardrop*), the BBC, the National Theatre, BAC, Punchdrunk and the Eden Project, where he was Design Consultant.

As Associate Designer with WildWorks recent productions include: *Wolf Child* (WildWorks and Norfolk and Norwich Festival 2015), *Yuletide Ark-Ive* (Eden Project 2014), *100* (the Lost Gardens of Heligan 2014), *Once Upon a Castle* (Kasteel Gaasbeek, Belgium 2014-15), *Babel* (WildWorks and BAC, World Stages London 2012), *The Passion* starring Michael Sheen (WildWorks & National Theatre of Wales 2011), *The Enchanted Palace* (Kensington Palace 2010-2011). Mydd has also worked in tribal communities in Africa for the Gallman Foundation, in Romania on the Four Generations Project with Romany gipsy communities and (with WildWorks) with refugee communities in Nablus, occupied territories of Palestine, to tell stories of their traditions, local community and pride of place.
www.myriddinwannell.com

JAMES WATSON /195

Graduate of Loughborough University (2009) with a First Class BA (Hons.) Drama. After graduating, James spent three years in residence for the Little Theatre Leicester, designing and implementing sets for a selection of their season of plays and annual pantomime, as well as for guest musical theatre companies. Shows included: *Sweet Charity, Carrie's War, Dick Whittington, Anything Goes, Cause Celebre, Spider's Web, Oklahoma, The Witches, Our Town, A View From The Bridge, Aladdin* (the Little Theatre, Leicester). Following a move to East London, James now works predominantly in an education setting, and tutors a technical youth theatre. Recent design work includes: *The Edelweiss Pirates, Paper Planes, Pronoun,* and *Joseph and the Amazing Technicolour Dreamcoat* (the Queen's Theatre Hornchurch), *The Crucible* (Fine Line Theatre), and venue design for the PIE Eyed Performance Festival (Romford).

FIONA WATT /197

Fiona trained with Motley at the Almeida, London.

In 2013, as curator for Design as Performance at World Stage Design in Cardiff, she created a series of projects (*The Intimate and the Epic, FOUR, The Marketplace* and *Wayfinding@WSD*) that engaged participatory practitioners, international emerging companies, early career artists and local entrepreneurs exploring design as a lead element of their work in the festival.

In 2012 she was a member of the core team delivering *Open Stages*, a Cultural Olympiad project for the Royal Shakespeare Company.

She was one of six international artists to lead *SIX ACTS*, a series of site specific interventions in the city for the Prague Quadrennial of Performance Design and Space 2011.

Fiona is Honorary Secretary for SBTD and UK Performance Design Commissioner for OISTAT (International Organisation of Scenographers, Theatre Architects and Technicians). She is co-ordinating *The View From Here* , the UK student submission to PQ2015 with SBTD colleague Peter Farley.
www.fionawatt.com

IAN WESTBROOK /202

Ian started with Lord Delfont Group on *Lenny Henry, Cannon & Ball, The Nolan sisters* and *Jim Davidson* summer shows. Since 1985, he has worked with all the major UK theatres creating over 650 productions from world arena tours for *Iron Maiden, Robbie Williams, The Spice Girls, Michael Flatly, Peter Gabriel, West Life, Blur.* Five Royal commissions for HM the Queen Elizabeth II inclue the Diamond Jubilee Beacon and Crystal Diamond at the Jubilee Concert. In London's West End: *Blythe Spirit* (Savoy), *All the Fun of the Fair* (Garrick), *Proof* (Arts), *Santa's Magic Adventures* (Ambassadors), *West Side Story* and *Men in Motion* (Saddler's Wells), Cy Colman's *See Saw* and *La Cage aux Folles* (Broadway). Since 2006, Qdos pantomime sets at Birmingham Hippodrome, and Cat Stevens' *Yusuf Islam* world arena tour.
www.3dcreations.co.uk/ian-westbrook-theatre-design.html

SIMON WILKINSON /196

Simon designs lighting for theatre in all shapes, sizes and locations. For the National Theatre of Scotland, he lit: *Dragon, The Day I Swapped My Dad For Two Goldfish, Roman Bridge, Truant* and *A Sheep Called Skye*. For Vox Motus, designs include: *The Infamous Brothers Davenport, The Not-So-Fatal Death of Grandpa Fredo, Bright Black and Slick*. He is an associate artist of Magnetic North, designing: *Kora, Sex and God, Pass the Spoon, Wild Life* and *After Mary Rose*. Other theatre designs include: *Bondagers, Cinderella* and *Christmas Carol* (Royal Lyceum), *After The End* and *Topdog / Underdog* (Citizens Theatre), *This Wide Night* (Tron Theatre), *Feral* (Tortoise in a Nutshell), *Chalk Farm* and *The Static* (ThickSkin). Simon has been nominated for three CATS Awards for Best Design. Over the years, his lighting has created a Guinness World Record, brought 30,000 people to a windswept Highland Forest, and caused reports of an alien invasion.
www.simonwilkinson.net

RICHARD WILLACY /37

Richard has over 20 years experience directing and producing a wide variety of experimental music theatre, multimedia and film. He presents work which advocates equality, enables social change and positions the arts as integral to a healthy society. Richard has been Associate Director with Birmingham Opera Company since the company's re-launch in 2001, and was subsequently appointed Associate Artistic Director in 2008 and Executive Director in 2014. He was Executive Producer on the world premiere of Stockhausen's *Mittwoch aus Licht* commissioned by London 2012 Festival. The production included a large-scale digital collaboration with The Space and was awarded the RPS Award for Opera and Music Theatre, acknowledging that participatory work can achieve at the highest artistic level.

MATTHEW WILLIAMS /205

Matthew, known to all as Wills, trained at Clwyd Theatr Cymru and the School Of Sound Recording, Manchester. Currently Deputy Head of Sound at Clwyd Theatr Cymru, under the artistic direction of Terry Hands, Wills has been sound designer for around 80 productions for Clwyd Theatr Cymru and various other companies, with designs in house, UK tours, London and New York. In addition to theatre sound design, film sound credits include the documentary, *I Told You I Was Ill: The Life and Legacy of Spike Milligan* and recording credits for Colin Towns and many radio advert voice over recordings.

Wills was a co founder of Liverpool based record label, Spank Records, working with various bands including, Antiproduct, The Relatives and The Quireboys. Other work includes around 20 releases by The Dogs D'Amour and their vocalist, Tyla, as engineer, producer, mastering engineer and video editor. Wills has also worked with a number of independent record labels including, King Outlaw, Cargo, Stone Me Records and Changes One. Other releases include three albums by various male voice choirs and two albums of original cast recordings for shows at Clwyd Theatr Cymru.

Randomly, Wills is also a co owner of a North Wales based dance school.
www.willswillsaudio.co.uk

LOUISE ANN WILSON /200

Louise Ann Wilson is a scenographer, director and performance maker whose company LAW co creates site-specific walking-performances in rural locations that seek to articulate, reflects upon, and transform significant life-events. Projects include: *Empty* (Spring 2015), an interactive mountain walk in Buttermere, Cumbria, which explores childlessness by circumstance. *The Gathering* (Sept 2014 with NTW), a site-specific walking-performance revealing the day-to-day and seasonal workings of a sheep farm located on Snowdon, Wales. *Ghost Bird* (Sept 2012), a silent walk and live-art installation in the Trough of Bowland. *Fissure* (May 2011), a cross-disciplinary walking-performance that unfolded over three days in the Yorkshire Dales and explored life, death, grief and renewal. *Still Life* (Sept 2008, rev.2009) and *Jack Scout* (Sept 2010) both co-productions with Sap Dance in response to two locations on Morecambe Bay, Lancashire.
www.louiseannwilson.com

JESSICA WORRALL /201

Designs include for Northern Broadsides: *Loves Labour's Lost, We are Three Sisters, Lisa's Sex Strike, Wars of the Roses, School for Scandal, The Bells, Macbeth, Twelfth Night, Oedipus, The Cracked Pot*. For People Show: *Fallout no. 124* (CCA Glasgow), *The Detective Show no.121* (Edinburgh, London, San Francisco), *The Ghost Sonata no. 119* (Sefton Park Glass House, Liverpool).

Other works include: *Grit* (Tramway), *The Knitting Circle* (Vital Xposure), *Alice Through the Looking Glass* (Egg Theatre); *Huxley's Lab* (Grid Iron), *Snow Queen* (Macrobert Stirling), *Turandot, Carmen* (Festival Theatre, Edinburgh) and *Peter Pan* (Theatre Royal, Bath). Film design: *Death of a Double Act* (Directed by Christine Entwistle) and *A Loss of Sexual Innocence* (directed by Mike Figgis). Artist Collaborations: *The Story of How...*(Artissima Turin), *Art Now Live* (Tate Britain), *The Slapstick Mystics* (Frieze Art Fair) with Joanne Tatham & Tom O'Sullivan. Exhibition Design: *Sadness and Gladness* and *Tait and Style* (Lighthouse, Glasgow).
www.jessicaworrall.co.uk

ELIZABETH WRIGHT /194

Elizabeth's designs include: *The Wonderful Wizard of Oz* (Octagon Theatre, Bolton and Hull Truck Theatre), *Queen of the North* and *Peter Pan* (Octagon Theatre, Bolton), *The Cherry Orchard* and *Fear and Misery of the Third Reich* (Manchester Metropolitan University), as well as numerous productions including: *Wallflowering, Blue/Orange, The Birthday Party, The Glass Menagerie, The Blue Room, Vincent in Brixton, 'Tis Pity She's a Whore* and *The Shape of Things*, at Theatre by the Lake, Keswick, where she began her career as a trainee designer. She trained at Bristol Old Vic Theatre School, studied English and Theatre at the University of Leeds and has a PhD (an oral history of British theatre design) from Wimbledon College of Art. Originally from Liverpool, she now lives in London.
www.elizabethwright.com

DESIGNERS

PRODUCTIONS

VENUES/COMPANIES

PHOTOGRAPHERS

Sincere thanks are due to:
- Victoria & Albert Museum
- The Backstage Academy, Wakefield
- Nottingham Trent University
- The Royal Welsh College of Music & Drama
- Cardiff Theatrical Services (CTS)
- Welsh National Opera (WNO)
- Bregenze Festspiele
  (loan of Magic Flute costumes)
- New National Theatre, Tokyo
  (loan of Yokai costumes)
- ROBE
- Stage Technologies Ltd
- White Light
- Association of Sound Designers
- Peter Ruthven Hall
- ETC
- SplinterScenery

Make/Believe draws on the resources and membership of the following organisations which include theatre designers, technicians, architects and academics:

- The Society of British Theatre Designers
- The Association of British Theatre Technicians
- The Association of Courses in Theatre Design
- The Association of Lighting Designers
- Equity Register of Designers
- Society of Theatre Consultants

Thanks are also due to the following for their inspiration, commitment, knowledge and hard work:

- Patricia Grasham: Make/Believe Coordinator, Exhibition Design and Management
- John Kirk: Construction Manager
- Kevin Smith: Production Manager
- Ben Stimpson: Technical Manager
- Brad Caleb Lee: Production Assistant
- Kay Denyer: Administrator SBTD
- Sean Crowley: Chair of SBTD
- Alice Cabanas: Marketing Advisor
- Kate Bailey: V&A Museum Theatre and Performance Curator
- Jesca Warren: Catalogue team
- Hannah Boothman: Catalogue team
- Irene Jade: Education team
- Shiona Little: Exhibition admin
- Jenny Harpur: Catalogue team
- Pat Ellingham: Catalogue team

Essays: Simon Banham, Dick Bird, Samal Blak, Paul Brown, Es Devlin, Mercedes Kemp, Bill Mitchell, Peter Rumney, Nettie Scriven, Andreas Skourtis, Myrriddin Wannell, Fiona Watt, Richard Willacy.

Peter Farley & Fiona Watt – ACTD PQ Project

Fiona Watt & David Cockayne SBTD Final Day Event organisers

Karen Lauke – Association of Sound Designers (ASD) Presentation Coordinator

Special thanks to the RWCMD Student Production team.

At Nottingham Trent University:
Ann Priest, Tracey Newton, Marjolijn Brussaard, Professor Terry Shave, Maggie Burnett and marketing team, Katie Senior, Patrick Connellan, Karen Bartlett, Carl Smith (CNC cutting), Shane Guy, Chris Green

All Staff, Technicians, Administrators and Students in BA (Hons) Theare Design and BA (Hons) Costume Design and Making courses.

All student volunteers from NTU, RWCMD, LIPA and other courses who have helped with Make/Believe -

THANK YOU!

Back cover
Die Fledermaus
Gary McCann
Norwegian National Opera December 2012